THE ANATOMY
OF THE AEROPLANE

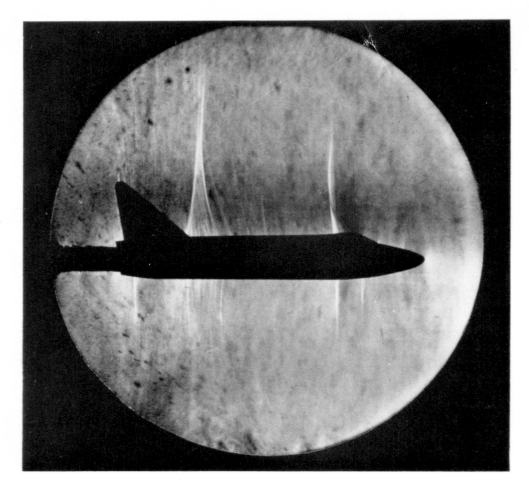

THEORY AND PRACTICE
Comparison between a Lightning at high speed in moist air and a Schlieren photograph of a wind tunnel model showing shock formation
(*By permission of the British Aircraft Corporation (Warton) and Flight International*)

THE ANATOMY
OF THE AEROPLANE

DARROL STINTON
MBE, CEng, FRAeS, MRINA, MIMechE, RAF (Retd)

OXFORD
BSP PROFESSIONAL BOOKS
LONDON EDINBURGH BOSTON
MELBOURNE PARIS BERLIN VIENNA

BSP Professional Books
A division of Blackwell Scientific
    Publications Ltd
Editorial Offices:
Osney Mead, Oxford OX2 0EL
25 John Street, London WC1N 2BL
23 Ainslie Place, Edinburgh EH3 6AJ
238 Main Street, Cambridge
    Massachusetts 02142, USA
54 University Street, Carlton
    Victoria 3053, Australia

Other Editorial Offices:
Librairie Arnette SA
1, rue de Lille
75007 Paris
France

Blackwell Wissenschafts-Verlag GmbH
Düsseldorfer Str. 38
D-10707 Berlin
Germany

Blackwell MZV
Feldgasse 13
A–1238 Wien
Austria

First published in Great Britain by
    G. T. Foulis & Co. Ltd, 1966
Reissued 1980 (ISBN 0-246-11447-9)
Reissued in paperback by Collins
    Professional and Technical Books 1985
Reprinted 1987
Reprinted by BSP Professional Books 1987,
    1989, 1994

Set by V & M Graphics Ltd,
Aylesbury, Bucks.
Printed and bound in Great Britain at
the University Press, Cambridge

DISTRIBUTORS

Marston Book Services Ltd
PO Box 87
Oxford OX2 0DT
(*Orders*: Tel: 0865 791155
        Fax: 0865 791927
        Telex: 837515)

USA: American Institute of Aeronautics & Astronautics
370 L'Enfant Promenade, SW
Washington, DC 20024-2518
(Orders: Tel: (202) 646-7400)

Canada
    Oxford University Press
    70 Wynford Drive
    Don Mills
    Ontario M3C 1J9
    (*Orders*: Tel: (416) 441-2941)

Australia
    Blackwell Scientific Publications Pty Ltd
    54 University Street
    Carlton, Victoria 3053
    (*Orders*: Tel: (03) 347-5552)

British Library
Cataloguing in Publication Data

A catalogue record for this book is
available from the British Library

ISBN 0-632-01876-3

For Julian and Caroline

Aircraft Design, a Continuing Problem . . .

'But it was just this instability that gave Camels* their good qualities of quickness in manoeuvre. A stable machine had a predilection for normal flying positions and this had to be overcome every time you wanted to do anything, whereas a Camel had to be held in flying position all the time, and was out of it in a flash. It was nose light, having a rotary engine weighing next to nothing per horsepower, and was rigged tail heavy so that you had to be holding her down all the time. Take your hand off the stick and it would rear right up with a terrific jerk and stand on its tail. Moreover, only having dihedral on the bottom plane gave a Camel a very characteristic elevation. You could tell one five miles off . . .

'With these unorthodox features, a Camel was a wonderful machine in a scrap. If only it had been fifty per cent faster! There was the rub. A Camel could neither catch anything except by surprise, nor hurry away from an awkward situation, and seldom had the option of accepting or declining combat. But what of it? You couldn't have everything.'

V. M. Yeates   *Winged Victory*

* Sopwith Camel, 1917.

Preface

One should never have too much reverence for ideas, no matter whose they are. Ideas are meant to be kicked around, stood upon their heads, and looked at backwards through mirrors. It is only in this way that they can grow up in the way that they should, without excessive self-importance. The ideas of one man are the food for thought of another. Perhaps Oliver Wendell Holmes had this in mind when he said something to the effect that: 'A man's mind stretched by a new idea can never go back to it's original dimensions'. And that is the reason for this book.

The Anatomy of the Aeroplane was started in 1960 as a set of supplementary notes to the author's annual lectures on Aero-Structures given at the Empire Test Pilot's School, at Farnborough in Hampshire. The lectures were intended to give embryo test pilots an insight into the reasons for aircraft not being shaped in ways that fitted the often more elegant theories. In so doing the inherent capabilities and limitations of an aeroplane became more apparent. The capabilities and limitations were seen to be functions of specific requirements: those formalized statements of human needs that cause aircraft to be made as useful and as safe as possible within the 'state-of-the-art' at a given time. The seeming dichotomy of the two worlds of theory and practice —usually more apparent to the practical man than the academician—is resolved by looking at the development of an aircraft as a response to a set of requirements.

The aim of the book is to show students of aeronautics how requirements affect the application of theories, causing aeroplanes to be twisted, bent, cambered and kinked, to end up without the flowing perfection of their original, idealized, forms. It is aimed in particular at students in developing countries who, the author has found, are bursting with the desire to learn and assert their own ideas, but who cannot yet gain the practice they require. To this end a number of specialized subjects are introduced and shown in relation to the end product of the finished aeroplane. In this way the student will be able to specialize later with some idea of where his own subject fits into the whole.

The treatment of the subject is such that the reader should be able to reason for himself why every salient feature of any aeroplane is shaped as it is. In doing this the book will probably make some enemies among those who cherish a professional mystique behind which to hide. That does not matter, for the book will have served its purpose if only one student gets a better feel for his subject than he might otherwise have had.

The word aeroplane is used throughout in preference to airplane, or the meaningless plane, for two reasons. The first is that it is a scholarly word applied to a particular order of a class of aircraft. The second is that it derives from two Greek words meaning, literally, air-wandering. That is excellent, for the word touches in part upon the spirit of aeronautics and the impulse to wander in the air that made men want to fly in the first place. The Concise Oxford Dictionary describes an aeroplane as a 'mechanically-driven heavier-than-air flying-machine'. Taking the definition further: the Glossary of Aeronautical Terms of the British Standards Institution defines an aeroplane as 'a power-driven heavier-than-air aircraft with supporting surfaces fixed for flight'. The name includes landplanes, seaplanes (float-seaplanes and flying boats), and amphibians (float-amphibians and boat-amphibians).

Unfortunately, precise definitions of this kind miss out the most beautiful of all winged machines, that comes nearer to wandering-in-the-air than any other: the sailplane. For the purposes of this book the definition will treat an aeroplane as a heavier-than-air flying-machine with fixed wings (*i.e.*, wings that do not beat the air as a means of propulsion, although they may be moved fore and aft in flight) while avoiding any need to specify the means of propulsion. There is no great inconsistency in doing so, for the first aeroplanes grew from kites and gliders, and the sailplane is a highly refined glider.

The evolution of powered aeroplanes is such that they outstrip the definition. Since sustained flight became a possibility, little more than half a century ago, the performance of the aeroplane has increased more than one hundredfold. Cruising speeds and heights, range and endurance, carrying capacity and weight (and complication) have all increased. In order to fly fast smaller wings are used to achieve optimum efficiency. But smaller wings bearing heavier loads require more space for take-off and landing, and space is at a premium. This has led, under pressure of military necessity, to the development of short and vertical take-off, STOL and VTOL aeroplanes. We may not like to recognize it, but most significant advances are brought about through military necessity. And now there are dreams of aeroplanes employing powered lift throughout the whole envelope of flight, for cruising as well as for take-off and landing.

The scope of the book is broad. Essentially it is a physical textbook, written in five parts, with a number of additional appendices. These have been added in order to focus attention upon some specific areas of operation: supersonic transports, airobuses, strike and reconnaissance aeroplanes of various kinds. As far as possible early project aeroplanes have been used as illustrations, for these show most clearly the first thoughts of designers, with little adulteration. Many of the aircraft shown are really in the form of feasibility studies—the stage before becoming a project, in which a particular way of doing a job is investigated to see if it is worth continuing with as a project.

Mathematical statements are simple, amounting to little more than $1+1 = 2$, or $3 = 6/2$, and using symbols to say so. Although British symbols are used these are defined, and repeated where relevant, so that the foreign reader should have no difficulty in converting them to the standard symbols of his own country. Equations are, for the most part, unit-less—although the ft-lb-sec system is used where stated. The reason for avoiding units is that the ideas count more than quantitative results, which belong properly in a handbook of aircraft design. Some basic calculus symbols are used, but it is only necessary to know what is meant by Δx and dx when they appear.

A significant departure from standard works on aerodynamics is that to explain the nature of aerodynamic phenomena and forces aeroplanes are considered in motion through the air, instead of the usual reverse. There is plenty of time for the reader to come round to the conservative point of view, of visualizing an aircraft somehow motionless in space, with air flowing past it. This view has been deliberately rejected, not only because aeroplanes do not fly that way, but because certain concepts—like circulation, and its effect upon aerodynamic forces—are more readily understandable if one goes straight to the point of trying to see what really happens to the air. Futhermore, stability and control (neither of which are easily mastered if one is not happy with textbook mathematics) become simpler when seen as the pilot sees them: as properties of a machine that, under his hands, seems to be alive as it moves through apparently living air.

The author is indebted to a large number of people who, directly and indirectly, have either helped by providing material, or have helped with the play of ideas thrown up as the book was written. Among these are three test pilots: Wing Commander N. F. Harrison, D.S.O., A.F.C., R.A.F., Don. Wright, and Squadron Leader G. M. Morrison, R.A.F. Others are Ernest Stott, the artist: Squadron Leader J. H. Maguire, M.B.E., R.A.F., Charles Gibbs-Smith (who provided the copy of the Sir George Cayley medallion), Derek Dempster, Alastair Pugh, Dr. M. H. L. Waters, W. T. Gunston, W. W. Coles, and D. Howe of the College of Aeronautics. Thanks are also due to the Blackburn and De Havilland Divisions of Hawker Siddeley Aviation Ltd, Bristol Siddeley Engines Ltd, the British Aircraft Corporation, Short Brothers and Harland Ltd, The Royal Aeronautical Society, Air et Cosmos, Flight International, Interavia, Shell Aviation News, and the Air Registration Board.

The quotation on page vii is taken from *Winged Victory* by V. M. Yeates and the author is grateful to Mrs. Norah Yeates and to Messrs. Jonathan Cape Limited for permission to reproduce it.

It should be noted that the views expressed are those of the author. The book does not reflect any policy or opinion of either Her Majesty's Government or the Royal Air Force.

Mattingley, January 1966   *D.S.*

Contents

APPENDICES

List of Plates

CONVERSION FACTORS BETWEEN THE BRITISH FPSR (FOOT, POUND, SECOND, RANKINE)

SYSTEM AND SI (SYSTÈME INTERNATIONALE) UNITS

Quantity	FPSR Units	Multiply by	To obtain SI Units	Multiply by	To obtain FPSR Units
Mass (M)	slug	1.459×10	kg	6.852×10^{-2}	slug
Length (L)	ft	3.048×10^{-1}	m	3.281	ft
Density (ρ)	$slug/ft^3$	5.155×10^2	kg/m^3	1.940×10^{-3}	$slug/ft^3$
Temperature (T)	$^{\circ}F + 460$ $^{\circ}R$	5.56×10^{-1}	$^{\circ}C + 273$ $^{\circ}K$	1.8	$^{\circ}F + 460$ $^{\circ}R$
Velocity (V)	ft/sec mph knot	3.048×10^{-1} 1.609 1.853 0.515	m/sec kph kph m/sec	3.281 6.214×10^{-1} 5.396×10^{-1} 1.942	ft/sec mph knot
Force (F)	lbf $slug\ ft/sec^2$	4.448	N (newton) $kg\ m/sec^2$	2.248×10^{-1}	lbf $slug\ ft/sec^2$
Work Energy (J)	$slug\ ft^2/sec^2$ BTU	1.356	Nm (joule)	7.376×10^{-1}	$slug\ ft^2/sec^2$ BTU
Power (W)	$slug\ ft^2/sec^3$ hp (550 ft lbf/sec)	1.356 7.456×10^2	Nm/sec (Watt)	7.376×10^{-1} 1.341×10^{-3}	$slug\ ft^2/sec^3$ hp (550 ft lbf/sec)
Pressure (p)	$slug/ft\ sec^2$ lbf/ft^2	4.788×10 4.788×10^{-4}	N/m^2 (pascal) bar	2.088×10^{-2} 2.088×10^3	$slug/ft\ sec^2$ lbf/ft^2
Specific Energy, etc	ft lbf/slug	9.290×10^{-2}	Nm/kg	1.076×10	ft lbf/slug
Gas Constant	$ft\ lbf/slug\,^{\circ}R$	1.672×10^{-1}	$Nm/kg\,^{\circ}K$	5.981	$ft\ lbf/slug\,^{\circ}R$
Coef of Viscosity (μ)	slug/ft sec	4.788×10	kg/m sec	2.088×10^{-2}	slug/ft sec
Kinematic Viscosity (ν)	ft^2/sec	9.290×10^{-2}	m^2/sec	1.076×10	ft^2/sec
Thermal Conductivity (k)	$lbf/sec\,^{\circ}R$	8.007	$N/sec\,^{\circ}K$	1.249×10^{-1}	$lbf/sec\,^{\circ}R$
Heat Transfer Coefficient	$lbf/ft\ sec.^{\circ}R$	2.627×10	$N/m\ sec\,^{\circ}K$	3.807×10^{-2}	$lbf/ft\ sec\,^{\circ}R$
Frequency	c/sec	1.0	Hz (hertz)	1.0	c/sec

List of Symbols

Symbol	Meaning	Symbol	Meaning
A	Aerodynamic aspect ratio (b^2/S)	c_d	Section drag coefficient
A	Cross-sectional area of a cylinder of air	c_l	Section lift coefficient
		c_m	Section moment coefficient
A	Cross-sectional area of a stream-tube	c_t	Equivalent tip chord
		c'	Thrust specific fuel consumption
A	Moment of Inertia about longitudinal (rolling) axis OX	$\bar{c}$	Geometric mean chord of wing
		$\bar{\bar{c}}$	Aerodynamic mean chord of wing
A_S	Structural aspect ratio ($b^2 \sec^2 \Lambda/S$)		(practically: $\bar{c}$)
A_w	Total wetted area of airframe	D	Total drag of aircraft
a	Acceleration along flight path	D_F	Zero-lift drag
a	Cross-sectional area of material specimen	D_L	Lift-dependent drag
		D_{fric}	Total frictional drag (sensibly D_F in subcritical flight)
a	Unspecified constant of proportionality	D_{pod}	Pod drag
		D_{press}	Total pressure drag
a	Velocity of sound	E_h	Total energy at a given speed and height
$a_1, a_2 \ldots$	Slopes of lift curves ($dC_L/d\alpha)_1$, etc		
		e_c	Compressive (bearing) strain
B	Moment of inertia in pitch about axis OY	e_t	Tensile strain
		F	Farenheit
b	Wing span	F	Net propulsive force
C	Centigrade	F_e	Static sea level thrust per engine
C	Moment of inertia in yaw about axis OZ	f	Equivalent parasite area of aircraft
C	Total fuel consumption	$f(\ )$	Some unspecified function
C_D	Total drag coefficient ($D = C_D qS$)	g	Gravitational acceleration 32·2 ft/sec^2
C_{DF}	Zero-lift drag coefficient		
C_{DL}	Lift-dependent drag coefficient (induced or vortex drag in subcritical flight)	h	Height above mean sea level
		h_e	Energy height ($h + V^2/2g$)
		I	Moment of inertia Mk^2
$C_{D\text{fric}}$	Frictional drag coefficient (sensibly C_{DF} in subcritical flight)	K	Factor of planform efficiency (or 'inefficiency')
$C_{D\text{min}}$	Minimum drag coefficient	K	Factor of principal tensile stress
C_L	Lift coefficient of complete aircraft $L = C_L qS$	K_S	Factor of take-off distance
		k	Radius of gyration
$C_{L\text{max}}$	Maximum lift coefficient	k	Unspecified constant of proportionality
C_{Lto}	Take-off lift coefficient		
C_M	Pitching moment coefficient $M = C_M qS\bar{c}$	L	Total lift
		L	Specified distance to applied load
C_{Mac}	Pitching moment coefficient about aerodynamic centre	L_F	Part of total lift supporting weight of fuselage
C_{MCG}	Pitching moment coefficient about centre of gravity	(L/D)	Lift/drag, the measure of aerodynamic efficiency
c	Chord of aerofoil section	$(L/D)_{\text{max}}$	Maximum lift/drag
c_c	Equivalent centre-line chord	$(L/D)_R$	Optimum range lift/drag (about 0·94 $(L/D)_{\text{max}}$)

Symbol	Meaning	Symbol	Meaning
l	Aerofoil section lift	s	Semi-span of aerofoil ($b/2$)
l	Overall length of aircraft	T	Absolute temperature (degrees Kelvin)
l_t	Tail moment arm		
M	Mach number	T	Torque
M_{crit}	Critical Mach number	T_W	Torque applied at wing root
$M_{crit D}$	Critical Mach number where wave drag becomes 'measureable'	t	Maximum thickness of aerofoil section
		(t/c)	Thickness ratio of aerofoil section
M	Bending and fixing moment	V	Relative velocity of airflow
M	Metacentre	V	True airspeed, TAS
M	Total (unspecified) pitching moment	V_A	Design manoeuvring speed
		V_B	Design speed for maximum gust intensity
M_W	Bending moment applied at wing root	V_C	Design cruising speed
M_{ac}	Pitching moment about aerodynamic centre	V_D	Design diving speed
		V_J	Jet velocity
M_{CG}	Pitching moment about centre of gravity	V_L	Relative velocity of airflow over lower surface of aerofoil
M_x	Bending moment at station x	V_U	Relative velocity of airflow over upper surface of aerofoil
m_a	Mass of air (W_a/g) acted on per second by engine	V_{AB}	Resultant velocity of circulation of two particles A and B
N	Number of alternating load cycles per second	V_{US}	Unstick speed of seaplane
N_e	Number of engines	V_a	Aquaplaning speed
N_p	Number of passengers	V_i	Equivalent airspeed, EAS
n	Normal acceleration (in units of g) = aeronautical load factor	V_1, V_2	Different TAS
		$\bar{V}$	Horizontal tail volume coefficient ($l_t S_T/\bar{c}S$)
$n_1, n_2, \ldots$	Different values of n		
P	Applied force	v	Component of root mean square velocity
P	Brake horsepower of engine		
P_e	Power required for flight (ft-lb-sec units) at constant TAS	v	Specific volume of a gas
		v_c	Rate of climb
p	static pressure	v_d	Rate of descent
p	Tyre pressure	W	Instantaneous weight
p_c	Compressive stress	W	Specified applied load
p_t	Tensile stress	W_A	Equipped airframe weight
p_o	Total static pressure head	W_E	Powerplant weight
p_1	Static pressure at engine compressor face	W_F	Fuel weight
		W_O	All-up weight
p_1, p_2	Different values of ambient pressure	W_P	Payload
		W_S	Structure weight
$\bar{p}$	Average pressure differential across aerofoil chord	W_a	Weight of air acted on per second by engine
$\bar{p}$	Specific weight of engine (engine weight/net thrust)	$W_{(w+u)}$	Weight of wing plus undercarriage
Q	Applied shear force	W_1, W_2, etc	Component weights
Q	Probability of failure	w	Downwash velocity
q	Dynamic pressure ($\frac{1}{2}\rho V^2, 0.7pM^2$)	w	Vertical gust velocity
q	Shear stress	w	velocity of propeller slipstream
R	Gas constant	X	Structural length
R	Probability of reliability	x	Distance measured in direction O–X
R	Radius of turn		
R	Range in still air	x_L	Moment of total lift about centre of gravity
R	Total resistance (air plus water drag) of seaplane	$x_{(w+u)}$	Distance of CG of wing plus undercarriage from CG datum of aircraft, along O–X axis
(R)	Unspecified requirement		
R_N	Reynold' number (Vc/v)		
$R_1, R_2, R_3 \ldots$	Component probable reliabilities	x_1, x_2, x_3, etc	Component distances from CG datum along O–X axis
r	Radius of rotation		
S	Wing area	$\bar{x}$	CG coordinate along O–X axis
S_T	Horizontal tail area		

Symbol	Meaning	Symbol	Meaning
y	Distance measured in direction $O-Y$	δ	An increment of small order
y_1, y_2, y_3, etc	Component distances from CG datum along $O-Y$ axis	η_o	Efficiency of overall propulsion process
$\bar{y}$	CG coordinate along $O-Y$ axis	η_p	Efficiency of mechanical propulsion process (ideal, Froude efficiency)
Z	Structural depth	η_t	Efficiency of 'internal' thermal process
z	Distance measured in direction $O-Z$	η_p'	Effective propulsive efficiency
z_D	Moment arm of total drag about CG	θ	Semi-vertex angle of Mach cone
z_F	Moment arm of net propulsive force about CG	Λ	Angle of sweep of aerofoil along the $\frac{1}{4}$ chord line
z_1, z_2, z_3, etc	Component distances from CG datum along $O-Z$ axis	Λ_{LE}	Angle of sweep of leading edge
$\bar{z}$	CG coordinate along $O-Z$ axis	Λ_{TE}	Angle of sweep of trailing edge
α	angle of attack	μ	Dynamic viscosity
β	Angle of sideslip	μ	Coefficient of friction between wheels and ground
γ	Ratio of specific heats of air (approx' 1·4)	ν	Kinematic viscosity (μ/ρ)
γ_c	Angle of climb	π	3·1417
γ_d	Angle of descent	ρ	Density at height other than sea level
Δ	Load on water	ρ_0	Density at sea level
Δ	An increment	σ	Relative density (ρ/ρ_0)
		ϕ	Angle of bank

Units

For all calculations it is necessary to use a consistent set of units. Those most commonly used in Britain are the slug for the unit of mass, M, the foot for the unit of length, L, and the second for the unit of time, T. The following table gives the dimensions and units of a number of terms used in aeronautical work.

Quantity	Dimensions	Units
Length* (chord c, tail arm l_t)	L	ft
Area (wing area S, wetted area A_w)	L^2	ft^2
Speed* (forward speed V)	L/T	ft/sec
Acceleration (gravitational g)	L/T^2	ft/sec^2
Kinematic viscosity v	L^2/T	ft^2/sec
Mass (mass airflow m_a)	M	slugs
Air density ρ	M/L^3	slug/ft^3
Force (lift, drag, thrust, weight)	ML/T^2	lb
Pressure p	M/LT^2	lb/ft^2
Moment of Inertia	ML^2	slug ft^2
Angle (attack α, yaw β)	—	radians (and degrees)

* Distance (length) is also measured in miles and speed in miles/hour: nautical miles and knots being used respectively in aeronautics. 1 n ml = 6,080 ft and 66 n ml = 76 st ml, while 1 hr = 3,600 sec.

PART 1

ENVIRONMENT

CHAPTER 1

The Atmosphere

1.1 Composition of the Atmosphere

The atmosphere is a fluid skin surrounding the earth and extending out to about 500 miles. It is a mixture of gases that are chemically indifferent to one another. Roughly half the total weight of the atmosphere is accounted for by the first 18,000 ft, and another quarter by the next 18,000 ft. Up to about 50 miles the composition of the air is more or less constant, except for variation of water vapour content. The proportions of the most important gases present are as shown in Table 1.1.

TABLE 1.1

Composition of the Atmosphere at Sea Level

Gas	Formula	Percentage Volume	Molecular Weight	Percentage Weight
Nitrogen	N_2	78·088	28·016	75·525
Oxygen	O_2	20·950	32·000	23·143
Argon	A	0·932	39·944	1·286
Carbon dioxide	CO_2	0·030	44·011	0·046

Together with small quantities of Neon, Helium, Krypton, Hydrogen, Xenon, Ozone and Radon

Up to the first five or six miles the water vapour content varies and depends upon the temperature of the air: the higher the temperature the more vapour that can be held in a given volume. The pressure and density of the atmosphere decrease with height. At very high altitudes the heavier gases fail to rise until, around 50 miles, hydrogen and helium are predominant. The pressure of the amount of oxygen needed to sustain life decreases rapidly with height until around 18,000 ft the danger limit for the human pilot is reached and thereafter oxygen must be fed mechanically. Around 100,000 ft there is no longer enough oxygen to support combustion in the most advanced turbojet engines now in service.

In temperate latitudes the first 36,000 ft marks the extent of the troposphere, the region of decreasing temperature with height. Above the troposphere and separated from it by a hypothetical boundary called the tropopause lies the stratosphere, a region of initially constant temperature that gradually increases from about $-56°C$ at

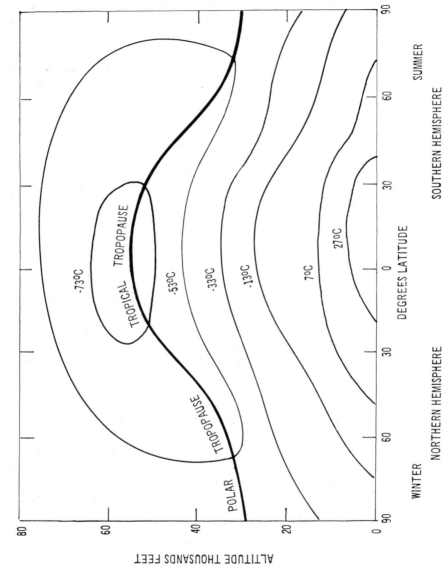

ALTITUDE THOUSANDS FEET

DEGREES LATITUDE

WINTER   NORTHERN HEMISPHERE   SOUTHERN HEMISPHERE   SUMMER

-73°C

TROPICAL   TROPOPAUSE

-53°C

-33°C

-13°C

7°C

27°C

TROPOPAUSE

POLAR

Fig. 1.1. Typical variation in atmospheric temperature along a meridian of longitude, summer in the southern hemisphere

20 miles to a maximum around $-20°C$ at 35 miles. The tropopause is not clear-cut in practice, varying from about 30,000 ft at the poles to about 54,000 ft at the equator, as shown in Fig. 1.1. It follows that much lower temperatures are encountered at altitude over the tropics than over the poles, because the higher tropopause allows the temperature of the atmosphere to fall further before the region of constant temperature is reached. For this reason most low temperature flight trials are carried out in the tropics.

The atmosphere is divided into further layers by different authorities. The simplest is into the mesosphere, adjacent to the stratosphere, in which the temperature again falls with height, reaching a minimum near $-88°C$ around 50 miles, where it is bounded by the mesopause. The rare noctilucent clouds—meaning 'shining at night'—occur near the mesopause, and are thought to be formed by volcanic meteoric dust and ice crystals, resulting from the amalgamation of hydrogen from outer space with atmospheric oxygen molecules. Above the mesopause lies the thermosphere, extending out to 350 miles or more and marked by increasing temperature with height. The relatively high temperatures are thought to be caused in part by ionisation of the atmospheric gases by various forms of cosmic radiation. Beyond the thermosphere lies the fringe region, or exosphere, that is poorly defined by limits assumed to lie between 350 and 600 miles, although some think 1,000 miles.

1.2 Phenomena Affecting the Operation of Aircraft

There are a number of atmospheric conditions and phenomena that affect the operation of aircraft:

(1) Aircraft and engine performance depend directly upon the physical state of the atmosphere: and in particular upon the pressure, density and temperature of the local air mass in which flight is taking place. The local conditions around an aircraft are referred to as ambient conditions.

(2) An aircraft is propelled through an air mass which is in motion relative to the surface of the earth. This introduces navigational problems that grow with flying-time and, therefore, affect the amount of special equipment carried by an aeroplane in order to operate in a specific role.

(3) The state of the weather affects operations and phenomena such as heavy rain, hail, snow, ice, fog and thunderstorms must be planned for. Temperature variations within the atmosphere cause air masses to move and interact, resulting in wind and turbulence. Turbulence is a major hazard affecting the structural design and planned life of the airframe, as well as stability and control criteria.

(4) Cosmic radiation, a generic term for a large number of solar and galactic radiations, has not presented much of a hazard until now. The appearance of the supersonic transport, or SST, is now highlighting some of the dangers to be expected from ionization of animal tissues. The maximum influence is found to occur around 75,000 ft, while the intensity of such radiation changes both with height and latitude.

(5) The presence of ozone, a toxic product of ionization, prevents the use of ambient air for cabin pressurisation at heights above 60,000 ft. This involves the aircraft designer in additional problems of air conditioning and design against pressure-cabin failure.

1.3 Physical Properties of the Atmosphere

Air is a compressible fluid that flows and changes shape when subjected to the minutest pressures. There is cohesion between molecules and this gives rise to friction. If there were no friction and the air was incompressible it would correspond with the mathematical concept of an 'ideal' fluid.

The vertical distribution of pressure throughout the atmosphere behaves in a fairly regular manner and decreases steadily with height. Under standard sea level conditions a cubic foot of dry air is assumed to have a defined density, one example of which is 0·002378 slugs/ft³. The slug is used as a convenient unit of mass in aerodynamics to avoid confusion between pounds force and pounds mass in the ft-lb-sec system. It is derived from Newton's law:

$$Force = Mass \times Acceleration$$

and one pound force causes a mass of one slug to accelerate at 1 ft/sec². It follows that as one pound force is equivalent to one pound weight, a mass of one slug is 32·2 times greater than a mass having a weight of one pound in the earth's gravitational field, where the acceleration is 32·2 ft/sec².

When air is compressed or expanded at constant temperature, a greater or lesser mass then occupies a given volume. Hence, at constant temperature the density is directly proportional to the pressure. However, the temperature changes in practice and the density is no longer directly proportional to pressure alone, and the three quantities are inexactly (but commonly) related by the ideal gas equation:

$$pv = RT \qquad\qquad (1\text{--}1)$$

or,
$$p = \rho RT \qquad\qquad (1\text{--}2)$$

where, p = pressure (lb ft²),
v = specific volume (ft³ lb),
R = a constant for a given gas (3,090 ft lb/slug/°C for air),
T = absolute temperature °Kelvin, i.e., (t°C + 273°C),
ρ = density (slugs/ft³).

1.3.1 The Standard Atmosphere

For the analysis of the manner in which air behaves when a moving body passes it is necessary to define a standard atmosphere to which all measurements can be related. There are many in existence and, for the purpose of this book, that defined by the International Civil Aviation Organization (ICAO) has been chosen.

The ICAO definition of the standard atmosphere is that: the air is a perfectly dry gas; the temperature at sea level is 15°C (i.e., 288°K); the pressure at sea level is 29·92 inches of mercury. The temperature is assumed to lapse at a rate of 1·98°C/1,000 ft from sea level to the altitude at which the temperature becomes −56·5°C, i.e., 36,090 ft, where the lapse rate changes. The word altitude is used instead of height to denote a vertical distance, based upon the defined pressure and measured from mean sea level. Clearly, an instrument measuring the pressure variation with distance above mean sea level, and calibrated to a precise law, will not give the 'tape-measure' height.

Such an instrument is called an altimeter. All altimeters have to be adjusted to a datum pressure whenever they are used, the datum pressure varying from hour to hour and being given out by the Meteorological Office. Elsewhere height is used when speaking generally. Fig. 1.2 shows the general characteristics of the ICAO atmosphere to an altitude of 1,000,000 ft. For convenience density, pressure and dynamic viscosity are shown relative to their sea level values, ρ_0, p_0 and μ_0. Above 80,000 ft the curves have been based on the broadly similar U.S. Standard Atmosphere 1962.

For simplicity the corresponding curve of relative kinematic viscosity, v/v_0, is not shown. The importance of kinematic viscosity will become clearer when we come to discuss 'scale effect' and its influence upon the relative magnitude of aerodynamic forces and behaviour of the air when similar bodies of different sizes pass through it. For the present it is enough to mention that the magnitude of the frictional force which opposes motion of the air is expressed in terms of the dynamic viscosity, denoted μ. Imagine several thin layers of air moving smoothly over each other, rather like sheets of notepaper in a pile that is being spread out (sheared) sideways. The quantity μ is the factor of proportionality between the shearing force per unit area (or shear stress) and the velocity gradient between the layers. At ordinary pressures the dynamic viscosity depends only upon the nature and temperature of the air. But the density of the air must always be taken into account in aerodynamics, and the ratio of dynamic viscosity to density—the kinematic viscosity—is more important in aerodynamic measurements than the magnitude of frictional forces alone. Hence we meet the following relationships in aerodynamics:

$$\text{Dynamic viscosity, } \mu = \frac{\text{shear stress between adjacent layers of air}}{\text{shear velocity gradient between adjacent layers of air}}$$

$$\text{and, kinematic viscosity, } v, = \frac{\text{dynamic viscosity}}{\text{density}}$$

i.e.,
$$v = \frac{\mu}{\rho} \tag{1-3}$$

1.3.2 Local Speed of Sound and Mach Number

The local speed of sound in air is of utmost significance, because the behaviour of the air and the associated pressure patterns set up by an aeroplane in flight change radically as the speed of flight approaches that of the local speed of sound. At low flight speeds the particles of air are displaced fairly smoothly by a body, because the particles have time to adjust themselves to the transient situation.

The root mean square of the speed at which the particles move is the speed of sound. When the speed of flight reaches the speed of sound the particles cannot move easily in time and are more violently displaced: the result is marked changes in the pressure field and in density and temperature. The aeroplane is then in the regime of compressibility.

The ratio of the speed of flight to the local speed of sound is called the Mach number, M, after Ernst Mach, the Austrian scientist who is famous for his early study of the behaviour of bodies travelling through the air at high speeds. Thus:

$$M = \frac{V}{a} \tag{1-4}$$

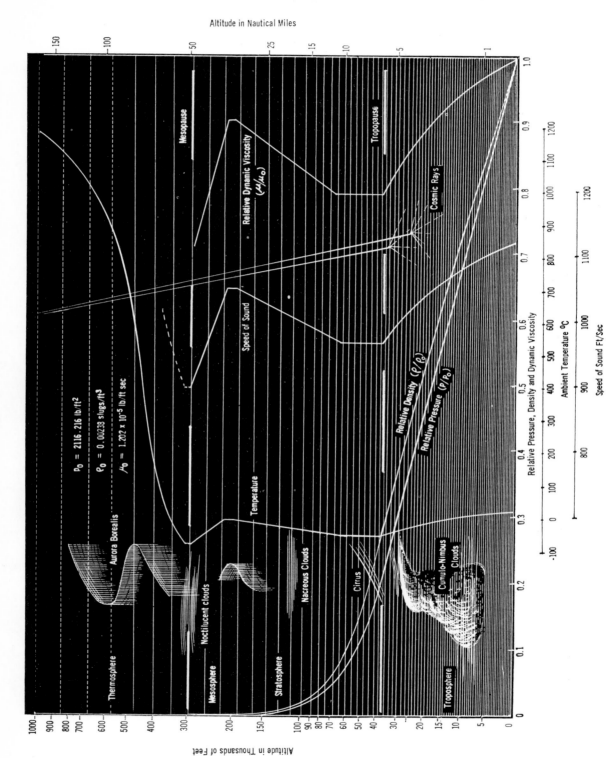

Fig. 1.2. General characteristics of the atmosphere (based upon ICAO and U.S. Standard Atmosphere 1962)

where, a = local speed of sound in air, which varies as the square root of the absolute temperature of the local air mass.

V = true airspeed of the aircraft.

No units have been specified because as long as they are the same for V and a, *i.e.*, ft/sec, mile/h or knots, then the ratio remains constant.

In Fig. 1.2 the speed of sound is seen to vary in a similar way to the curve of absolute temperature.

1.3.3 True and Equivalent Airspeed

An aircraft has two significant speeds. The first, called true airspeed, or TAS, is measured relative to the undisturbed air. The second, called equivalent airspeed, or EAS, is a fiction that is of prime importance in aerodynamic calculations, because the forces acting on an aeroplane depend upon EAS. The two speeds are denoted V and V_i respectively.

Both TAS and EAS are identical at sea level in the standard atmosphere, but they differ according to a simple law at altitude. The reason for the difference can be explained by imagining what happens as an aeroplane flies through a mass of initially undisturbed air. Through impact and friction every molecule will eventually have momentum imparted to it by the aeroplane in its passage. Some will be swept along at the same speed, others more slowly, and so on down to those that are barely influenced at all. The first molecules which are swept along at the same speed may be thought of as being brought to rest relative to the aeroplane, but work has been done during the action of accelerating from their initially undisturbed state to the speed of flight, V. Every cubic foot of air so accelerated to the TAS has, therefore, an additional kinetic energy q, where:

$$q = \tfrac{1}{2}\rho V^2 \qquad (1-5)$$

It is convenient to use this expression in aerodynamic measurements of all kinds, while referring to q as the dynamic pressure. Aerodynamic forces are expressed non-dimensionally as pure numbers multiplied by the dynamic pressure and the wing area. It may be shown that for an aeroplane to generate the same forces at altitude as in flight at sea level, it must be flown at such a speed that the dynamic pressure remains constant, regardless of any difference in density of the ambient air. It follows that, in Eq. (1-5), the maintenance of constant dynamic pressure at different altitudes involves one in flying at different airspeeds. The sea level airspeed, where the density is ρ_0, is the TAS. At any other altitude, where density is ρ, the result is achieved by flying at the EAS. It may be shown quite simply that:

$$V_i = V\sqrt{(\rho/\rho_0)} = V\sqrt{\sigma} \qquad (1-6)$$

Where σ is the relative density. Fig. 1.3 shows the theoretical relationship between TAS, EAS and Mach number.

There is another useful form of expression for the dynamic pressure given in Eq. (1-5), which is of increasing importance when making calculations for flight at high Mach numbers. The relationship giving the speed of sound in ft/sec:

$$a = \sqrt{\left(\frac{\gamma p}{\rho}\right)} \qquad (1-7)$$

where: γ = the ratio of specific heats for air, approx. 1.4.

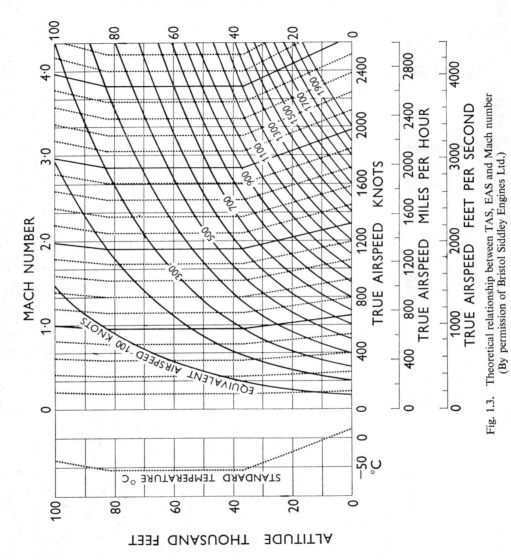

Fig. 1.3.   Theoretical relationship between TAS, EAS and Mach number
(By permission of Bristol Siddley Engines Ltd.)

Fig. 2.4. The Swallow polymorph. For flight at high Mach numbers the aircraft becomes a slender delta with the middle region of the trailing edge cut away

(a)
F-16A
(single seat)

(b)
F16/79 two seat
tactical fighter

(c)
F-16 XL with a
larger cranked arrow
wing, composite
wing skins,
enhanced
performance
and active
(fly-by-wire)
controls
(USA, 1974)

Fig. 2.5   Examples of different marks of one type of aeroplane: the General Dynamics F-16
(*By permission of the* General Dynamics Corporation *and* Flight International)

and, a, p and ρ have their earlier meanings, and it may be shown from this that:

$$\tfrac{1}{2}\rho V^2 = \tfrac{1}{2}\gamma p \mathrm{M}^2$$

i.e.,
$$q = 0{\cdot}7p\mathrm{M}^2 \tag{1-8}$$

1.3.4 Aerodynamic Heating

The addition of kinetic energy to the air by an aeroplane in flight is measurable (if instruments could be made accurately enough) in terms of a temperature rise. The highest temperature that could be measured is called the stagnation temperature: the temperature of those surfaces which lie locally at right angles to the direction of motion. Such parts of the airframe impart the full change of momentum to the particles of air which, in becoming 'attached', may be thought of as being swept along at the TAS. The adiabatic temperature rise ΔT is given by:

$$\Delta T = \left(\frac{\text{TAS in mile/h}}{100}\right)^2 {}^\circ\text{C} \tag{1-9}$$

to within three parts in 1000. Alternatively, the temperature rise of the boundary layer of air adjacent to the skin at high altitude is given by:

$$\Delta T = 75\mathrm{M}^2\,{}^\circ\text{F} \tag{1-9a}$$

What does this mean in real terms? At $\mathrm{M} = 3$ the temperature of the leading edge of the wing of an aircraft flying at high altitude reaches at least 600°F: 100° hotter than is needed to roast a side of beef. Kinetic heating becomes critically important at high speeds when it affects structures, causing distortion and internal stress concentrations; it can also involve fuel cooling and similar problems. It is discussed in more detail in the chapter on structures.

From the foregoing we see that air is a mixture of gases which, for practical purposes, can be treated as one gas. The air has temperature (the measure of internal energy of the molecules), density, pressure and viscosity. The behaviour of the air in the presence of a moving body can be changed by the rate at which the body is moving. An aeroplane flies, therefore, in a pressure field that is a function of height, speed and Mach number. At this point we may begin to think of an aeroplane having an operational environment.

CHAPTER 2

The Operational Environment

The term operational environment is used here to include every aspect of the flight and ground environment of any aeroplane that is carrying out the role for which it was designed. For example, military aeroplanes are designed for more strenuous operating conditions than their civil counterparts: a civil transport for the North Atlantic route is used in more stately operations than a military machine supplying a battlefield. Every aeroplane is designed to operate best in one particular regime of the operational environment. The flight regime is broadly defined by Mach number: *i.e.*, low-subsonic, high-subsonic, transonic, supersonic and hypersonic. Within the design flight regime lies the design point, defined specifically by the speed and height at which the particular aeroplane is assumed to spend the most important part of its working life.

The operational environment is determined by the operator's requirements, by the design requirements, the availability of power plants, the state of the aerodynamic art, materials, technology, sociology and economics. Every aeroplane is a mass of compromises. Each compromise represents a balance between sets of conflicting demands. The picture is complicated by the interdependence of many demands. For example, an airline operator is in business to make money and does not want his aeroplanes to cost more to run than his competitor's. To achieve economy when cruising requires the minimum fuel consumption in that condition and, hence, the minimum power to achieve the required cruising speed. But an aeroplane with just enough power for economical cruising will be under-engined when it comes to meeting the case of take-off and baulked approach to landing with an engine-failure. Being under-engined results in longer take-off runs and runways, the inability to climb away safely with engine-failure, spending longer at relatively low altitudes over built-up areas (thereby causing sociological problems with noise) and the need to reduce payloads in some hotter parts of the world.

2.1 The Flight Envelope

The operational environment of an aircraft lies within a boundary, drawn on a basis of speed and height, called the flight-envelope, as shown in Fig. 2.1. The outline marks the limit of performance in one particular configuration: the arrangement of the aircraft at the time, including external stores carried.

The left hand side of the figure marks the speed at any height below which there is insufficient lift to fly straight and level. The dip in the curve around Mach 1 is caused by the increased drag and a decrease in aerodynamic and propulsive efficiency. Some aeroplanes exhibit this characteristic to a marked extent, others hardly at all.

10

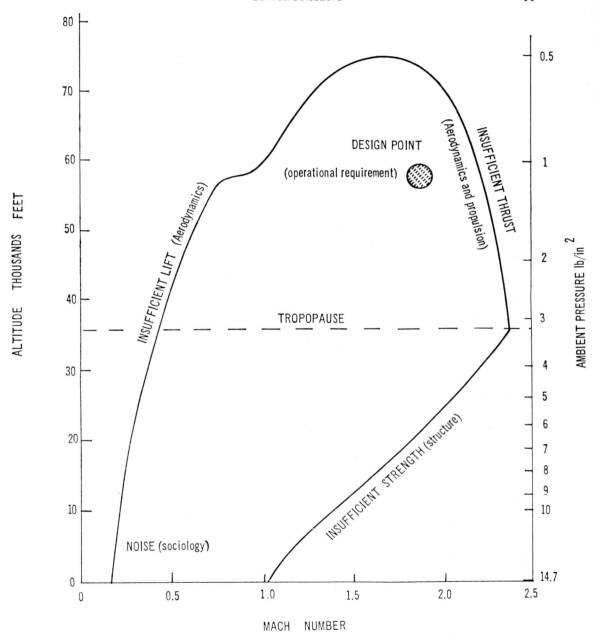

Fig. 2.1. Typical flight envelope of a supersonic aeroplane

The top of the curve marks the region where the minimum level speed coincides with the maximum speed that can be attained with the particular combination of engine and airframe. While the right hand side of the curve represents the propulsive limit, and the structural limits: where higher speed, kinetic heating and higher dynamic pressure would require an excessively strong and heavy airframe.

A boundary similar to Fig. 2.1 can be drawn for any aeroplane, the actual shape of

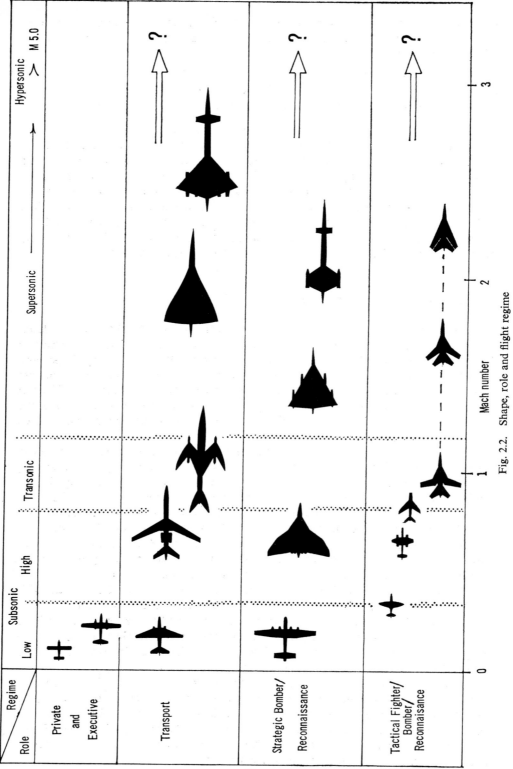

Fig. 2.2. Shape, role and flight regime

12

the boundary being determined by the role for which the machine is intended. Typical roles are: transport, freight, aerial work, fighter, bomber, etc. Transport aircraft, for example, are either:

(1) Long haul, *i.e.*, designed for ranges in excess of 2,500 n ml.
(2) Medium haul, for ranges of 1,500 to 2,500 n ml.
(3) Short haul, for ranges less than 1,500 n ml.

The first two tend to be called 'strategic', the third 'tactical'.

A further consideration is that although the picture was once fairly simple, in that one type of aeroplane did one job, now aeroplanes are so expensive that they are expected to work efficiently in a variety of roles. The trend is towards one aircraft for all related roles. Costs shown in millions of pounds are becoming meaningless today, but in 1961 the cost of one V-bomber was equivalent to the cost of more than eight bombers in 1946 (although the nuclear weapon carried was more than 500,000 times more powerful than the conventional bomb of that period). The cost of one Lightning fighter is roughly equal to the cost of 100 wartime Spitfires.

2.2 Classification of the Aeroplane

The name aerodyne means that an aeroplane belongs to a class of flying-machines that are heavier than air—as distinct from aerostats, such as the airship, which in being lighter than air derive their lift from buoyancy. There are many shapes and sizes of aeroplanes, some of which are shown in Fig. 2.2, most of which are as diverse in appearance as others are similar. All can be placed in two broad families. The first family, called the classical family, because it is the commonest, embodies all of the characteristics of the traditional aeroplane. The second is the integrated family, which employs a new approach to aerodynamics.

In its simplest form the classical family is marked by an arrangement of clearly distinguishable lifting and non-lifting parts. The basic units are the payload-carrying fuselage supported by the wings, which are in turn stabilized by the wing-like tail surfaces. The 'tail' surfaces need not appear at the tail. The horizontal tailplane may lie ahead of the wing, in which case the surface is called a canard—because of the duck-like neck of the long forward fuselage. The primary function of the wing is to provide lift, while that of the fuselage is to house the useful (revenue earning) load, powerplants and crew. Nacelles, which are smaller non-lifting bodies, generally house powerplants and landing-gear, and are usually placed along the wings.

The family of integrated layouts, in its purest form, possesses no clearly distinguishable non-lifting parts. The difference between the classical and integrated layout is shown in Fig. 2.3. In the idealized illustration the payload of the integrated design is shown spread spanwise and lengthwise within the wing. Nearly the whole of the integrated surface contributes to the lift throughout the flight envelope but the arrangement is best suited to supersonic flight conditions.

Although at first sight it might seem that both families are quite distinct, both are in fact near relatives. The relationship can be most clearly seen in the slender polymorphous design of Dr. Barnes Wallis, shown in Fig. 2.4, which changes the wing shape in flight to maintain minimum drag conditions. The principle has been adopted in America by Boeing, for a supersonic transport and by General Dynamics for the F-111, a tactical strike and reconnaissance aircraft.

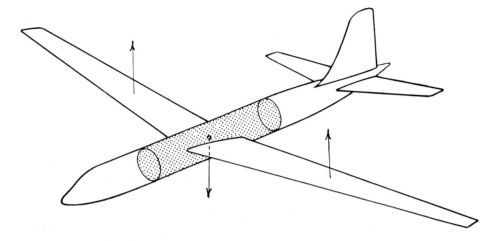

a. The 'classical' layout of an aeroplane   (discrete lift)

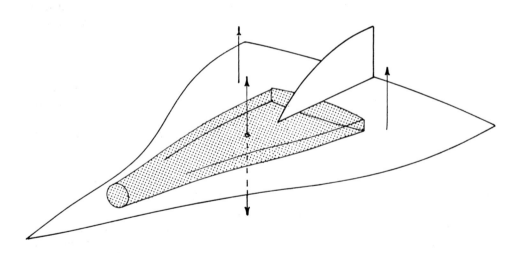

b. An 'integrated' layout (distributed lift)

Fig. 2.3.   The two basic families of aeroplanes

The classical family dominated the aerodynamic field for the first fifty years. Much of the trouble that aeroplanes ran into when they met the hypothetical 'sound barrier' in the 1940s was due to the attempt of designer and aerodynamicist to extend the classical layout into a region of new aerodynamic phenomena. The most characteristic change in the classical layout was to sweep back the lifting surfaces.

With the sweeping back of wings came thinner wing sections, sharper leading edges, increasingly slender bodies, so that changes in the gradient of the surfaces of the aeroplane did not take place too rapidly for the molecules of air to negotiate. The very slender integrated layout represents the ultimate result of these trends.

2.2.1 Group, Type and Mark

Within a family are found many variants, in fact an infinity of possible shapes. Each shape is a function of the role of the aeroplane and the flight regime within which it is designed to operate. The different shapes featured in Fig. 2.2 represent different groups of aeroplanes.

Each group of aeroplanes contains a large number of different types, each one of which represents the ideas of the people who built it about the best way of meeting the operational and design requirements.

Although the final configuration of a type is determined by an apparently incontrovertible set of scientific principles and disciplines, in reality fashion plays an important part, so that the thinking of a designer is channelled by what is generally referred to as current practice. Every so often the pattern of aeronautical development breaks away from current practice: sometimes through the obvious courage and clarity of thought of an individual, often through a technical breakthrough in materials, techniques and principles.

During the life of an aeroplane various improvements may be important enough to cause fundamental changes in design. Such changes are referred to as marks of a particular type. Fig. 2.5 illustrates different marks of one single type of aeroplane.

2.3 Configuration

So far the aeroplane has been fitted into the context of an operational environment, and it has been said that the external shape is determined primarily by the aerodynamic properties required in the intended flight regime. In fact an aeroplane may be thought of as having three separate aspects of shape which, when combined, make up its configuration: *i.e.*, the unique arrangement of wings, fuselage, control and stabilizing surfaces and power-units.

The first aspect of configuration is the aerodynamic shape: the arrangement of the essentially aerodynamic parts. The second aspect is the internal shape, again largely aerodynamic, for it is important to duct air into and out of the aeroplane for economic and efficient use by the propulsion system, which includes the engines and associated ducting. The third aspect of configuration is the internal shape determined by the payload and structural layout. If, therefore, the payload and design point within a flight regime are given, then the final configuration of the aeroplane will be a function of three independent variables:

$$\text{Configuration} = \text{Aerodynamics} + \text{Propulsion} + \text{Structure}$$
$$= f(R) \tag{2--1}$$

where $f(R)$ is some unspecified function of the Requirements.

The point of emphasis is that no design can ever be successful if the right account is not taken of each variable in relation to the others. In the past good designs have depended as much upon the intuition and artistry of the designers in their interpretation of requirements and juggling of the variables, as they have upon the logic of their reasoning.

It must be remembered, however, that an aeroplane is in many ways a living thing, in that once in flight each aeroplane has handling and control characteristics that are unique, to a degree. The handling and control characteristics depend upon the response of an aeroplane to disturbances, either from the air in which it is flying, or from the pilot. The problem of response is largely one of configuration: the effect of the arrangement of aerodynamically sensitive surfaces and the various masses making up the aeroplane upon the dynamic condition of flight. Although an aeroplane may be statically in balance, according to all calculations, and although it may appear to have the right arrangement and size of control and stabilizing surfaces, in certain flight conditions it may display uncontrollable tendencies. Finding these conditions and proposing ways of avoiding and curing the tendencies is the task of the test pilot, working with the designer, aerodynamicist and engineer.

Although the interaction between the inertia of an aeroplane about different axes and the aerodynamic properties is largely a modern problem, associated with long heavy fuselages and relatively small wings, this does not mean that designers have now to face different problems from their predecessors. They still have to find ways of carrying the maximum load with the minimum airframe. To find the right power units at the right time in the development of an aeroplane to enable it to carry the load. To find adequately strong materials to provide maximum strength with minimum weight under a wide band of operating conditions. And to make the aeroplane stable and controllable throughout the flight envelope.

Because the problems are immutable there is much to be gained from the study of aeronautical history. Although there have been occasional jumps—or, more accurately a steepening in the rate of development—in the evolution of the aeroplane, aeronautical history should be viewed as a continuous process. The steepening of the rate of development has corresponded with breaksthrough in propulsion, fuels, materials and techniques. An apposite example was the advent of the gas turbine and the tremendous advance in high speed performance that followed. History can be studied most fruitfully if attention is paid to the pitfalls as well as the triumphs, for man always learns most from adversity.

PART 2

REQUIREMENTS

CHAPTER 3

Requirements and the Specification

The configuration of an aeroplane is a function of the requirements that it is designed to satisfy: in other words the operational environment fixes the shape. Inevitably the converse is true: that the shape given to an aeroplane by the designer limits what it will do. This lies at the root of many present problems, for the designer needs to know at an early stage in the development of a design just what can be fixed, so that plans can be made for production. While the operator—the military operator especially—wishes to leave a design fluid and himself as much flexibility as possible, to ensure that the limitations of a design will be small when matching it to rapidly changing requirements.

3.1 Operational Requirements

Operational requirements are either civil or military. They arise directly from the world situation and, as the world situation changes constantly so too do the operational requirements. One day there may be a need for an aeroplane capable of delivering a nuclear weapon, as a traditional bomber, anywhere within 5,000 n ml radius of base. The next day finds the same aeroplane needing to carry an airborne ballistic missile that can be launched a long way from the target, because the aircraft has become vulnerable to a new development in enemy air defence. In time the second requirement becomes redundant, because of still newer developments.

There are many civil analogies: one of the most apposite being the supersonic transport, or SST. The technical advances needed to make such an aeroplane a success are roughly proportional to the cruising range and Mach number. But both range and Mach number required by a particular operator depend upon geography, politics, economics, population needs and national pride. Of these, politics is really much too simple a word to use, because there is a sort of national strategy involved too, that springs from nationalist predilections, prejudices and desires. These in turn depend upon geography and national history—in fact one may talk of geopolitics.

The high cost of making aeroplanes has led to rationalization of the aircraft industry in the U.K. In the developed parts of the world the aircraft industries, impelled by the need to design and develop war material, have tended to become the leader industries for research and development in a vast number of fields. At this time, however, there is an equally imperative need for simpler aircraft for use in the remoter and less developed parts of the world, to which the younger generation in aeronautics could well devote more energy and attention than has been done in the past. The benefits that would accrue from such attention cannot be measured in terms of cost.

3.1.1 Operational Criteria

The essential thing to grasp is that whatever the aeronautical aspirations of an operator, or the national predilections and prejudices that govern his thinking, aeroplanes are costly to build and fly. To avoid wasting money aeroplanes must be productive. They have inherent potentialities and limitations, and the design of an aeroplane must be such that the greatest potentialities are realized before too much money has been spent on development. Nearly every machine has to last longer than at first expected. But an aeroplane will sell better if the inherent development potential is readily apparent when the design first appears, for in this way the aircraft acts as a stimulant to further rapid development, sometimes in quite unexpected directions.

An aeroplane must be matched to the needs of the country concerned. One of the most interesting exercises at this time is, for example, looking at ways in which aircraft might be used to improve the *per capita* income in developing countries. A recent survey showed the *per capita* income of the U.K. to be about £470 per annum: in India and East Africa it is about £28. Most developing countries have *per capita* incomes below £70 per annum, and usually more than 60 per cent of the population engaged in agriculture—while in a developed country it is less than 20 per cent. When one realizes that a modern long range jet transport may cost nearly £20 per lb of equipped airframe weight, Eq. (3–2), so that in many parts of the world a man might expect to be able to buy 4 lb of empty aeroplane in a year, then we see just how important it is that certain definite criteria should be borne in mind when assessing the aeronautical needs of a region.

The study of operational criteria would become a book in itself, and only the simplest and broadest note should be taken here of what is probably most useful:

(*a*) Climate, this affects the air-conditioning (the environment that must be provided for passengers within the aircraft) and also the choice of structural materials.

(*b*) Population, which requires a survey of the people likely to need air transport for various purposes.

(*c*) The transport needs of the population, which are a function of the economy, and thus dependent upon (*b*).

(*d*) Availability of airfields and landing areas, all of which depend upon topography.

(*e*) Routeing, and hence, range and altitude, which depends upon topography and should be related to (*d*).

It must be apparent that none of the criteria can be considered in isolation for very long. Climate and topography, latitude, longitude, distance from the sea, are related to affect the local economy. Transport needs depend upon the local economy and upon the geographical factors already mentioned. Communications are of vital importance in all aircraft operations, and these depend upon topography. The availability of land or water for operations, and the approaches to landing grounds, affect the excess of power and lift that must be built into a machine to enable it to operate safely and surely when needed.

All of the criteria have an effect upon the ultimate configuration of an aeroplane matched to a set of operating requirements. Their influence is shown very generally in Fig. 3.1., which also serves to show the broad development of the rest of the book. As soon as the criteria are listed, however, they lead one to look into more specific aspects of design: the prime influence of payload, and of disposable load as one whole, upon the range of an aeroplane; and at break-even load factors, and economics as applied to aeronautics.

Payload

Versatility in type and distribution of payload has an important bearing upon ability to achieve high load factors (roughly: payload carried/payload that could be carried). An aircraft should have an inboard profile that allows the maximum payload volume to be used all of the time. If there is such scope, then loading is less of a problem—although large movements of the centre of gravity, or CG, can be expected. Large trimming surfaces will be needed for stability, and the stability requirements must be balanced against the need for manoeuvrability. In this respect the aeroplane scores over the helicopter in terms of stability, but not in manoeuvrability.

Passenger aeroplanes usually seat 4 or 5 abreast. Ideally a cabin should be high enough for a man to stand erect, but much depends upon the role of the aeroplane. An aircraft intended for fairly short duration flights is less likely to require such a high cabin than one designed for flights of several hours. Similarly, long distance aircraft must be designed to cater for the more exacting needs of the hard-to-please passengers of the developed countries. But some reduction in average standards of passenger comfort can be tolerated for low-cost transports designed for short block times (total time taken from start to stop), e.g., 50 minutes for a 250 mile stage.

Freighter aeroplanes must carry pre-packaged loads, as well as comparatively heavy and bulky equipment of many kinds. Large and accessible freight holds are needed with ample room for manhandling awkward loads. Ideally there should be provision for nose and tail loading, so that one load can be rolled from the rear of the hold as the other is rolled into the front. However, the arrangement is often hard to achieve without recourse to swing-noses and tails, which are inevitably more complicated than simple doors.

Payload-Range

A basic criterion of transport operational requirements is the distance, the range, that a given payload can be carried. This criterion, called the payload-range is defined as:

$$\text{Payload-range} = \text{payload} \times \text{distance, ton-miles} \qquad (3\text{--}1)$$

The weight of fuel + payload with which an aeroplane can take-off is called the disposable load. Additional fuel is carried for emergencies.

For a given disposable load, payload and range are interchangeable to a certain extent. Neglecting, for the moment, the effect of improved propulsive efficiency and

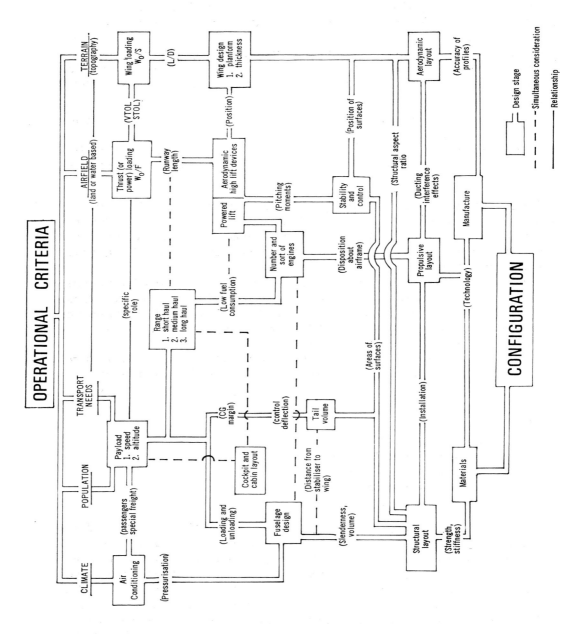

Fig. 3.1. Influence of operational criteria on final configuration

20

improved lift/drag ratio upon range-flying ability as the aeroplane grows lighter; and assuming that the disposable load can be carried entirely as fuel, then the distance flown for any quantity of fuel burnt is as shown in Fig. 3.2(*a*). The slope of the graph is a function of the lift/drag ratio, which is the measure of aerodynamic efficiency. The less the drag the further an aircraft flies on a given quantity of fuel.

In practice there are restrictions to the exchange between payload and fuel weights. Fuel can be carried within thin wings, but passengers cannot. Fuel should not be carried in the fuselage along with passengers. Fig. 3.2(*a*) becomes modified therefore by:

(i) The maximum payload, by weight as well as volume, that can be carried within the fuselage.

(ii) The total amount of fuel that can be carried within the structure. Fuel carried in the wings relieves the bending loads at the wing roots and enables a lighter structure to be built.

The modified figure is as shown in Fig. 3.2(*b*). It should be noted that the range is now shown along the base of the graph, as Fig. 3.2(*a*) has been rotated. Point B is the hardest to place, as it is fixed by the structure weight and this in turn depends upon among other things, the dispostion of fuel tanks, engines and the type and position of the undercarriage units.

The line A–B marks the cut-off, by volume or weight, of the payload that can be carried. Point C marks the maximum distance that can be flown with the fuel carried —clearly it would be uneconomical to design for maximum range with the maximum payload. The line C–D marks the slightly increased ranges that may be flown with the full fuel load, by reducing the payload carried.

The total weight of an aeroplane is made up of the weights of the payload, structure systems, equipment, fuel and engines. These can be put together mathematically as:

$$W_O = W_A + W_E + W_F + W_P \qquad (3\text{--}2)$$

where,

W_O = all-up weight, lb;
W_A = equipped airframe weight, lb;
W_E = powerplant weight, lb;
W_F = fuel weight, lb;
W_P = payload, lb.

Although the sum is simply stated, most of the components are interdependent. For example, one may not alter a design to carry more fuel without having to increase the fuel system weight and also the structure weight (unless the fuel can be so placed along the wings as to give bending relief—one of the reasons for podded overload tanks suspended beneath wings and wing-tips). Similarly, one may not 'stretch' a design to carry more passengers without also increasing the weight of structure, furnishings, fittings and allied equipment and, hence, the equipped airframe weight. The equipped airframe weight is composed of the structure weight, the weights of the fuel system and power services and equipment, and the weights of furnishing and other fittings for the payload.

The proportion of the all-up weight taken by the payload is quite small in all but the shortest range aircraft: that of a subsonic transport is of the order of ten per cent, while that of a supersonic transport may be around five per cent. It is salutary to

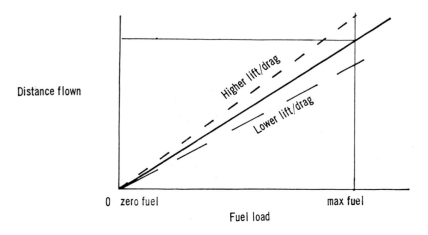

Distance flown

Higher lift/drag

Lower lift/drag

0   zero fuel   max fuel

Fuel load

a. Range flown against fuel carried

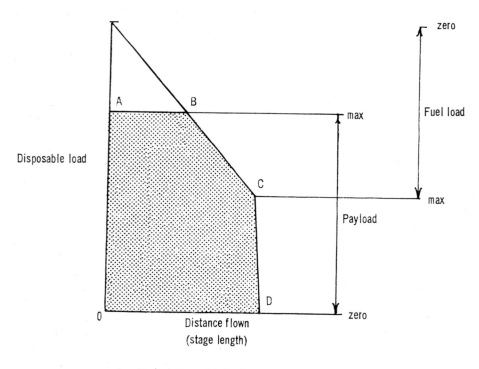

Disposable load

A   B

C

D

0   Distance flown
          (stage length)

zero

Fuel load

max

max

Payload

zero

b. Typical disposable load : range relationship

Fig. 3.2. Disposable load and payload-range

remember that the bumblebee, which is extremely efficient as a flying-machine, is said to carry a payload around forty-six per cent of its all-up weight over considerable distances.

Economics

Operational requirements must always take account of the economic health of a country. In aeronautical affairs this depends upon the health of a country's industry. The criterion of a sensible operational requirement, an OR, is that it must result in an aircraft that will pay for itself with the returns that it brings, either financially or in increased security.

The economics of an aeroplane can be viewed as a pair of scales. On one side is the cost, on the other is what can be afforded. The amount of money to be spent on a project has three aspects:

(i) The first arises from the designer and manufacturer, their choice of layout, powerplants and equipment.

(ii) The second depends upon the financial policies of the government, and upon its long and short term interests. A typical example might be the favouring of a design by a manufacturer situated in an industrially depressed area, even though that design might not satisfy requirements to quite the same extent as one from another area.

(iii) The third aspect arises from the operator himself who has his own specialized needs in mind, and who may have to compete in a cut-throat market with small margins for error close to the limits of his knowledge.

It may be that although a designer might specify a certain engine when discussing a project with an operator, the operator himself wants another engine, not quite as well matched to the design, but with exceptionally good economics and reputation. Similarly, the operator often specifies a particular type of equipment to be carried. Hence the designer must be a mixture of diplomat, mentor and psychologist in his dealings with a potential operator. And the potential operator must ensure that his requirements are so couched that the resulting aeroplane will be right for as many other buyers as possible, for the best way of ensuring that prices are kept down is through financial load-spreading over a wide market.

The most useful way of comparing the economics of aeroplanes and of weighing the merits of a project in meeting a set of requirements, is to study the operating costs. These fall into two categories: direct operating costs, which depend directly upon the physical characteristics of the aeroplane: and indirect operating costs which, although depending in part upon the physical characteristics, depend much more upon the service offered and the circumstances of the operator. The first is the sum of all costs of flying and maintenance, together with insurance, obsolescence and depreciation of airframe, engines and equipment. The second criterion arises from the attraction of traffic and general administration. However, unit costs, which are the costs per ton-mile (calculated by dividing the total hourly cost by the block speed and the payload) give an immediate measure of the commercial efficiency of an aeroplane, and may often be used instead of direct operating costs.

The Break-Even Point

If seats or capacity are sold on an individual basis at a fixed rate, then a percentage of seats or capacity must be sold in order that the net revenue equals the cost of the operation. The percentage of seats or capacity is called the break-even load factor. There are a number of break-even points with which we are not concerned here. The

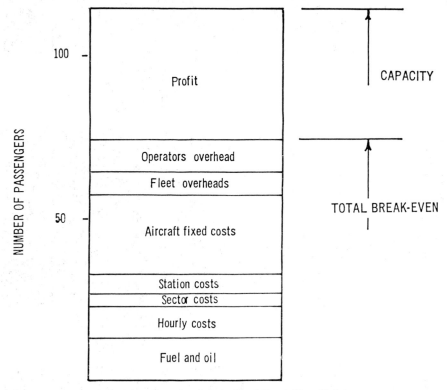

Fig. 3.3. Capacity and the Total Break-Even Point

total break-even point is shown in Fig. 3.3. The break-even points are not constant for any particular aircraft type. In computing break-even points all costs (including financial charges) must be taken into account. These vary with stage lengths and different routes and should, therefore, be considered as an important part of any operational requirement where they are relevant to the aircraft concerned.

Airfield Requirements

The airfield requirements affect the design of an aeroplane in the following important ways:

(i) Take-off distance available. The distance can usually be reduced by using more powerful engines, although this results in the aircraft being overpowered when cruising and using more fuel than is necessary during that stage of the flight.

Fig. 5.10. Behaviour of wool tufts on a wing with local boundary layer separations

Fig. 7.16. Jet lift, the VSTOL AV-8B Harrier (1981), built jointly by McDonnell Douglas and British Aerospace (*By permission of* McDonnell Douglas *and* Flight International)

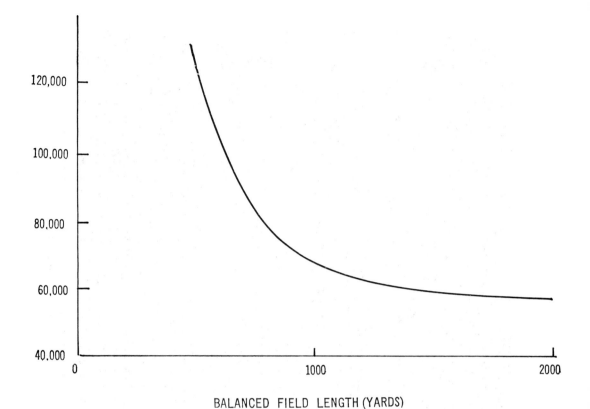

BALANCED FIELD LENGTH (YARDS)

Fig. 3.4.   Typical relationship between aircraft all-up weight and airfield size for a turbo-prop transport carrying 60 passengers 1,000 nautical miles at 350 knots

   (ii) Landing distance available. The landing distance is reduced by fitting high-lift devices to the wings, to enable the aeroplane to land at lower forward speeds. If cruising performance is not the most important criterion, then larger wings may be used.

(iii) Runway and taxiway strength. This affects the design of landing-gear: the number of wheels and types of tyres to be used.

(iv) Noise restrictions. The higher the thrust and power loading (Eq.(4–8) *et seq*) of the engines, the flatter is the climb-out path and, the longer does take-off noise disturb those on the ground.

If one is to design an aeroplane for shortened take-off and landing distances, then there is an inevitable increase in the all-up weight. The weight increase is brought about by increased size of engine to generate the necessary power, and the addition of high lift devices and their attendant mechanisms. Fig. 3.4 shows a typical all-up weight trend for a turbo-prop aircraft designed to carry 60 passengers 1,000 n ml at 350 knots. The balanced field length is the distance in which the aircraft can be brought to rest in the event of an abandoned take-off.

3.2 Design Requirements

The act of designing an aeroplane is governed by stringent regulations that ensure, as far as is theoretically possible, that the aircraft will be well behaved and safe in practice. The regulations have been introduced for all classes of aircraft and lay down certain minimum standards with which their designs must conform.

In Britain there are two sources of requirements: those for civil aeroplanes being embodied in British Civil Airworthiness Requirements, of the Air Registration Board: and those governing the design of aircraft for the Royal Air Force and Royal Navy, of the Ministry of Aviation. Their scope embraces all operational functions, and they cover the following broad aspects:

(1) The comfort and safety of passengers and crew. Guidance is given as to the placing of controls, the design of seats, and the adequacy of the pilot's view and other allied matters.
(2) The flying qualities of the aircraft, both in pilot handling and in performance.
(3) Considerations of basic engineering design, strength and stiffness. These considerations are intended to ensure that the aeroplane will operate safely in the design role without danger of structural failure.
(4) The installation of engines, fuel and oil systems, and various other power systems and services.
(5) Servicing and reliability to ensure efficient operation and a reasonable life.
(6) Flight testing by the manufacturer before an aeroplane is delivered to the operator, or before the delivery of a new type to a test establishment.

Compliance with BCARs also ensures that an aircraft satisfies the corresponding ICAO standards of airworthiness.

Only when every consideration of precise performance and every detail of engineering design has been approved, does an aeroplane receive a Certificate of Airworthiness, or C. of A. There are several categories of the certificate and it must be renewed whenever an aeroplane is modified.

3.3 The Specification

Specifications arise from requirements and amount to rational statements of what is wanted in an aeroplane so that it may best satisfy the requirements in terms of what is possible at the time. The specification must always take account of the current state-of-the-art of aeronautical technology and practice.

The specification is the yardstick against which the resultant aircraft is measured. In theory it is drawn up by the customer before submission to the manufacturer. But in practice there is an increasing tendency to write the specification as the aircraft is progressed through the various states of design and construction. The practice is inevitable as advanced aeroplanes must be planned well ahead of the time they are due to be used operationally. In that time there may be large attendant changes in technology as research and development precedes design.

Because specifications are practical documents one finds that the clean lines first drawn by the designer are greatly altered by what is achieveable in practice. The real aeroplane also grows heavier than was at first estimated. Fig. 3.5 shows the sort of

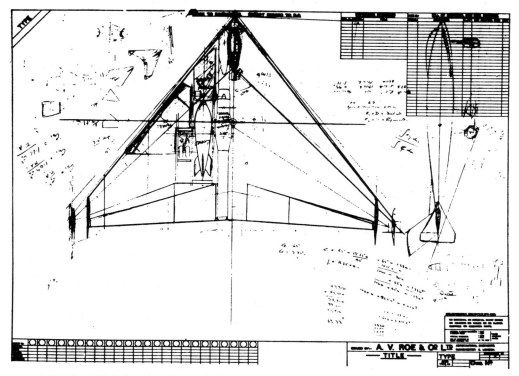

a. An historic sketch, believed to be the very first Avro 698 delta drawing, by the late Roy Chadwick and his team.

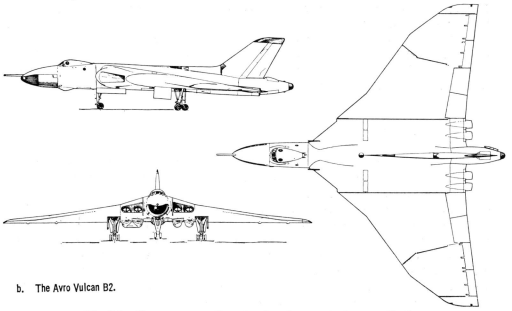

b. The Avro Vulcan B2.

Fig. 3.5.   The emergence of an aeroplane in response to a specification

changes that appear between the first sketching of an aeroplane and the emergence of the latest version. In this example the aircraft is the Avro Vulcan, designed to a specification formulated by the British Air Staff in 1946 which led to the V-bombers still used by Bomber Command of the Royal Air Force.

The contents of a specification are normally agreed before signing the contract between the manufacturer and his client. After that, the responsibility of meeting the specification is in the manufacturer's hands. The specification is a precise document and failure to meet it by only a fraction can result in penalty payments under the guarantee. It is more usual for civil operators alone to lay down such limits as military aeroplanes involve too many political considerations to make the exacting of penalties a reasonable proposition.

Generally speaking, the smaller the tolerances by which a design might be allowed to fall short of what is required, and the greater their number, the more expensive will be the eventual aeroplane. The tolerances are set by the operator, typical examples being:

(1) Range within ± 3 to 5 per cent at optimum range-speed.
(2) Maximum speed within ± 3 per cent.
(3) Equipped airframe and structure weights within ± 2 or 3 per cent.
(4) Take-off and landing distances within ± 5 to 7 per cent.
(5) Noise levels no more than 2 or 3 decibels above that specified.

The tolerances usually include upper and lower limits, although one of them represents a bonus for the operator. If the bonus is too large, however, one should suspect that some other quality of the design has suffered.

Occasionally one still finds a specification being written around a completely new aircraft that has been designed and built as a private venture. Such was the practice on several notable occasions before the Second World War. Two of the most famous aeroplanes so designed were the Supermarine Spitfire and the de Havilland Mosquito. Apart from the private venture, the specification gives the designer his first ideas of how big and how heavy the eventual aeroplane will be. We shall, therefore, now look at some of these aspects of interpreting the requirements that determine what form the configuration will take.

CHAPTER 4

Interpretation of Requirements

the Beginning of an Aeroplane

Before the first outline of an aeroplane can be sketched three questions must be considered, although they are probably never posed consciously at the same time:

(1) What priorities should be singled out from the operational requirements, *e.g.*, is the aeroplane a heavy weight-lifter, or for flying long ranges with moderate payloads?
(2) What might be achieved within the present state-of-the-art?
(3) How far might the basic design require future development beyond the present requirements. In other words, might the basic requirements be expected to change very much with time?

The answers to these questions all depend upon the required performance. In order to appreciate the answers it will help to look at some of the design parameters affecting the performance of an aircraft.

4.1 Forces Acting on an Aeroplane in Flight

Fig. 4.1 illustrates a number of the performance modes that might be encountered during a typical supersonic sortie. The motions of the aeroplane in the various modes are of two kinds, rectilinear and curvilinear. The first is motion in a straight line, without accelerations applied normal to the line of flight. The second is motion along a curved flight path due to applied normal acceleration. This is termed manoeuvring, and is of great importance because the magnitude and direction of the normal accelerations directly affect the structural design.

In order to move and manoeuvre, a system of forces must be set up in such a way that it can be controlled at will, with the minimum of delay. Movement is a function of applied power, through the propulsion system and the aerodynamic controls. Manoeuvre is a function of the response to applied power, and this depends upon the size and weight, the distribution of weight throughout the airframe, and the stability of the aeroplane.

4.1.1 Unaccelerated (rectilinear) Flight

In its passage through the air an aeroplane sets up a pressure field, due to the reaction of the air over the whole airframe surface. The pressure acts at right angles

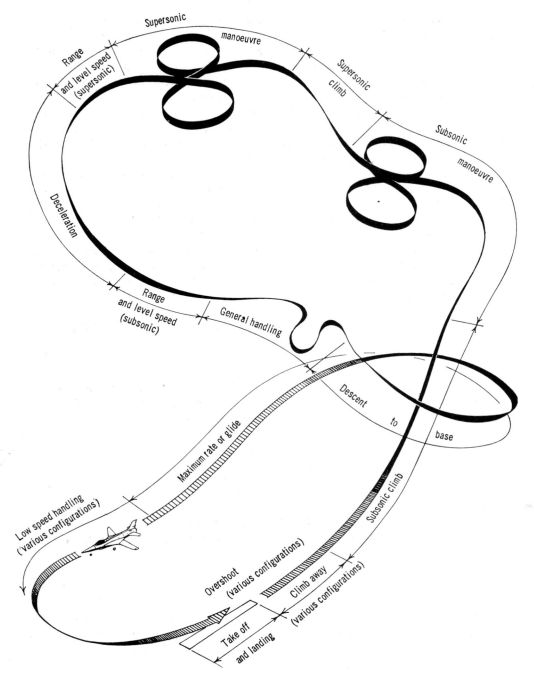

Fig. 4.1. Performance modes

30

to the skin contour at any point, but the pressure can be resolved into components normal and tangential to the line of flight, taken in the plane of symmetry of the aircraft. Those normal to the line of flight, when summed, give rise to the resultant lift, L. It should be noted that lift is contributed to by the whole airframe and not the wings alone. The tangential components, when summed, give rise to the resultant drag, D. The nature of lift and drag is considered in some detail later.

In powered flight the drag is opposed by the net propulsive force, F. This is the resultant force generated by the propulsive system after the sum of the gross thrust of the engine, the internal drag of the propulsive system, and the inclination of the thrust line to the line of flight have all been taken into account.

The final force in the picture is the weight of the aeroplane, W, acting through the centre of gravity. Fig. 4.2 shows the simplified system of forces, all acting through the CG at this juncture, in unaccelerated flight. It should be noted that the lift is only equal and opposite to the weight in straight and level flight. When climbing and descending the lift component is less than the weight.

In Fig. 4.2(a) and (b) two velocity diagrams show the relationship between the angles of climb and descent, γ_c, γ_d, and the rates of climb and descent, v_c, v_d. These are given with respect to the TAS, V. However, it should be noted that v_c and v_d are usually given in ft/min, which involves an adjustment of V from the usual form of knots or miles per hour.

From the force and velocity diagrams we see that in straight and level flight:

$$F = D \qquad (4\text{--}1)$$
$$L = W \qquad (4\text{--}2)$$

When climbing and descending, however, the force vector balancing the weight is composed of two components: the lift (which, as we have observed, is less than that in straight and level flight) and the resultant of $(F-D)$, such that:

$$\gamma_c = \sin^{-1} \frac{(F-D)}{W} \qquad (4\text{--}3)$$

whence,

$$v_c \text{ or } v_d = \frac{(F-D)}{W} V \qquad (4\text{--}4)$$

the sign, which differentiates v_c from v_d being determined by the sign of $(F-D)$.

In the case of gliding flight, when the net propulsive force is zero, the rate of descent can be approximated, from Eq. (4–2), to:

$$\text{gliding } v_d = -\left(\frac{D}{L}\right)V \qquad (4\text{--}4a)$$

when the angle of glide is very shallow. Hence, the gliding efficiency of a sailplane depends upon achieving the highest possible lift/drag ratio, (L/D). Although a sailplane or glider descends constantly through the air, it will climb away from the ground as long as the air is ascending with a velocity greater than v_d.

4.1.2 Accelerated (curvilinear) Flight

Although an aircraft may be in accelerated flight when changing speed along a rectilinear path, here accelerated flight applies to the special condition of changing

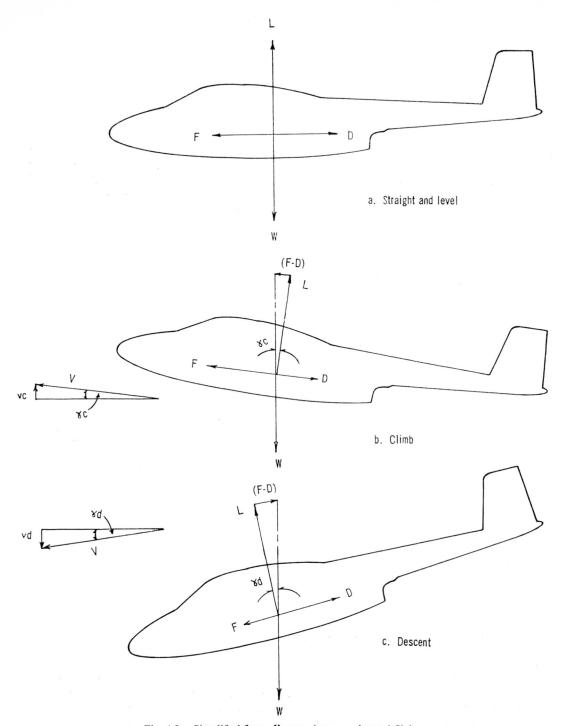

Fig. 4.2. Simplified force diagram in unaccelerated flight

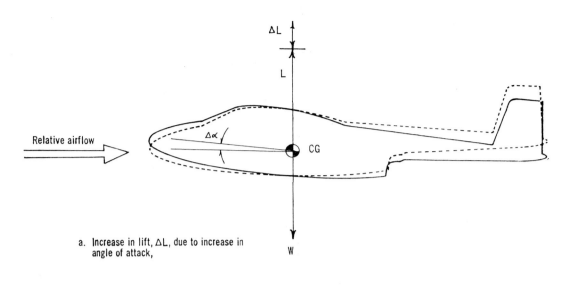

Relative airflow →

a. Increase in lift, ΔL, due to increase in
   angle of attack,

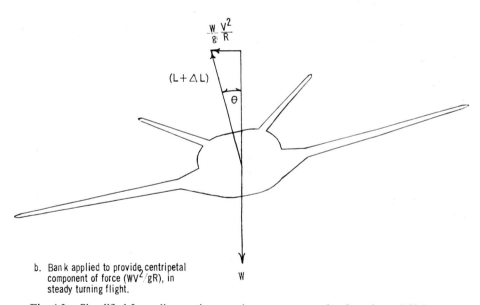

b. Bank applied to provide centripetal
   component of force (WV²/gR), in
   steady turning flight.

Fig. 4.3. Simplified force diagram in a steady turn, an example of accelerated flight

direction, which involves a component of acceleration normal to the flight path.
Curvature of the flight path is achieved by changing the magnitude and direction of
the lift component away from the equilibrium condition of Fig. 4.2(a). The change
can be brought about either by a change of speed, or a change of the angle of attack,
$\Delta\alpha$, of the aeroplane to the relative airflow.

Fig. 4.3 illustrates the simplest manoeuvre mode, that of level turning flight, in
which the angle of attack is increased by movement of the control surfaces. An

increase in engine power is needed to maintain speed by countering the increased drag, while the aeroplane is banked until the vertical component of the new lift is equal and opposite to the weight. If θ is the angle of bank, then the radius of turn is given by:

$$R = \frac{V^2}{g \tan \theta} \qquad (4\text{--}5)$$

where, R = radius of turn,
         g = gravitational constant,
         V = TAS, reduced to a velocity,
         θ = angle of bank.

The normal acceleration is given by the ratio of the lift/weight, L/W. The more steeply banked the turn, the more the lift that is needed and the higher the normal acceleration (commonly referred to as 'g'). Accelerated flight involves more than turns alone and includes: stalling, which is a loss of lift through a breakdown of the airflow over the lifting surfaces; spinning, which is rotation of the aeroplane about its axes when the lifting surfaces are stalled asymmetrically. Similarly rolls, pull-ups, push-overs and their various combinations produce normal accelerations for which the designer must cater, if they lie within the requirements. Additionally, accelerated flight results from horizontal and vertical gusts which, in being associated with atmospheric-turbulence, are of critical importance at high speed. It may be shown that the resulting normal acceleration varies with TAS and inversely with wing loading (the weight of aircraft carried per unit wing area). For that reason low-level strike aircraft, like the TSR2 in Fig. E.3.1 have small, short wings.

4.1.3 Flight Loads

During flight an aeroplane is subjected to a wide range of combinations of normal accelerations, speeds and altitudes. The normal method of measuring acceleration is to call the straight and level case zero, describing applied accelerations as +ve and −ve about it. The aeronautical engineer differs in his approach, calling the straight and level case $1g$ and meaning that the inertia force to which an object is subjected in this condition is 1·0 times its weight. The table is self-explanatory:

TABLE 4.1

Case	Normal method of expressing acceleration	Aeronautical method	Lift ÷ weight of aeroplane	Inertia force on weight ΔW
Free fall	$-1g$	0	0	0
Level flight	0	$1g$	1	ΔW
General	$(n-1)g$	ng	n	$n\Delta W$

The V—n Diagram

There are two significant families of curves, referred to generally as V—n diagrams, that are used for representing the limiting combinations of speed and normal acceleration for which an aircraft must be designed. The first, the basic manoeuvring envelope applies to symmetric flight, *i.e.*, flight in which the aircraft is not yawed at an angle to the flight path when, for example, an engine has failed. The second, the basic gust envelope applies to symmetric flight in vertical gusts. A gust alters the angle of attack of the lifting surfaces by an increment $\tan^{-1} w/V$, where w is the vertical gust velocity. As the lift is a function of the angle of attack, the inertia forces applied to the structure by manoeuvring are altered by the gust conditions. Typical diagrams are shown in Fig. 4.4. The basic manoeuvre envelope corresponds for a civil aircraft, with Table 4.2.

TABLE 4.2

Load* Factor (*i.e.* inertia) force)	Category		
	Normal	Semi-aerobatic	Aerobatic
n_1	$2 \cdot 1 + \dfrac{24000}{W_0 + 10000}$ but n_1 need not be greater than 3·5 and not less than 2·5	4·5	6·0
n_2	0	0	0
n_3	1·0	1·8	3·0
n_4	0·75 n_1 but not less than 2·0 2·5	3·5	4·5

W_0 ... lb ... is design all-up weight

* See Fig. 4.4 (*a*)

4.2 Performance

The performance of an aeroplane depends upon the degree to which a designer can:

(1) Achieve combinations of excess lift and net propulsive force (thrust) over weight and drag.
(2) Stabilize and control the combination of forces throughout the flight envelope.

Both lift and drag depend upon the aerodynamic design of the aeroplane. The choice of powerplant depends upon the flight regime. The weight depends upon both the aerodynamic design and choice of powerplant. And the stability and control of the machine depends upon flight regime, aerodynamic design and powerplant arrangement. Clearly then, the performance is seen to depend very much upon the propulsion system: a term used here to include any mechanical means of moving or supporting an aeroplane in flight.

4.2.1 Powerplant Choice

All propulsive systems perform the same basic function of transforming the heat energy of fuels into propulsive thrust. The development of an aircraft engine depends, perhaps more than anything else, upon the availability of a fuel suited to the particular function of the engine. Air-breathing engines use the ambient air for oxidizing the

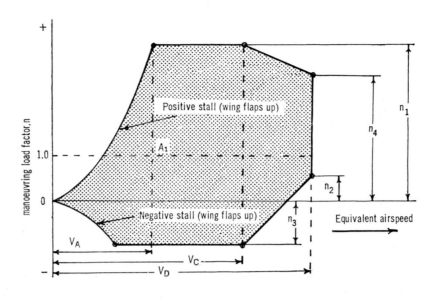

a. Basic manoeuvring envelope

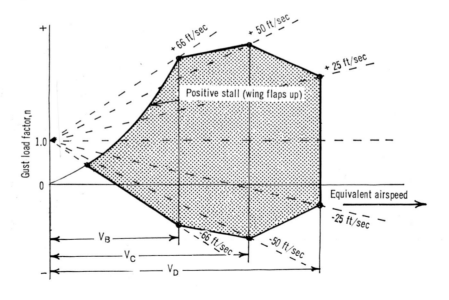

b. Basic gust envelope

Fig. 4.4. Typical V-n Diagrams

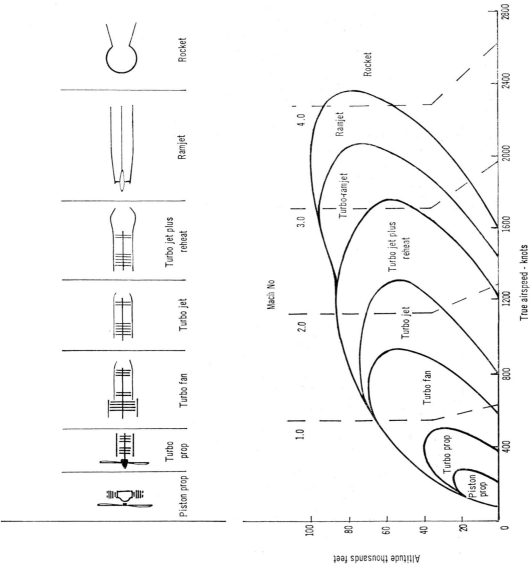

Fig. 4.5.   The level flight propulsion picture

37

fuel and, therefore, can only be used up to heights where there is enough air to support combustion. For practical purposes at this time the limit is around 100,000 ft. Air-breathing engines develop thrust either by means of a propeller, or by the ejection of combustion gases in the form of a jet. The two basic types of air-breathing engine are the reciprocating (or piston) engine and the gas-turbine. The rocket carries the oxidant needed to release the energy of the fuel. Although the rocket is, therefore, unlimited by ambient conditions, the weight of oxidant required makes the use of the rocket prohibitive for any aircraft that must fly for more than a few minutes.

Later in the book we will be concerned with aspects of powerplant installations, that affect the aerodynamic and structural design of aeroplanes. For the present it is enough to note the broad propulsion picture illustrated in Fig. 4.5, in which are shown the general flight envelopes of each type of powerplant.

Powerplant Performance

Powerplant performance has three important aspects: the net thrust produced per pound of dry engine weight: the net horsepower produced per pound of dry weight; and the thrust specific fuel consumption.

The net thrust of the engine (for small inclinations of the thrust line to the line of flight sensibly equal to the net propulsive force) is the useable thrust when installed. Fig. 4.6(a) shows typical values of net thrust/lb dry weight for a number of power-plants, and these curves should be related to Fig. 4.5.

The net horsepower of the engine is proportional to the net thrust multiplied by the velocity of flight. It is useful in that when compared with the drag horsepower one obtains a measure of the residual power left over for doing work, either by changing altitude or increasing speed. Fig. 4.6(b) shows typical values of net horsepower/lb dry weight.

The overall efficiency of a propulsion system is indicated by the specific fuel consumption, defined as the number of pounds of fuel used to produce one horse-power for one hour. In the case of gas turbine engines, which may be used over large bands of speed and height, the mass flow through the engine changes markedly with environment. It is therefore more useful to use the thrust specific fuel consumption, the weight of fuel needed to maintain unit thrust for one hour. Fig. 4.6(c) shows typical values of thrust sfc in lb/hr lb.

4.2.2 Basic Performance

Basic performance problems are concerned with the general cases of changing speed and height, *i.e.*, with acceleration, level speed, climb and descent.

Energy Height

Basic performance may be conveniently treated in terms of an equation expressing the rate at which the total energy of an aeroplane is being changed. At any instant the total energy is the sum of the potential and kinetic energies:

$$E_h = W\left(h + \frac{V^2}{2g}\right) \qquad (4\text{--}6)$$

where, E_h = total energy at a given speed and height,

   h = height above mean sea level,

   g = gravitational constant,

   V = TAS, expressed as a velocity,

   W = instantaneous weight of aircraft.

The term in brackets is usually called the energy height, because it has the dimensions of length and is a measure of the total energy per unit weight of aircraft. The energy height is denoted by the symbol h_e, where:

$$h_e = \left(h + \frac{V^2}{2g} \right) \qquad (4\text{--}6a)$$

   Now, power is the rate of employment of energy with time so that, on differentiating Eq. (4–6) with respect to time we have:

$$\frac{d}{dt}(E_h) = W \left(\frac{dh}{dt} + \frac{V}{g}\frac{dV}{dt} \right) \qquad (4\text{--}6b)$$

But, dh/dt is the rate of climb, v_c (or of descent v_d) and dV/dt is the acceleration (or deceleration), a, of the aircraft along the flight path. Furthermore, as power is equivalent to the rate of doing work, we may say that the power of the aeroplane when flying at a given speed is:

$$V(F-D) = W \left(v_c + \frac{Va}{g} \right)$$

i.e.,

$$(F-D) = W \left(\frac{v_c}{V} + \frac{a}{g} \right) \qquad (4\text{--}7)$$

From this it can be seen that the residual propulsive force (the net propulsive force minus the drag) of the aeroplane can be used to change either the height, or the speed or both. If the net propulsive force is less than the drag, then the aeroplane descends or decelerates.

   Very high performance aeroplanes possess high kinetic energies. For this reason they are able to 'zoom climb' to heights that are well above their normal ceilings, by simply exchanging kinetic for potential energy in Eq. (4–6). For example, an aeroplane pulling up into a climb at M 2·0 and decelerating to M 1·0 might gain some 15,000 ft without the pilot touching the throttle. It follows too, from Eq. (4–7) and Fig. 4.2, that the angle of climb or descent is obtained by dividing through the equation by W, as long as a steady speed is being maintained.

   Fig. 4.7 illustrates net propulsive force and drag curves of a typical supersonic fighter in level flight. From these may be seen the ways in which $(F-D)$ varies with height in Eq. (4–7). It should be noted that the maximum level speed is determined by the intersection of the curves, highest values being obtained at the higher altitudes.

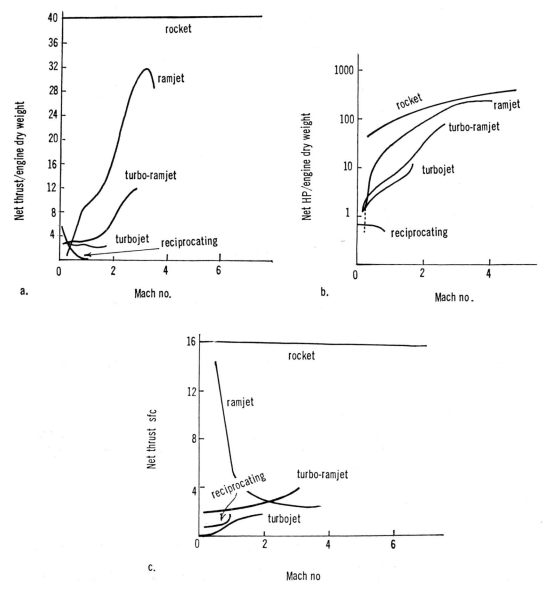

Fig. 4.6. Comparison of typical performance characteristics of several different power plants

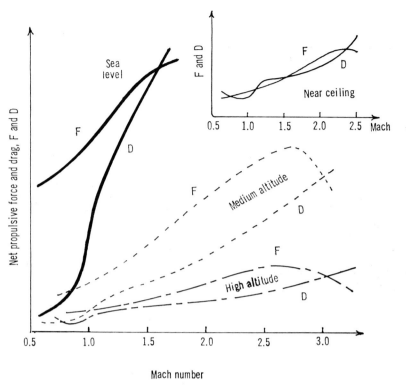

Fig. 4.7. Typical variation of net propulsive force and drag of a supersonic fighter in level flight at different altitudes

Power for Flight and Wing Loading

Eq. (4–7) is of particular importance, because we may deduce from it a relationship between the power and the wing area required to fly an aeroplane of a given weight. At constant airspeed (Eq. (4–7) becomes:

$$(F-D) = W\frac{v_c}{V}$$
$$= W \sin \gamma_c \quad \text{(from Fig. 4.2}(b))$$

The potential energy of the aircraft is being increased at a steady rate: work is done in drawing the weight of the machine upwards.

The power required, P_e, is equivalent to $(F–D)V$, the product of the resultant thrust and the airspeed—in fact V is assumed to be the speed of the aircraft in still air, so that it is also the speed relative to the earth, the ground speed, which is used in dynamic calculations. If we now rearrange Eq. (4–7) as follows:

$$\frac{(F-D)V}{W} = v_c$$

but substitute P_e and $v_c = V \sin \gamma_c$ for the respective sides of the equation, we have:

$$\frac{P_e}{W} = V \sin \gamma_c \qquad (4\text{--}7a)$$

If the inclination of the flight path to the horizon remains unchanged, then $\sin \gamma_c$ is a constant, and this is the condition in which we wish to determine the minimum power for steady flight. If the angle, γ_c, is shallow—in fact tending to 0—then the lift L is sensibly equal to the weight, W. Now, it may be seen from Eq. (5–8) that lift is the product of $C_L/2$, a constant fixed by the flight conditions of constant angle of attack and airspeed, and $\rho V^2 S$, which contains the wing area, S, and a pair of airflow terms. The wing loading, W/S, is equivalent to L/S under these conditions, so that transposing Eq. (5–8) and using W in place of L we see that

$$V \text{ varies as } \sqrt{\left(\frac{W}{S\rho}\right)}$$

and Eq. (4–7a):

$$\frac{P_e}{W} = k \sqrt{\left[\left(\frac{W}{S}\right)\frac{1}{\rho}\right]} \qquad (4\text{–}8)$$

The constant of proportionality, k, between the power and wing loading terms depends upon the lift and drag characteristics of the aircraft at the particular speed and height. The ratio, P_e/W, is the reciprocal of the power loading, at one TAS, V.

If, instead of P_e/W we use $(F–D)V/W$, and L/D in place of W/D, Eq. (4–8) becomes:

$$\left(\frac{F}{W} - \frac{1}{(L/D)}\right)V = k \sqrt{\left[\left(\frac{W}{S}\right)\frac{1}{\rho}\right]} \qquad (4\text{–}8a)$$

where F/W is the reciprocal of the thrust loading, and L/D the lift/drag for the particular flight conditions.

From the last equation we may deduce that:

(i) For a given aerodynamic efficiency, (L/D), the lower the wing loading the lower are the power and thrust requirements.

(ii) With the propulsive and aerodynamic characteristics fixed, the higher we wish to fly the lower must be the wing loading.

(iii) For a given wing loading the higher the aerodynamic efficiency of the wing (really the whole aeroplane, not the wing alone) the lower are the thrust and power requirements.

The thrust and power requirements affect the choice of powerplant and the number of engines to be used.

Although the foregoing arguments have been made in terms of flight at altitude, they apply equally well to the take-off and landing cases, for all airfields have limitations in runway lengths and directions, and the altitude of an airfield affects the performance of aircraft using it. Simply: the smaller the airfield, the hotter the day, and the higher the airfield above sea level, the more the thrust (or power) and the lower the wing loading that must be used for take-off. The airfield characteristics determine the design wing loading of large aircraft.

We see that to achieve high speed, rate of climb and acceleration throughout the flight envelope an aeroplane must have engines developing high thrust. The engine installation must be efficient, while the overall lift/drag must be as high as possible.

4.2.3 Special Performance

Take-off and landing, and range and endurance flying are really special perform-ance problems. It is now apparent that to satisfy take-off and landing requirements account must be taken of the size, type, geography, altitude and climate of the most critical airfields from which it is intended to operate. For example, airfields in Russia, the U.S.A., and India and Africa pose fewer climb-out problems than airfields in Western Europe or Greece. Australia has few really difficult approaches to her air-fields, while Norway is beset with them.

Take-off

The shortness of take-off depends upon how quickly lift greater than the weight can be generated. Excess lift can be obtained with wing area in excess of that required for cruising, but that is uneconomical. Where cruising efficiency is of secondary importance, large cheap benefits accrue from low wing loadings. Where cruising efficiency is of primary importance one finds aeroplanes fitted with slots, flaps and other forms of high lift devices. In recent years lifting-engines have appeared to shorten take-off runs still further, but at a high price in fuel consumption.

The generation of lift early in the take-off run can also be achieved by low power and thrust loadings, (W/P), (W/F), enabling faster accelerations to be made. The two forces to be overcome are due to the inertia of the aeroplane, $a(W/g)$, and the rolling friction, $\mu(W{-}L)$, as shown in Fig. 4.8. As far as the second is concerned, the lift may be increased by the use of flaps and other high lift devices, and by lengthening the nosewheel leg to set the aircraft at a higher angle of attack and generate a thrust component in the lifting plane. The coefficient of friction, μ, is not only affected by tyre size and tread pattern, but by wheel arrangement. For example, bogie wheels are increasingly common on large aircraft and tandem wheels cause less drag when running through standing-water and slush than side-by-side arrangements. Such drag may well prevent the nosewheel from being lifted off the ground, and the aircraft from taking off at all.

Landing

The approach and landing path is similar in all respects to that on take-off, but in reverse. The forces acting on the aeroplane are the same, except that ground drag is increased by the use of brakes and braking parachutes, arrester gear (in the case of naval aeroplanes) and thrust-reversing engine installations.

The steepness of the approach path depends upon the lift/drag ratio. For this reason one finds high drag flaps and airbrakes used when landing, but in order to maintain adequate power for emergencies the high drag also enables the engines to be run at high rev/min, which reduces their acceleration time to full power.

It is essential that the pilot should be able to change the approach path rapidly. The amount of control he can exercise depends upon the effectiveness of the control surfaces, upon the rate at which lift can be 'dumped' or drag increased by spoilers and flaps, and upon the approach speed itself. The approach speed may be as much as

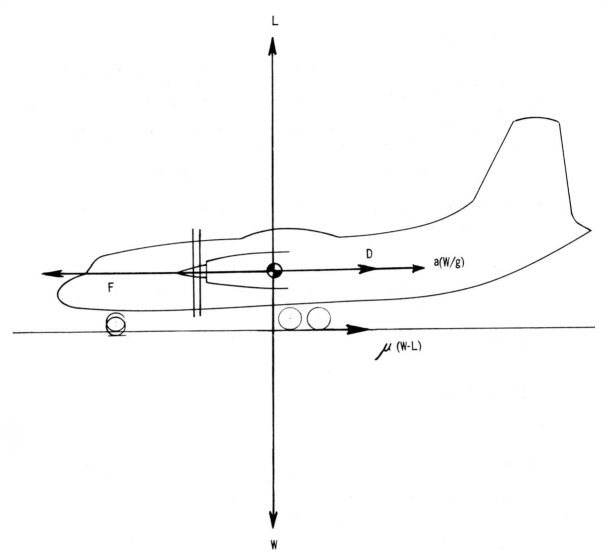

Fig. 4.8. Forces acting on take-off

forty per cent higher than the stalling speed, to give an adequate safety margin. The stalling speed increases as the square root of the normal acceleration, while the lift and effectiveness of the control surfaces increases as the square of the air speed. However, there are limits to the approach speed, which is the most important single parameter governing the ability of a pilot to break cloud after an instrument approach and line up on the runway. One manufacturer has said that it is possible to 'side-step' a transport aircraft more than a 100 ft laterally at 100 k on a 3° glide path, with 100 ft between the cloud base and the ground. As the approach speed rises the distance decreases until at 120 k the limit of the 'side-step' is about 80 ft, at 140 k about 40 ft and only about 20 ft at 160 k.

Range and Endurance Flying

We have already seen that payload-range is a basic operational requirement for most aeroplanes. Let us now consider the design factors, and their particular relationship one with another, which determine how far, or for how long, a projected aeroplane might fly.

Now range, or more accurately the specific air range (the air-miles flown per pound of fuel) multiplied by the fuel available, can be written as:

$$\text{Range} = \frac{\text{miles per hour}}{\text{lb per hour}} \times (\text{total fuel} - \text{fuel needed for other flying})$$

In a turbojet engine, the simplest and most representative unit at this time, the fuel consumption is given by:

$$C = c'F \qquad (4\text{--}9)$$

where, c' = thrust sfc,

F = net propulsive force, for our purposes approximately the same as the thrust of the engine.

If the whole of the fuel, W_F, could be used for flying range, R, the range could be stated as:

$$R = \frac{V}{c'F} W_F$$

But, in level flight:

$$F = D$$

and,

$$L = W$$

so that,

$$R = \frac{V}{c'} \frac{L}{D} \frac{W_F}{W} \qquad (4\text{--}10)$$

Or, converting to Mach number by applying Eq. (1–4):

$$R = a \frac{M}{c'} \frac{L}{D} \frac{W_F}{W} \qquad (4\text{--}11)$$

It should be noted that the range is given as a simple ratio of the total fuel weight to some average weight of the aircraft along the stage length. In practice this is hard to calculate and much less useful than the ratio of the total fuel weight to the all-up weight of the aircraft on take-off. We therefore find range more conveniently stated in a form of the Breguet range equation:

$$R = k \frac{V}{c'} \frac{L}{D} \log_e \left(\frac{W_O}{W_O - W_F} \right) \qquad (4\text{--}12)$$

in which k is a constant to reconcile the units.

We see then that the range of an aeroplane depends upon three parameters: V/c' or M/c', a measure of the speed that can be derived from unit weight of fuel (in effect an indication of the efficiency of the engine installation); L/D, a measure of the aerodynamic efficiency; and $\log_e (W_O/W_O - W_F)$, a measure of the structural efficiency.

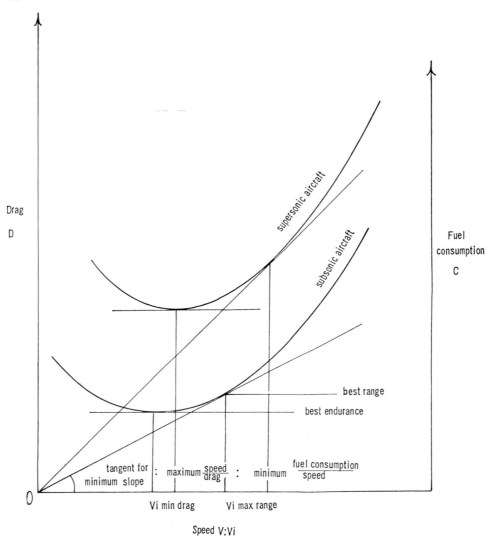

Fig. 4.9. Range and endurance of a turbojet aircraft in level subsonic flight

With certain exceptions the maximum range of a jet aeroplane increases markedly with height, being commonly twice as great at 30,000 ft as at sea level. The opposite is the case with the piston-propeller aircraft, which flies more efficiently for range at low altitudes. Turboprop aeroplanes lie somewhere between the two.

Maximum endurance is achieved when the minimum amount of fuel is used to keep the aeroplane flying. It follows that the speed for best endurance corresponds with the minimum drag speed of a turbojet aircraft, and the minimum power speed of a piston aircraft. The range and endurance speeds of a jet aeroplane are shown in generalized form in Fig. 4.9.

Summarizing for both aspects of specialized performance. Attention must be paid to design for the lowest drag. Engine economy is of utmost importance; and the structure of the aircraft must be as light as possible.

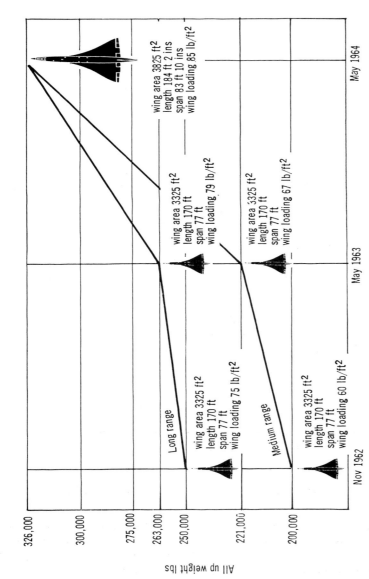

All up weight lbs

Nov 1962   May 1963   May 1964

326,000
300,000
275,000
263,000
250,000
221,000
200,000

Long range

wing area 3325 ft²
length 170 ft
span 77 ft
wing loading 75 lb/ft²

Medium range

wing area 3325 ft²
length 170 ft
span 77 ft
wing loading 60 lb/ft²

wing area 3325 ft²
length 170 ft
span 77 ft
wing loading 79 lb/ft²

wing area 3325 ft²
length 170 ft
span 77 ft
wing loading 67 lb/ft²

wing area 3825 ft²
length 184 ft 2 ins
span 83 ft 10 ins
wing loading 85 lb/ft²

Fig. 4.10. Diagram showing the way the B.A.C.-Sud Concorde is reported to have grown in weight and size since it was first announced as a firm project. The aeroplane has therefore grown 63 per cent heavier and 14 ft longer in a little more than eighteen months

47

4.3 The Effect of 'Stretching' Requirements

The commonest ways of 'stretching' requirements are to increase the payload, or the fuel load, both of which increase the all-up weight. Increased payload involves stretched fuselages: it is significant that few transport aeroplanes designed in recent years have remained unmodified for long in their original form. Increased fuel loads involve either overload tanks, hung beneath wings and fuselage, or wings of larger area.

Increased weight with unchanged wing area increases the wing loading: which may be thought of as a pressure applied to the supporting air by the wing surfaces. There is a relationship between wing loading and dynamic pressure, $\frac{1}{2}\rho V^2$, or $0\cdot7\,pM^2$, (as given in Eqs. (1–5) and (1–8)) that must be maintained if the aeroplane is to continue flying at the most efficient angle of attack to the air. In the next chapter we shall examine the aerodynamic picture to see the way in which the aerodynamic forces vary with speed and attitude to the air. If the wing loading is increased, then it must be met with increased dynamic pressure, and this can only be done by a reduction of height, for to increase speed at the same height involves running the engines off-design and, hence, inefficiently.

The effect of increased wing loading is to shrink the boundaries of Fig. 2.1 towards the centre, by increasing the stalling speed, decreasing the ceiling and decreasing the maximum and cruising speeds. Increased stalling speeds result in higher landing speeds and greater kinetic energies to be absorbed by the wheels and brakes. For example, an aeroplane weighing seventeen tons (34,000 lb) touching down at 165 k represents about 41,000,000 ft lb of kinetic energy: enough to kick a five-ton elephant 4,000 ft straight up into the air. If the aircraft could be landed at 110 k, then the reduced energy would be only 18,000,000 ft lb: the saving being equal to the heat potential to melt 100 lb of steel.

If, on the other hand, it is possible to increase the wing area at some stage in the design, then the wing loading may be maintained or even reduced. Of course, the increased wetted area being moved through the air may well result in a decreased overall lift/drag, but this is offset by reduced landing speeds when most of the fuel has gone. Unfortunately, stretching requirements tends to result in weight increasing faster than wing area, as initially indicated in Fig. 4.10, which shows the growth of the medium and long range versions of the B.A.C.-Sud Concorde from November 1962 to May 1964. The initial wing loading increased from 60 lb/ft² to 79 lb/ft²: a growth of more than thirty per cent. It must be remembered, however, that the growth was brought about by the building-in of more advanced features and advantages.

Increased weight without alteration of structural strength is equivalent to flying at increased normal acceleration, in that smaller margins are left within the manoeuvre envelope. Manoeuvring has to be carried out more gently and smaller accelerations must be applied if strain and failure are to be avoided. Most aircraft are now fitted with cockpit accelerometers that measure the normal acceleration in flight. Most heavy aeroplanes are also fitted with V–g recorders which maintain a continuous count of acceleration levels exceeded on every flight.

PART 3

AERODYNAMIC SHAPE

CHAPTER 5

The Generation of Aerodynamic Forces

Although it may often seem that the picture of Nature at work is clouded by attempts to explain phenomena in the shorthand of mathematics or the concepts of classical science, more often than not the abstraction is the nearest approach to the truth that can be made at the time. One such example is the common tendency to imagine an aircraft to lie somehow at rest, with the air flowing past it and behaving in a rationalized way. This picture is used in almost every textbook and is accepted so naturally, that even flying-men are heard to say that: 'the airflow is brought to rest at . . .' (some point or other on the airframe) and going on to talk then of an 'undisturbed flow' that passes, river-like, from infinity upstream to infinity downstream. The picture is fair enough when one considers what happens in wind-tunnel or water-channel experiments, where a gas or a liquid is arranged to flow past a static model. It tells us very little about the real world of seemingly alive aeroplanes, or of how to bridge the gulf between the often superficially incompatible worlds of theory and practice. Let us consider then what happens when an aeroplane moves through air that is relatively at rest.

5.1 The Nature of Aerodynamic Forces

Imagine an aeroplane passing through a mass of air, drawn as a cylinder in Fig. 5.1. The particles of air within the mass are deflected in all directions, but if the aeroplane is in straight and level flight the motions of the particles will be symmetrical either side of a vertical plane along the centre line. Broadly speaking the particles would be seen to move in two kinds of motion: translational, in which movement is a pure displacement without spin; and rotational, in which the particle spins about one or more of its axes.

Both displacement and rotation of the mass of a particle require work to be done, energy to be expended, and the energy is taken from the fuel of the aeroplane via the combination of engines and airframe. Every particle affected by the aeroplane is given an acceleration in unit time (it does not matter here whether the acceleration is linear or angular) and the reaction of the particles to acceleration is felt over the surfaces of the aeroplane as a field of varying pressures.

In fact there are two sources of resistance to motion through the air. The first arises from pressure alone, due to displacement. The second is due to friction between the separate particles of air, and the air and the airframe. One cannot avoid generating both pressure and friction when moving through the air. The aim of aerodynamic research is to discover shapes and combinations of shapes which enable the aircraft designer to use the inevitable aerodynamic forces to the best advantage.

If we could see the air in the cylinder after the aeroplane had passed we would see that a new downward motion had been imparted, in effect a downwash, which is the origin of the lift. If the aeroplane flies quickly a large mass is affected in unit time, but the downwash velocity is relatively small. When flying slowly a smaller mass is affected but the downwash velocity is larger. Hovering aircraft produce strong downwashes. The lift is the reaction resulting from imparting a downwards momentum to the air.

The pressure field varies around the aeroplane, but in general the pressure is higher around the under surfaces than it is around the upper surfaces of the airframe.

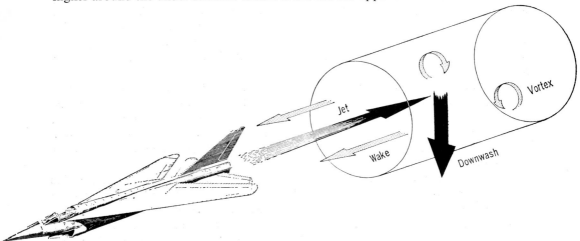

Fig. 5.1.   The effect of an aeroplane upon a mass of air through which it has just passed

The net normal reaction of the pressure field is therefore upwards, as lift. Allied with the downwash and the associated pressure field is the trailing-vortex system, in which a large scale rotation of the air takes place about two axes lying in the wake of each wing tip. The vortices are part of the circulation of the wings and are caused by the air flowing outwards from the high-pressure under surfaces, upwards around the tips and inwards again over the low-pressure upper surfaces. Within the boundary of each tip the air sweeps downwards, and this gives rise to the predominant downwash pattern. There is a circulation around every lifting surface—no matter what the direction of the lift vector. If the lift vector is downwards over a part of the span, then the local circulation is in opposition to the main circulatory system. Circulation theory, pioneered most notably by Lanchester (1878–1946) and given practical mathematical form by Prandtl (1875–1953), is the basis of modern wing theory. We will shortly consider the physical explanation of circulation in greater detail.

Now consider the motions of the air in the direction of flight. The aeroplane derives propulsive thrust from a slipstream of air driven rearwards by a propeller or a jet engine. The momentum added to the air is a measure of the thrust reaction. Some of the air is gathered by the aeroplane and swept along with it for some distance before being shed as a wake. The wake is therefore given a change of momentum in a direction opposite to the propulsive slipstream. The change of momentum given to the wake is reacted as drag, the force opposing motion through the air. The total drag is made up of a number of components and may vary from as little as $\frac{1}{30}$th of the lift of a very high performance sailplane, to as much as $\frac{1}{5}$th of the lift of a supersonic transport. In the latter case the engines of a machine weighing 300,000 lb would have to produce a combined thrust of 60,000 lb (30 tons) at Mach 3 and 70,000 ft.

5.1.1 Pressure and Streamlines

When air is 'at rest'—in effect the particles are moving at random—the static pressure on a surface is the ambient pressure at that altitude. The static pressure is the mean force/unit area due to the bombardment of the surface by particles moving at the root mean square of the molecular velocity. That velocity, which corresponds with the velocity of sound at that altitude, may be thought of as the typical limiting velocity at which a pressure pulse may be transmitted through the air. As long as the temperature of the air is unchanged by the passage of a body, the speed of sound remains constant.

The static pressure varies with the head of air above the level at which it is measured. The head of air possesses energy in that it has potential energy due to position, and the static pressure is capable of doing work. If the air is in motion at the pressure level the particles also possess kinetic energy, measured in terms of the dynamic pressure $\frac{1}{2}\rho V^2$. As soon as the air is in motion in a particular direction the motion is no longer random but directed.

Now consider a flexible tube immersed in air with equalized pressures both inside and out as shown in Fig. 5.2(a). If one end of the tube is separated from a low pressure chamber by a diaphragm which is then punctured, the air within the tube will flow with directed motion towards the low pressure chamber. If the pressure difference is sufficiently small then the density and temperature of the confined air will be unaffected and the particles will move with a velocity less than the velocity of sound a. One might then draw a vector diagram for a particle in which the vector resultant is equivalent to the velocity of sound, Fig. 5.2(b). Clearly, the component of velocity, v, normal to the wall of the tube is less than when the motion is random. Therefore the static (normal) pressure is reduced and the walls collapse inwards. The higher the directed velocity V the lower the pressure p_1.

The phenomenon is expressed in a theorem of Daniel Bernoulli, (1700–1782) which states that in the flow of an incompressible fluid—if we disregard gravity (i.e., any change in potential energy) and friction—the sum of the pressure head and velocity head is a constant:

$$p + \tfrac{1}{2}\rho V^2 = \text{a constant} \tag{5-1}$$

The argument can be extended by replacing the flexible tube in Fig. 5.2 by a streamtube bounded by streamlines in a directed mass of air—a streamline being an imaginary line along which motion is wholly tangential. When a body is immersed in such a mass of air, particles are displaced at different velocities by different parts of the body surfaces. Where local velocities are increased, the pressure is decreased and the streamlines move together. Where local velocities are decreased, the pressure increases and the streamlines move apart.

In reality air is compressible, but another relationship helps us to visualize the behaviour of a streamtube when the density and static pressure of the air are changing.

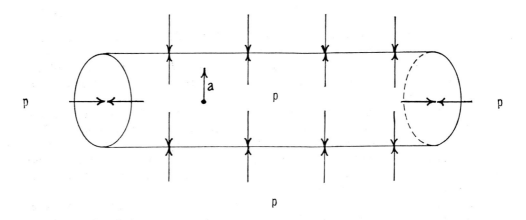

a. Initial shape of flexible tube with
equalised pressure inside and out.

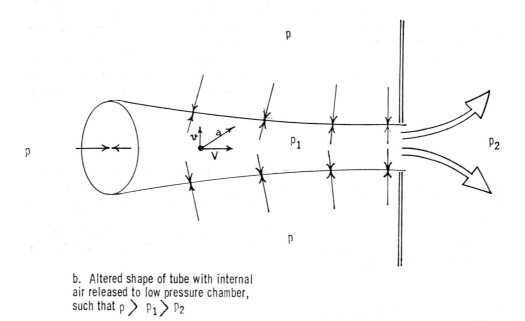

b. Altered shape of tube with internal
air released to low pressure chamber,
such that $p > p_1 > p_2$

Fig. 5.2. Effect of directed motion on static pressure within a flexible tube containing air
particles having root mean square velocity a

The relationship depends upon the conservative nature of the air: *i.e.*, mass is neither lost nor gained, so that the mass contained within a streamtube and moving with velocity V is:

$$\rho A V = \text{a constant} \qquad (5\text{--}2)$$

where A is the cross-sectional area of the tube. If the density remains unchanged then a decrease in A is accompanied by an increase in V, and vice versa. If the velocity increases greatly and the pressure drop is large enough to decrease the density of the air, then the change will be accompanied by a smaller decrease in the cross-sectional area of the streamtube.

The foregoing explanation presupposes that the mass of air is in directed motion— but, as we said earlier, this has nothing to do with the reality of air being more or less at rest with an aeroplane passing through it. Under these conditions the surfaces of the aeroplane gather up some of the air to a certain extent, and it follows that those particles swept along by the aeroplane impose a reaction against the surfaces of the airframe which is felt as increased pressure.

Eventually the particles free themselves to return to their undisturbed condition and the pressure decreases again. When the particles are swept along they have the lowest velocity relative to the aeroplane and exert the highest pressure. When they are in the process of returning to their undisturbed condition their relative velocity increases, and the pressure begins to drop. The pressure distribution over the surface of the body is therefore a function of the relative velocity, and it is that velocity which is used in aerodynamic calculations.

In this way two quite different situations may be treated in the same way mathematically. But because a fixed body in a windtunnel can have the same aerodynamic laws applied to it as an identical body in motion through air, we must not fall into the lazy trap of confusing the one with the reality of the other.

These relationships are the root of a most important design technique: that if we wish to obtain a particular sort of pressure distribution around a part of the airframe at a given design point, then it is possible to calculate the necessary profile to induce it.

5.2   Subsonic Flight

In subsonic flight the aeroplane can be considered to be made up of discrete parts each with its own independent function. Aerodynamic design seeks to achieve the maximum efficiency of each part as a separate entity, while minimizing the interference between them.

Lifting surfaces, generically called aerofoils, include all wing and stabilizer surfaces. Aerofoil sections are specially shaped for generating high lift/drag, typical values in subsonic flight being from 17 to 20.

5.2.1   Aerofoil Section Geometry

A symmetrical aerofoil profile is shown in Fig. 5.3(*a*) and below it the same section modified, by the introduction of camber. The aerofoil definitions are based upon the American NASA (ex NACA), National Aeronautical and Space Administration series of sections. It should be noted that the thickness distribution along the

a.   Basic symmetrical section.

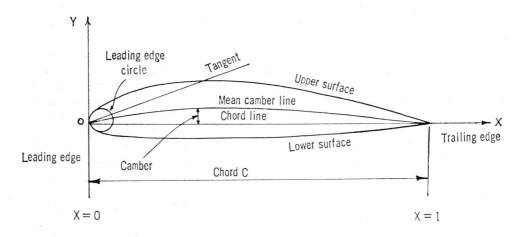

b.   Cambered section with definitions.

Fig. 5.3.   Aerofoil section geometry

chord of the section, the position and amount of camber and the radius of the leading edge circle determine the curvature and slope of the upper and lower surfaces at any point.

The pressure over an aerofoil surface is made up of three components, the last two of which have been combined here. The resultant pressure is approximated to the algebraic sum of:

(a) The pressure arising from the displacement of the air around the basic symmetrical section at zero angle of attack—clearly a function of the thickness distribution along the chord.

(b) The pressure distribution over a thin plate having the same camber distribution and generating the same lift as the aerofoil in question.

Many factors are taken into account when choosing the aerofoil sections for wings and tails, simply because no one section possesses all of the needed qualities. A fully cantilever monoplane wing requires a thicker section than an externally braced wing, such as a biplane might use. The final choice depends upon the relative importance of the aerodynamic, structural and stowage properties of wings.

To aid the designer in his choice various useful families of related sections have been designed in different countries at different times. The best known is the N.A.S.A. series of America. There is no precise equivalent in the United Kingdom, although a historical series of R.A.F. (Royal Aircraft Factory, later the Royal Aircraft Establishment) sections was used during and after the first World War.

Let us now consider the way in which section geometry determines aerodynamic properties.

5.2.2   Circulation and Vortices

Imagine a mass of air particles being met by an aerofoil section moving with velocity V (the argument is much the same if the air is moving instead towards a stationary aerofoil, as in a wind tunnel). Two particles, A and B, are deflected above and below the section which, because of the camber and angle of attack, presents upper and lower surfaces of different lengths and curvatures to the air it meets, Fig. 5.4(a).

The major effect of the aerofoil surfaces is to give both A and B a forward impulse, at the same time separating them: A upwards, B downwards. In doing so the particles are crowded into the mass of air ahead of the leading edge and the local pressure is increased. Each particle is able to slip, with friction, over their respective surfaces. After a small interval of time, when each is adjacent to station 1 (upper and lower), the impulse given by the surfaces has decreased, because of the reduced slope of each— although the impulse given to A is larger than to B, because the slope of the upper surface is steeper than the lower.

As the aerofoil passes, the slope of the surfaces decreases, and the high pressure of the particles crowded ahead of the aerofoil is able to thrust A and B rearwards, over the crest at the point of maximum thickness of each surface. The surfaces are shaped like the tube with curving walls in Fig. 5.2(b), and as the particles move rearwards the static pressure falls. Beyond the crest, however, the air displaced by the retreating aerofoil comes crowding back, forwards, inwards, to fill the rarified regions left by its passage. A and B are therefore retarded in their rearward motion and squeezed (as it were) by increasing pressure forwards and inwards again. Until, agitated and displaced downwards (relative to their original positions) they are left in the wake behind the retreating section.

If one could draw the locus of each particle at successive intervals, corresponding with stations 1 to 10 across each surface, it would be seen that A and B had been forced to circulate around paths looking rather like those in Fig. 5.4(b). The circuits of each would be in opposition, but the algebraic sum of the two motions would be dominated by the more vigorous motion of A (because of A's greater displacement in the time), leaving a resultant clockwise motion with average velocity of rotation ΔV_{AB}, as shown in Fig. 5.4(c).

An aerofoil surface can be replaced, theoretically, by a chordwise sheet of bound vortices stretching from tip to tip—for the circulation shown in Fig. 5.4(c) could well apply at any average station across the chord. In fact ΔV_{AB} varies from station to station as the particles are initially accelerated, and then decelerated again behind the crests of the upper and lower surfaces. We are not concerned with the mathematics of

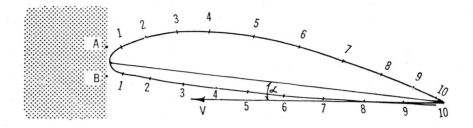

a. Simplified picture of aerofoil meeting undisturbed air mass.

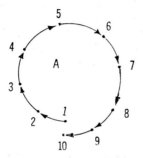

b. Loci of particles A and B during passage of upper and lower surfaces of aerofoil.

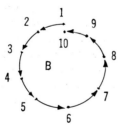

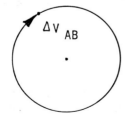

c. Simplified algebraic sum of motions a and b.

Fig. 5.4. The generation of circulation by an aerofoil in its passage through a mass of air

such a vortex system. Suffice it to say that by postulating such a system, and then adding vectorially the relative velocities around each vortex to the undisturbed relative airflow, V, we may obtain a reasonable approximation to the relative airflow around the aerofoil. This is shown in Fig. 5.5.

The vector sum across the chord of an aerofoil of biconvex section, such as we have used for illustration, shows an increase in relative velocity of the airstream over the crests of the surfaces. But the relative velocity is higher over the upper surface than over the lower. If we now apply Eq. (5–1), using the relative velocity at any point, we may calculate the pressure distribution across the chord. The spanwise pressure distribution is as shown in Fig. 5.6(a). Clearly, if the pressure is lower across the upper surface than across the lower surface, there is a net lift across the chord of every spanwise station. The spanwise lift distribution varies with different planforms and body arrangements, and this will be discussed shortly.

In theory a vortex can neither begin nor end in a fluid, it must form either a closed loop, or end at a surface. The sheets of bound vortices do not end at the tips of an aerofoil but are shed across the span, to wrap themselves into the large trailing vortices already mentioned, lying in the wake of each tip. In fact the vortices die away eventually due to friction and turbulence behind the aircraft, forming a horseshoe vortex system when taken as a whole.

5.2.3 Pressure, Loading and Pitching Moment

The differential pressure and aerodynamic load distributions in Fig. 5.6 show the origin of lift but not drag. The static pressure acts at right angles to every point on the 'wetted' surface area of an aeroplane. It is convenient to resolve the force due to pressure acting over unit area into components that are normal and tangential to the flight path, as shown in Fig. 5.7(a). The frictional forces must also be taken into account, as shown in (b). The sum of the normal pressure components is the lift generated aerodynamically. The pressure drag components, when summed over the whole airframe, give the total pressure drag, D_{press}; while the sum of the frictional components gives the skin friction drag, D_{fric}. Hence, the total drag of an aeroplane is given by:

$$D = D_{\text{press}} + D_{\text{fric}} \qquad (5–3)$$

The estimation of drag is a complex problem. The pressure components in particular are affected by a large number of factors that cannot be controlled by the designer as finely as he would wish.

Circulation and Downwash

We have seen that circulation is the motion around curved paths of the particles of air affected by the passage of an aerofoil surface. In fact circulation is generated by any body moving through the air at subsonic speeds. The art is to make circulation work by generating lift. Ways of increasing the local circulation of an aerofoil involve local increases of camber. Wing flaps, and all flap-like control surfaces are camber-changing devices and as such are employed to alter local lift distributions. Similarly one often sees cambered leading edge extensions over parts of the span of

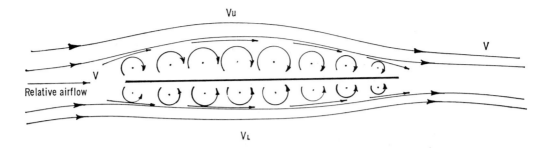

a. Theoretical replacement of upper and lower aerofoil surfaces by two sheets of vortex filaments, upon which is superimposed the undisturbed relative airflow, giving a resultant flow as shown:

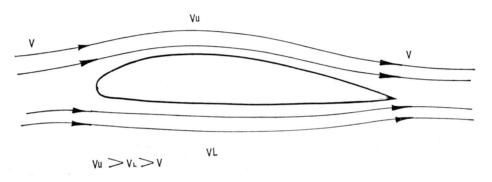

$V_u > V_L > V$

b. Idealised relative airflow around aerofoil section showing similarity to a

Fig. 5.5. The relative airflow pattern around an aerofoil due to circulation around an induced vortex system

some wings, and these are employed to smooth out local airflows and maintain efficient circulations.

Now, the downwash momentum imparted to the air is also a measure of the lift of an aerofoil, and it follows that there is a direct connection between the strength of circulation (*i.e.*, the product of the air velocity around a curved path and the length of the path) and the downwash velocity. To generate a given lift at a given airspeed an aerofoil of long span has to impart a smaller downwash to the air it meets than an aerofoil of shorter span. The reason for this is that the mass of air affected in unit time is proportional to the product of the distance flown and the span: double the span and twice as much air is affected. As momentum is the product of mass and velocity, doubling the span halves the required downwash velocity to produce a constant rate of change of momentum: the force known as lift. It follows, therefore, that a long span aerofoil generates less circulation per unit span than a shorter aerofoil generating the same lift. In fact we may summarize by saying:

(i) Downwash velocity varies directly with strength of circulation.

(ii) Strength of circulation varies inversely with aerofoil span.

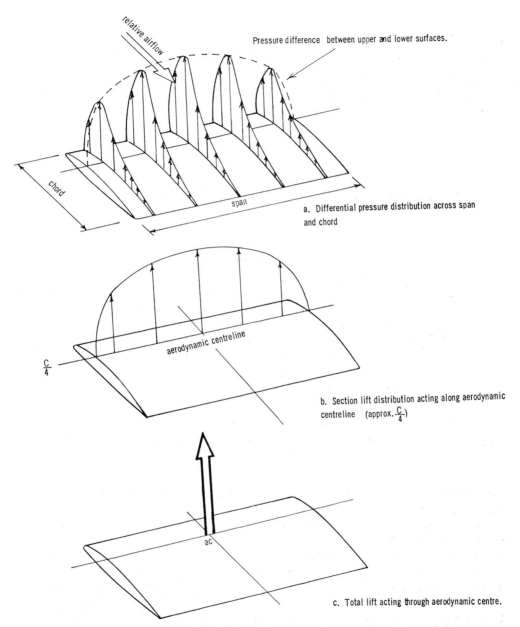

a. Differential pressure distribution across span and chord

b. Section lift distribution acting along aerodynamic centreline (approx. $\frac{C}{4}$)

c. Total lift acting through aerodynamic centre.

Fig. 5.6. Aerodynamic load distribution on a subsonic rectangular aerofoil

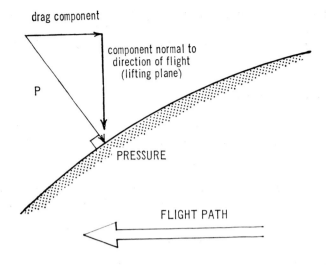

a. Static pressure: resolution into lift
and drag components.

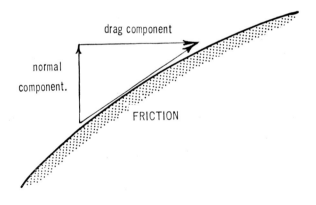

b. Skin friction drag component

Fig. 5.7.   The aerodynamic components of static pressure and skin friction

By imparting a circulation to the air an aerofoil experiences an equal and opposite
reaction from the air. The reaction, in effect a torque, is called the pitching moment,
which is denoted M and is nose down when the lift acts in the normal sense. The
greater or lesser the lift, the greater or lesser the pitching moment.

The pressure and frictional forces acting on a lifting aerofoil section produce a
resultant force that may be resolved into lift and drag components. Although the
force and moment relationship depends upon the angle of attack of the aerofoil
surface, it also depends upon the size of the surface, the airspeed and altitude. It is
convenient, therefore, to state the lift, drag and moment characteristics of a section in

terms of dimensionless coefficients that are independent of size and of ambient conditions. Actual forces and moments can then be calculated for surfaces of different sizes and for different flight conditions by applying the appropriate factors.

Dimensionless Force and Moment Coefficients

If the average differential pressure across a strip section of an aerofoil is denoted $\bar{p}$ and the area of the strip of chord, c, is $(c.\Delta y)$ then the lift of the section is:

$$l = \bar{p}(c\Delta y) \qquad (5\text{--}4)$$

To eliminate the ambient factors ρ and V we may transpose Eq. (5–4) for $\bar{p}$ and divide by the dynamic pressure, obtained from Eq. (1–5) which, it will be observed, is expressed in terms of:

$$q = \tfrac{1}{2}\rho V^2$$

The ratio of $\bar{p}/q$ is the lift coefficient of the section, c_l where:

$$c_l = \frac{\bar{p}}{q} = \frac{l}{q(c\Delta y)} \qquad (5\text{--}5)$$

The section drag and moment coefficients are derived in the same way, such that:

$$c_d = \frac{d}{q(c\Delta y)} \qquad (5\text{--}6)$$

and, introducing the chord c a second time, to make the moment dimensionless:

$$c_m = \frac{m}{qc^2\Delta y} \qquad (5\text{--}7)$$

If the total wing area of the aeroplane is denoted S, then the total lift, drag and pitching moments are given by:

$$L = C_L \tfrac{1}{2}\rho V^2 S \qquad (5\text{--}8)$$
$$D = C_D \tfrac{1}{2}\rho V^2 S \qquad (5\text{--}9)$$
$$M = C_M \tfrac{1}{2}\rho V^2 S c \qquad (5\text{--}10)$$

Aerodynamic Centre

The pitching moment of an aerofoil varies with lift and, if an aeroplane is to be stable: i.e., if it is to return automatically to a required attitude after a transient disturbance: stabilizing surfaces must be used that are not uneconomically large and heavy. Fortunately there is a point between the leading and trailing edge of an aerofoil about which the pitching moment is constant with attitude (angle of attack). This point is called the aerodynamic centre of the aerofoil. The aerodynamic centre, or ac, lies roughly one quarter of the way back from the leading edge, near the $0.25\,c$, or $\tfrac{1}{4}\,c$ point. The aerodynamic centre is important, because the centre of gravity is arranged to lie near it. Lift, drag and pitching moment are usually related to the aerodynamic centre, as in Fig. 5.8.

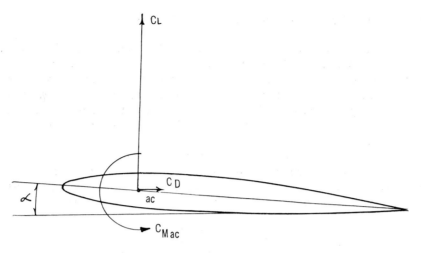

a. General expression of lift, drag and pitching
moment using dimensionless coefficients and
the aerodynamic centre

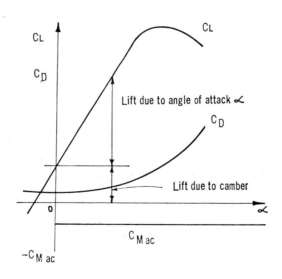

b. Variation in lift, drag and pitching
moment about the aerodynamic centre
with angle of attack.

Fig. 5.8.   Aerodynamic characteristics of an aerofoil

5.2.4 The Boundary Layer, Separation and Loss of Lift

In Fig. 5.8(*b*) the C_L curve is humped and the lift decreases beyond the hump with increasing angle of attack. When the loss of lift is sharp the aeroplane is said to have a clearly defined stall. One wing may stall before the other, in which case a wing-drop occurs. Stalling usually occurs with combinations of large angle of attack and low airspeed, although an accelerated stall can be caused when manoeuvring with large normal acceleration and angle of attack. The loss of lift is caused by a decrease in local circulation.

The decrease in circulation causing the stall is brought about by the changing behaviour of the boundary layer: a mass of air which, in lying close to the skin of the aerofoil, is dominated by the viscous forces that cause skin-friction. Outside the boundary layer the forces arise more from displacement than from viscosity.

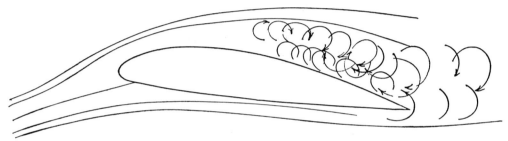

Fig. 5.9. Relative airflow past an aerofoil beyond the stall

In Fig. 5.9 is shown the motion of the air relative to an aerofoil beyond the stalling angle of attack. The picture of the streamlined flow in Fig. 5.5(*b*) below the stalling angle is necessarily idealized to illustrate the idea of laminar flow, in which the air is assumed to move in smooth sheets relative to the aerofoil. As we saw earlier, however, the air particles are really moving in directed paths, impelled by an aerofoil moving relative to them. The two views are complementary: the essential point linking them is that the motion is directed and the pressure changes are controlled.

Above the stalling angle of attack the particles move in a highly disturbed random manner, in apparently unconnected swirls, eddies and vortices. Because the motions are no longer directed and the relative velocity is decreased, the pressure increases. The stall follows the attainment of peak suction over the upper surface of the aerofoil and one may imagine the suction to have been so intense that the air, in returning around the last part of the circuit in Fig. 5.4(*b*), is drawn far forward in the wake of the aerofoil by the intense pressure gradient. Therefore, instead of the air being left in the vicinity of its undisturbed position when the aerofoil has passed, it is now swept forward with an additional momentum, that represents additional power taken from the aeroplane. The boundary layer is said to have separated from the aerofoil surface when the stall occurs. Separations are accompanied by drag rise and sharp drops in the lift/drag ratio. Airframe buffeting is the result of flow separation.

Near the trailing edge of the aerofoil there is a reversal of the relative airflow, as air creeps round the trailing edge from the lower to the upper surface. The sense of the motion is opposed to the sense of the lifting circulation, and as such may be thought of as reducing the net circulation and lift. Fig. 5.10 shows the behaviour of wool tufts on the upper surface of a wing with local separations.

Various artificial methods of controlling separation and circulation are discussed in the next chapter.

5.2.5   Aerofoil Platform—Aspect Ratio

The aspect ratio of an aerofoil has a most important bearing upon the lift/drag ratio and is defined as span^2/aerofoil area. In the case of a wing the aspect ratio is given by:

$$A = \frac{b^2}{S} \qquad (5\text{--}11)$$

When an aerofoil is rectangular the area is bc and the aspect-ratio is, therefore, b/c. Any planform may be reduced to an equivalent rectangle having the same span and area. The chord of the equivalent rectangular aerofoil is called the mean chord, denoted $\bar{c}$, and there is no point here in defining differences between the geometric mean chord, $\bar{c}$, which we shall use, and the slightly different aerodynamic mean chord, $\bar{\bar{c}}$, both are the same for most practical purposes. Fig. 5.11 shows the areas of the wing included in aspect-ratio and aerodynamic calculations, together with the mean chord and approximate location of the centre of gravity, at $\frac{1}{4}c$.

Geometrical Construction of Mean Chord $\bar{c}$

A simplified planform of one half of the wing is drawn as in Fig. 5.11(a), with an equivalent tip chord, c_t, constructed parallel with the plane of symmetry of the wing, as shown in the inset to (a). The leading and trailing edges of the wing are produced to intersect the plane of symmetry, thus forming chord c_c. The chords c_c and c_t are bisected and a line drawn joining their bisectors.

The tip chord is extended forward a distance c_c, the centre-line chord rearwards a distance c_t. The two ends of the extended chord lines, are then joined by a diagonal. The intersection of the diagonal and the line bisecting the centre-line and tip chords gives the distance of the mean chord outboard of the plane of symmetry. A line parallel to the plane of symmetry drawn through the lateral position and joining the leading and trailing-edges gives the length of the mean chord, $\bar{c}$.

When compound taper is used the same construction can be applied, but this time each separate portion of the wing is treated as a complete entity, as shown in Fig. 5.11(b). Mean chords $\bar{c}_1$ and $\bar{c}_2$ are determined for the inboard and outboard portions respectively. Leading and trailing edges are drawn joining c_1 and c_2 to form a mean wing. The chords $\bar{c}_1$ and $\bar{c}_2$ are then treated as c_c and c_t for the construction of a mean chord between them. The method can be applied *ad infinitum* for taper of more complicated compound forms.

Aspect Ratio, Span Loading and Lift Dependent Drag

We have already noted that the strength of circulation varies inversely with aerofoil span. It follows, therefore, that the lower the aspect ratio of an aerofoil the more

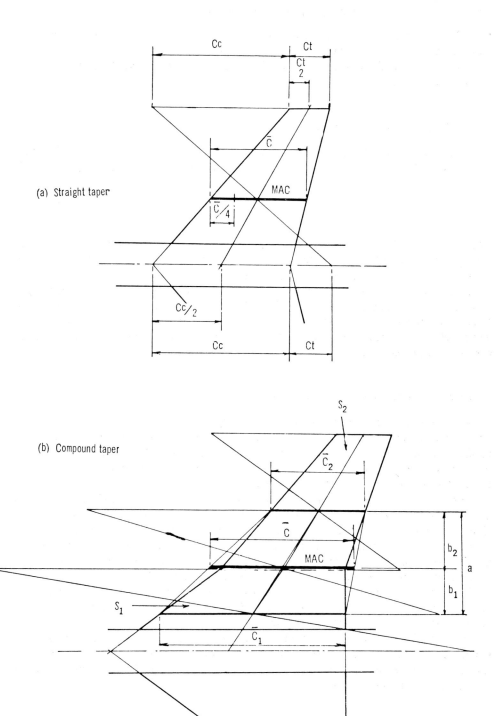

(a) Straight taper

(b) Compound taper

Fig. 5.11. The treatment of wing planform for aspect ratio and meanchord calculations

65

intense the circulation required to generate a given lift. The stronger downwash behind a low aspect ratio wing reduces the effective angle of attack compared with a wing of higher aspect ratio, so that the lower aspect ratio wing has to be flown at a larger angle of attack to generate the same lift. The stronger circulation around the low aspect ratio wing has the effect of inclining the resultant force rearwards, as shown in Fig. 5.12. The relative airflow is no longer almost tangential to the flight path (it is only tangential in theory, when an aerofoil is infinitely long and the distant tips have moved the trailing vortices right out of the picture). As both lift and drag are resolved relative to the flight path, the drag component must therefore be increased by a reduction of aspect ratio.

The drag increment that varies with aspect ratio is called the vortex drag—sometimes it is still referred to as induced drag. The vortex drag is a measure of how much the trailing vortices are intruding to affect the total airflow, and pressure field, around an aeroplane. The vortex drag is a part of the lift-dependent drag of the whole aeroplane, and this depends upon other factors besides aspect ratio, which influence the whole pressure field surrounding the aircraft.

Once the planform of a wing is fixed, however, in terms of area and aspect ratio, the lift dependent drag varies inversely with the span loading: defined as the lift carried per unit span, and equal to the weight/wing span (W/b). Examination of Eq. (5–4) shows that:

$$\frac{l}{\Delta y} = \bar{p}c$$

$$= \text{lift/unit span for the strip of aerofoil}$$
$$\text{considered.}$$

For a given wing, in which the chord distribution is already fixed, the span loading is, therefore, dependent only upon the value of $\bar{p}$, the average pressure differential between the upper and lower surfaces. And from Eq. (5–5) we see that at a given speed and height ($q = $ constant) the pressure differential is a measure of the lift coefficient of the wing—in other words, the angle of attack of the wing to the air. We may argue that, for a given set of ambient conditions and fixed wing geometry, the lower the span loading the lower the lift dependent drag. For simplicity we may say vortex drag instead of lift dependent, as long as we remember that we are neglecting certain other aspects that alter with, for example, angle of attack at high Mach numbers.

The lower the span loading, the lower the wing loading of a given wing. And it follows from the foregoing arguments that all else being equal: the longer the span of the wing and the lower the weight of the aeroplane the smaller will be the lift dependent drag.

The reduced effective angle of attack of very low aspect ratio wings delays the stall considerably. Some delta wings have no measurable stalling angle up to 40° or more inclination to the flight path. The drag is so high that the flight path is usually inclined downwards at a steep angle to the horizontal, with the aircraft descending rapidly. Apart from a rapid rate of descent and possible loss of stability and control, such aircraft may have a shallow attitude to the horizon that can be deceptive to a casual observer. The condition is called, picturesquely, the superstall or deepstall, although the wing may be far from a true stall and still be generating appreciable lift. Superstalling is a characteristic of the geometrically 'slender' aircraft (see Table 12.3).

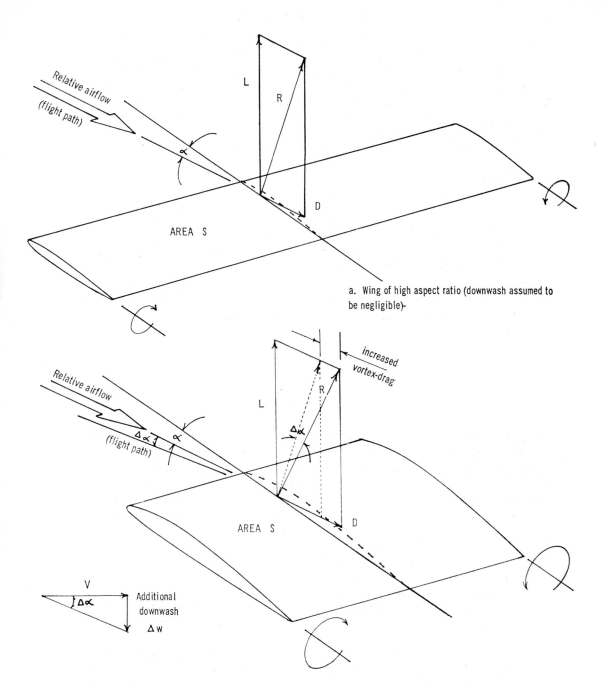

Relative airflow

(flight path)

L

R

D

AREA S

a. Wing of high aspect ratio (downwash assumed to be negligible).

Relative airflow

(flight path)

$\Delta\alpha$

α

increased vortex-drag

L

R

$\Delta\alpha$

D

AREA S

V

$\Delta\alpha$

Additional downwash

Δw

b. Low aspect ratio wing, angle of attack altered by downwash, Δw

Fig. 5.12. The effect of aspect ratio upon wings of equal area generating equal lift (note increased attitude of low aspect ratio wing to flight path)

Taper

Rectangular chord wings are heavy and uneconomical, the ease of manufacture no longer offsetting the structural weight penalties when aeroplanes are larger than a certain size. Taper is therefore employed, to shift the spanwise loading inboard, which reduces the bending moment at the root. Furthermore, taper enables a deeper root to be built, so that a lighter structure can be used in that region to resist the stresses set up by bending and torsion.

Taper has an aerodynamic disadvantage, however. Each slice, or section of an aerofoil may be thought of as generating a circulation that is modified by the adjacent sections. If the span of an aerofoil is sliced into sections of equal width, those inboard, having broader chords and greater thicknesses than those outboard, generate more powerful circulations. The tip vortices do not originate at the tip—vortices are shed across the whole of the trailing edge, but roll into a vortex-skein behind the tip, rather like the strands of a rope. The strong inboard vortices cause a powerful upwash out-board that cancels the downwash inboard of the weaker outboard vortices shed from the trailing edge. Their effect is, therefore, the opposite of that illustrated in Fig. 5.12(*b*), in which the effective angle of attack is decreased by the downwash. With a tapered aerofoil the effective angle of attack outboard is increased by the upwash effect out-board of the stronger vortices, so that the effective angle of attack near the tips is increased. The tips work at higher lift coefficients and tend, therefore, to stall first. Tip stalling is undesirable, for it leads to asymmetric wing dropping and the danger of a spin. We often find that wings are twisted nose down towards the tips: *i.e.*, they are washed-out, by having a smaller angle set at the tip than at the root. In this way tip stalling may be averted.

The ideal planform for minimum vortex drag is an ellipse, because the downwash is then constant across the span. The spanwise lift distribution is also elliptical. When an aerofoil is joined to a non-lifting body there is a loss of lift at the junction, and a trough occurs in the spanwise lift distribution. Fairings and fillets are therefore fitted to smooth out the troughs, for decreased lift means lost circulation: vortices shed in the wake without doing useful work first: increased drag and reduced performance.

Fairings and fillets are never too large, however, because they increase wetted area and skin friction drag. Where a junction is right-angled one finds either small fillets or none at all. Fillets are most commonly employed for very high or very low wing-fuselage combinations, for then the angle between curved wing and fuselage is acute and generates the most interference.

5.3 Supersonic Flight

The phenomena of lift and drag have been discussed so far in the context of pressure changes in the air that are too small to significantly affect the density. Changes of pressure caused by the passage of an aeroplane at a speed less than that of sound can be transmitted to other particles well away from the surface of the airframe, and the air can be thought of as being prepared in advance for the disturbance to come.

When an aeroplane flies faster than sound pressure changes cannot be transmitted ahead of it, so that the aerodynamic shape is determined by reactions from the air that are different from those at subsonic speeds. Aeroplanes grow longer and thinner:

curves are shallower: leading edges grow sharp instead of being rounded: surfaces are more nearly tangential to the flight path, so that the rate of displacement of the particles of air is kept as small as possible. The supersonic picture has two aspects that together help to explain the different shape of the supersonic aeroplane.

5.3.1 Compression and Expansion Waves

Imagine the source of a pressure pulse to be the pointed nose of a projectile (although any other point would do—in fact a sharp leading edge is made up of a line of such points). At very low speed the disturbance of the air by the moving point would spread out spherically through the surrounding air, like the much larger waves from a chiming bell. The waves all travel away from the source at the local speed of sound. As the source accelerates to higher speeds, however, the pressure pattern begins to change as each pulse is made further and further ahead of the previous one. These two cases are shown in Fig. 5.13(a) and (b), in which the source is initially almost stationary and is then seen moving at a speed half that of sound, M = 0·5. As long as pulses precede the source the air particles lying in its path receive warning of its approach and can begin to adjust themselves beforehand for the coming displacement. The acceleration of each particle is therefore smaller than if it received no warning, and the force required to cause displacement is less.

When the source moves at the speed of sound it moves forward with the advancing pressure pulses, as shown in Fig. 5.13(c). Ahead of the source lies a zone of silence, behind is a zone of action—while between them is a sharp pressure wave formed by the piled up pulses. When the source moves faster than sound successive pulses are sent out from points ahead of the preceding ones, and the pressure wave generated by the source takes on a conical form. The resulting Mach cone is unique in that the semi-vertex angle, θ, is related to the Mach number by:

$$\text{M} = \frac{V}{a} = \text{cosec}\,\theta \tag{5-12}$$

Now consider the airspeed relative to the source. If the source is considered to be stationary the air ahead of it is moving towards it with speed V, while behind the cone the relative airspeed is less than V. This is the situation in a wind tunnel where the formation of shock waves (the Mach cone is a conical shock wave—shock, because of the sharp pressure change through it) marks a deceleration in the flow relative to the source. Clearly, for a relative deceleration to have taken place, the air in the zone of action must have been swept along to a certain extent by the moving source.

It follows that if the air behind the Mach cone has been swept along by the source, then such a wave must be a cause of drag. Applying Bernoulli's theorem, the static pressure must be higher in the air behind the cone than in the silent region ahead. If the source is part of an aeroplane, then there must be another process of changing the pressure of the air back again to the undisturbed value as the aeroplane passes. The process of decreasing the pressure is by accelerating the air again, relative to the aeroplane through an expansion wave.

Consider a supersonic body passing through a mass of air contained within an imaginary cylinder, as in Fig. 5.14. The cylinder defines the limit of the undisturbed air during the interval of time between the nose and tail passing a datum point. Beyond the cylinder the air is only disturbed after the body has passed. Inside the cylinder the air is disturbed during the actual passage. The cylinder has a cross-sectional area, A, that is reduced from a maximum to a minimum at the mid point of the body, increasing to a maximum again at the tail. As the body is moving along the cylinder of air faster than pressure pulses can be transmitted, the air is compressed by the forward surface of the body, with a corresponding decrease in velocity relative

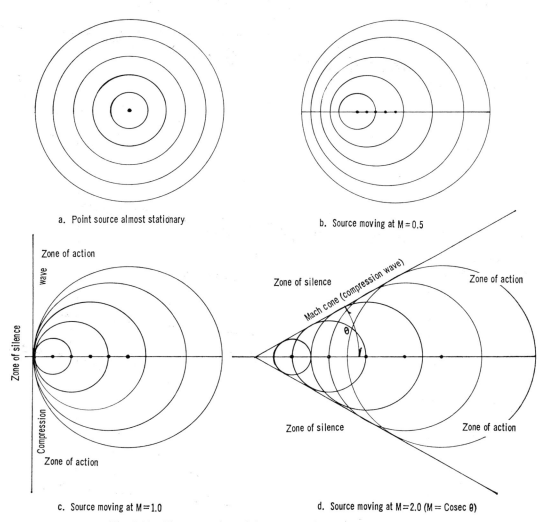

a. Point source almost stationary

b. Source moving at M = 0.5

c. Source moving at M = 1.0

d. Source moving at M = 2.0 (M = Cosec θ)

Fig. 5.13   The generation of the compression wave and Mach cone

to the body and an increase in pressure. As the slope of the forward facing surface decreases, however, the compression is reduced until, as the mid point of the body passes, the area opens out, allowing the compressed particles of air to expand again. The air is therefore accelerated, relative to the body (in reality only trying to move back to where it was pushed away from), and the pressure in that region is decreased to a suction over the rearward facing surface. This is the opposite of the case at low speed, when the air is sensibly incompressible. A shock wave occurs at the tail where the

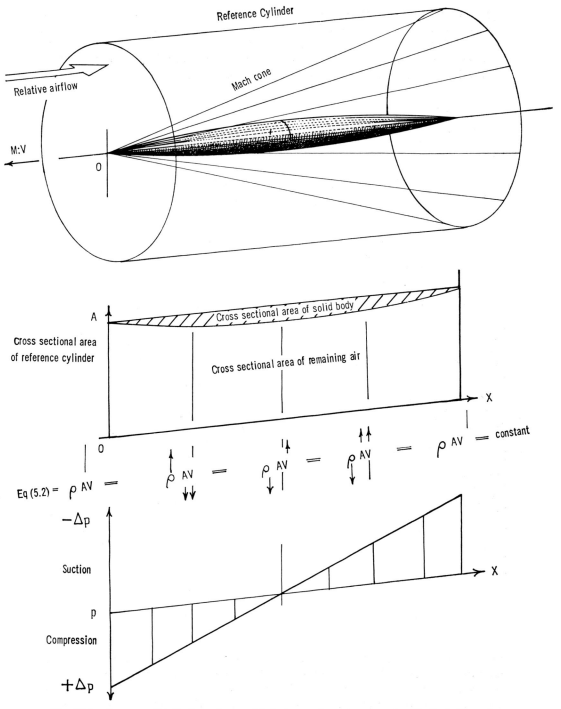

Fig. 5.14. Pressure distribution along solid body moving at zero angle of attack through a compressible fluid

71

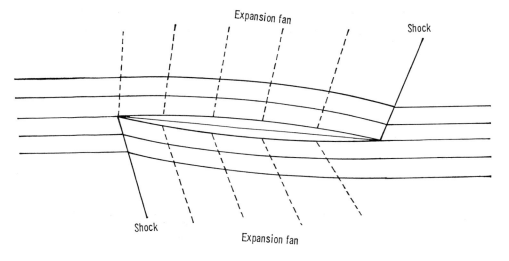

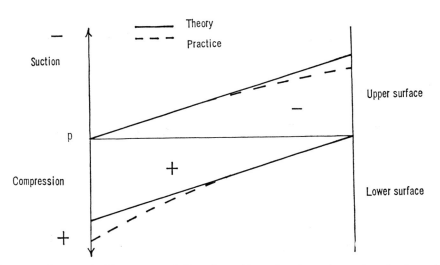

Fig. 5.15. Supersonic biconvex aerofoil section with angle of attack equal to leading edge
surface angle, showing lifting pressure distribution

rearward movement of the air is terminated and the pressure finally readjusted back
to the ambient value.

The frontispiece shows very clearly the formation of shock and expansion waves
experimentally and in practice. The expansion waves on the Lightning are marked
by water vapour condensing as mist.

The drag caused by compressibility of the air is termed wave drag which has
two components. The first is due to the distribution of volume along the length of a
body, and this is independent of the lift generated. The second is due to the lift
generated, as may be seen from Fig. 5.15, in which the slope of the pressure diagram

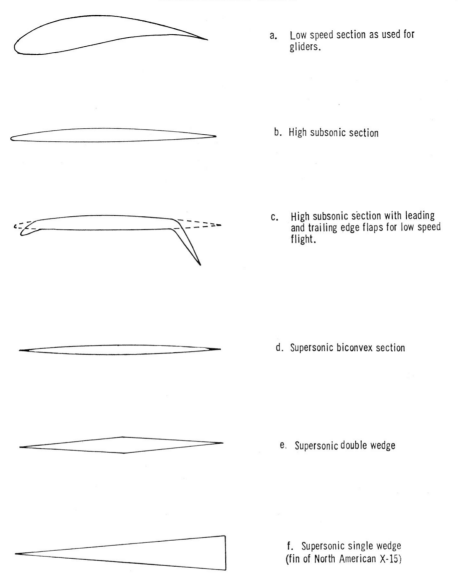

a. Low speed section as used for gliders.

b. High subsonic section

c. High subsonic section with leading and trailing edge flaps for low speed flight.

d. Supersonic biconvex section

e. Supersonic double wedge

f. Supersonic single wedge (fin of North American X-15)

Fig. 5.16.   Typical aerofoil sections

is similar to that shown in Fig. 5.14, except that the values have been altered by the angle of attack and, hence, the inclination of the surfaces to the air.

The double wedge aerofoil section is a simpler section to make than the biconvex version, although a biconvex section gives a more flexible performance throughout the flight envelope. When an aircraft is designed for one kind of performance mode (*e.g.*, an anti-aircraft missile) then a wedge is more convenient. The experimental North American X-15, employs single wedge fin surfaces, Fig. 5.16(*f*), and in this way eliminates the rear-facing wedge surfaces which, in experiencing a suction, contribute to the drag as much as a flat base. In this way the weight of the fin surfaces has been reduced without loss of control effectiveness.

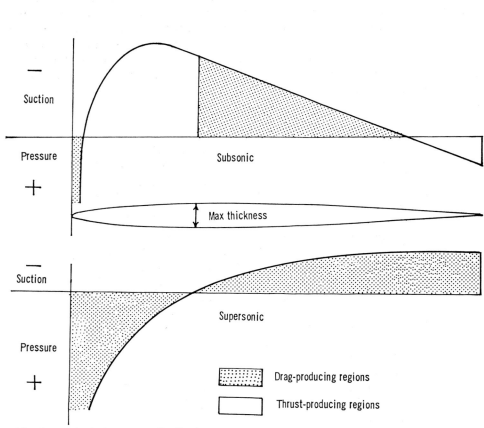

Fig. 5.17. Typical pressure distributions over an aerofoil at subsonic and supersonic speeds
(Compare with Fig. 5.14.)

The wave drag is minimized by selecting the optimum area, or volume-distribution along the length of the body. A Sears-Haak profile, rather like Fig. 5.14, is such an example. Area and volume distribution is an important design technique that will be discussed under area-ruling, in the next chapter.

5.4 Lift and Drag Summary

The generation of lift is achieved by establishing a favourable pressure distribution over aerodynamic surfaces. At subsonic speeds, where the air is assumed to have negligible compressibility, this is achieved by an induced motion of the air particles known as circulation. Circulation is the origin of the vortex system accompanying a lifting surface, which in turn is the origin of the vortex drag: the price to be paid to nature in return for the lifting-service rendered. The pressure distribution, even when the surface is not lifting, contributes to the drag—along with friction arising from the viscosity of the air.

At supersonic speeds lift is generated by the establishment of a pressure distribution that arises from a different motion of the air particles. The particles no longer circulate: they have not the time before a body has passed: instead they suffer a much more violent piston-like displacement which causes an initial compression, that must be followed by expansion back to the initially undisturbed condition. The supersonic pressure distribution generates higher drag, because of the more intense compression and suction forces. The additional drag is called wave drag. Skin friction drag is still present. Fig. 5.17 compares the typical pressure distribution over a wing section at subsonic and supersonic speeds.

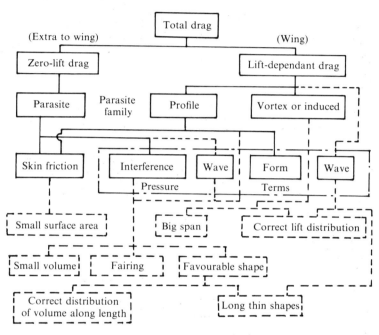

Fig. 5.18. Total drag components. The dotted lines show features that reduce the various drag components, but some features work against others, *e.g.*, big span versus long thin shape

At subsonic speeds aeroplanes have wings of high aspect ratio and the span may exceed the length of the body. At supersonic speeds aeroplanes must grow longer in the direction of flight and, so that drag may be minimized, they are also arranged to lie (as far as possible) inside the Mach cone shed from the nose of the body. It follows that for minimum supersonic drag aeroplanes have lower aspect ratios than their subsonic counterparts. At subsonic speeds a supersonic aeroplane has a higher drag than a subsonic machine of comparable size, generating the same lift. Fig. 5.18 summarizes the various drag components and the aspects of shape that contribute to the magnitude of each.

5.5 Scale Effect and Reynold's Number

As long as the relative airflow patterns around geometrically similar bodies are similar, then the forces generated are comparable, the proportionality being as the square of the scale. This is apparent from Eq. (5–8), for example, in which the lift varies as the wing area (*i.e.*, length^2), all other factors remaining equal: double the linear scale of the wing and both area and lift are quadrupled.

The forces depend also upon gravity, and the pressure, viscosity and inertia of the air. The first two can be neglected as far as the effect of scale is concerned. The last two are important because the actual motion of the particles of air depends upon the relationship between their viscosity and inertia, *i.e.*, upon μ and their mass/unit volume, ρ.

We have seen how, for example, the lift coefficient of an aerofoil section can be expressed in terms of the ratio of the average static pressure difference between upper and lower surfaces to the dynamic pressure. The pressure field around the aerofoil depends in turn upon the state of the boundary layer and upon the point at which transition from a laminar to a turbulent layer occurs. Turbulence is started mechanically at a point on the surface of an aeroplane by an irregularity of some kind. The rate at which the disturbance spreads as turbulence is a function of the diffusing effect of viscosity, which in effect carries motion outwards into successive layers of air. Inertia (the reluctance of the air to move out of the way of a body and then to close in behind) resists the effect of diffusion. The greater the 'momentum' (the product of density and relative velocity) of the relative airflow, the larger is the scale of a disturbance needed to alter it. On the other hand, the larger the scale of a surface the more slowly does any change of momentum take place. The condition of the pressure field can be defined, therefore, in terms of a number relating scale, inertia and viscosity. As long as such a number (called the Reynolds' number after Osborne Reynolds, Professor of Engineering in the University of Manchester (1883)), remains constant, then the aerodynamic conditions in the relative airflow remain comparable as far as the force coefficients are concerned.

The Reynolds' number is expressed as:

$$R_N = \frac{Vc\rho}{\mu} \qquad (5\text{–}13)$$

$$= \frac{Vc}{v} \qquad (5\text{–}13a)$$

where c is the chord of the aerofoil section. This is a most important relationship, for it enables data measured on a model in a wind tunnel to be applied to the full scale aircraft. Similarly, aerodynamic characteristics of several aerofoil sections should only be compared at the same Reynolds' number.

CHAPTER 6

The Control of Lift and Drag

So far we have considered the generation of lift and drag in general terms, by the use of suitably shaped aerodynamic surfaces. Once an aircraft of a given size is specified, and the design point settled, there arises the particular problem of determining the optimum shape of the aeroplane. The optimum shape is not the 'pure' basic shape to satisfy conditions at the design point, for aircraft must be flexible enough to operate safely and with reasonable economy off-design.

The optimum shape has three aspects:

(a) The basic shape in its purest form, satisfying the conditions at the design point alone.

(b) Changes of the basic shape in flight to improve off-design performance, the aspect being considered under the general heading of 'variable geometry'. Under this heading we can include the application of power to establish the required airflows.

(c) Fixed modifications of the basic shape to improve local airflows. This aspect covers the various kinds of aerodynamic palliatives that are employed, and the treatment of wing-body junctions to reduce losses through interference.

The resultant aerodynamic efficiency of the aeroplane is measurable in terms of the lift/drag. The three aspects of shape must all be balanced according to the role requirements, but for the purposes of discussion these are considered with regard for the optimum lift/drag when range flying.

6.1 The Basic Aerodynamic Shape

We know that the shape of an aeroplane varies with role and flight regime, for this has been shown in Fig. 2.2. In considering the aerodynamic reason we shall simplify the problem by only thinking of the wing plus body combination: the stabilizing surfaces belong to a further problem, that of keeping the aeroplane flying at the required attitude to the air.

6.1.1 Design for Subsonic Flight

The principal aerodynamic features of subsonic aeroplanes are the lack of wing sweep and the presence of a fuselage that is discrete from the wing in every respect.

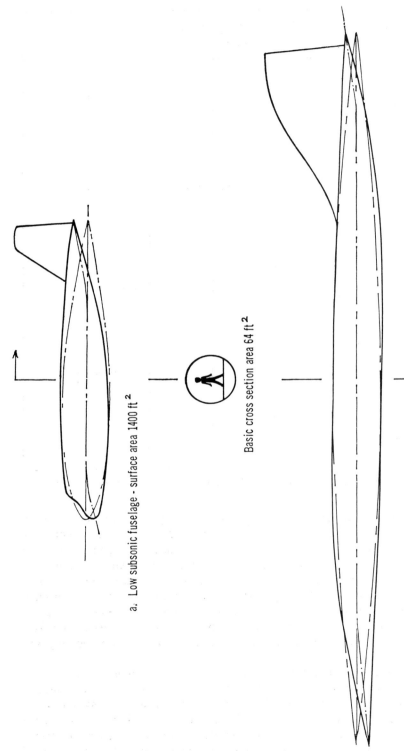

a. Low subsonic fuselage - surface area 1400 ft^2

Basic cross section area 64 ft^2

b. Supersonic fuselage - surface area 3250 ft^2

Fig. 6.1. Comparison of typical low and high speed transport fuselages. Approximately equivalent aerofoil thickness distribution shown

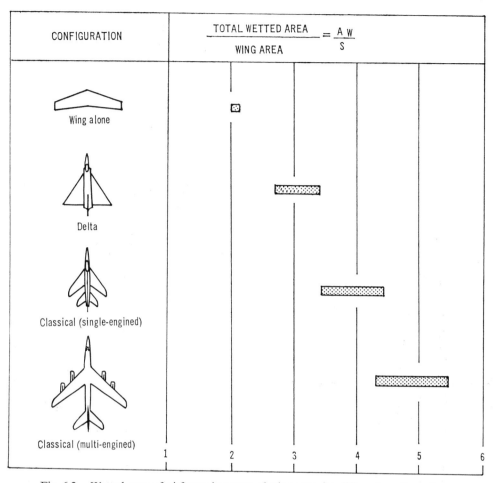

Fig. 6.2.   Wetted area of airframe in terms of wing area for different configurations

The shape of the fuselage usually resembles a streamlined cylinder, that may also be considered as a very low aspect ratio aerofoil. The profile thickness distribution is similar to that of the aerofoil sections used in the particular flight regime, as may be seen in Fig. 6.1, in which a low-subsonic fuselage is compared with a supersonic fuselage of the same minimum cross-section, as determined by the height of a man. It should be borne in mind that the supersonic fuselage shown carries about double the payload of the subsonic version. The existence of a discrete fuselage, as well as any other discrete body, alters the wetted area of the aeroplane and, hence, the skin-friction drag in the proportions shown in Fig. 6.2. The proportions apply equally well to all flight regimes.

The sweep of a wing requires some definition, for some subsonic aeroplanes appear to feature swept wings but the reason is different from that for aircraft designed for higher speeds. A wing is said to be unswept if it has zero sweep to any spanwise line between 25 and 70 per cent of the chord. Swept wings have appeared on low-subsonic aeroplanes as aids to stability: either as a way of arranging the centre of gravity and aerodynamic centre in the correct relationship, or as a means of increasing the moment arm of a control surface in a tailless design. On subsonic aircraft designed for higher speeds we shall say more in a moment.

Wing section thickness ratios are of the order of 12 per cent, while the point of maximum camber lies well forward, making sections humped-looking, with well-rounded leading edges. Aspect ratios are high, being around 10, with lift/drag ratios of 15 to 20. Invariably the stabilizing surfaces appear at the tail in the form of tail-plane and elevator, fin and rudder.

The subsonic aeroplane represents the 'classical' layout in what is probably its most efficient form. The classical layout had been used successfully for so long that it was adapted and modified as much as possible in the years following the appear-ence of the turbojet. It is only recently that technology has advanced far enough for reasonably efficient supersonic-cruise aeroplanes to be designed. Although supersonic lift/drag is lower than subsonic, and the sfc of supersonic engines is high, speeds have now been reached where the product:

$$\frac{V}{c'}\frac{L}{D} \text{ in Eq. (4–10)}$$

falls within a range of 'good' values for range flying efficiency. Until the truly supersonic aeroplane appeared high speed aircraft were really only transonic, in the sense that their shapes were designed in such a way as to make the air behave in a subsonic fashion, as though nothing unusual was happening to it.

Transonic Design Features: Sweep and Area Ruling

The outstanding feature of the transonic aeroplane is the swept wing in its different guises. The use of wing sweep to delay the onset of compressibility was suggested by A. Betz in 1939, after Busemann had drawn attention to such advantages of the swept wing at supersonic speeds at the Volta Congress in Rome in 1935.

To understand the effect of sweep (swept aerofoils are often referred to as yawed or sheared aerofoils) let us reconsider what happens to the air when impelled to move by a body at a speed very near to that of sound (the speed at which air adjusts itself to a disturbance). We have seen that as particles of air are forced over the surfaces of an aerofoil they are impelled to move relative to their undisturbed positions: to circulate. The magnitude of such movement depends upon the thickness-distribution of the aerofoil section and the camber, which together determine the slope of the surface impelling the air to move. If an aerofoil is swept (forwards or backwards) through an angle, $\wedge$, then the geometrical effect is to decrease the thickness-distribu-tion of the section. In Fig. 6.3 a parallel chord aerofoil is shown, in which case the thickness ratio decreases in proportion to cos $\wedge$. Clearly then, the air is displaced by the finer section in a longer time, so that the air has more time in which to adjust itself to the disturbance. Since drag-rise is roughly proportional to the square of the maximum thickness/chord, the aerodynamic advantage of thin sections is obvious (but thin sections raise many structural strength problems).

If lines are drawn joining all points of equal pressure over an aerofoil surface they form a family of isobars as shown in Fig. 6.3. There are two important features to be noted about isobars, both of which determine the pressure gradient across a surface:

  (i) the intensity of pressure that each represents;
  (ii) their spacing.

If the change of pressure is intense, or the isobars are close together, then the pressure gradient is steep and it is likely that the ultimate readjustment of the air to its undisturbed condition will be violent, with undesirable characteristics.

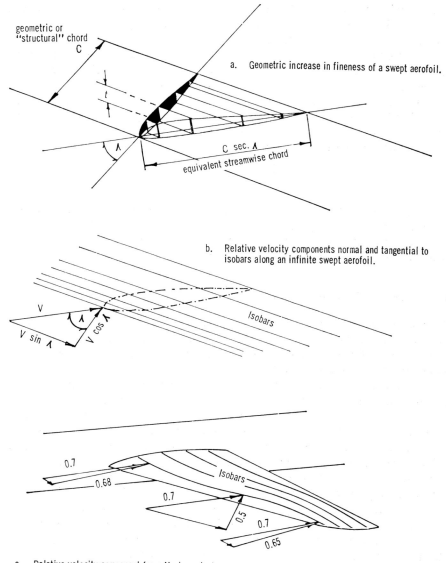

a. Geometric increase in fineness of a swept aerofoil.

b. Relative velocity components normal and tangential to isobars along an infinite swept aerofoil.

c. Relative velocity component (as a Mach number) normal to a given isobar near the leading edge of a wing moving at M 0.7,

Fig. 6.3.   The theory of sweep

It follows that the critical conditions governing the behaviour of the air on a surface are to be found on a line along which the gradient is measured, lying normal to the isobars through the region in question. We may now apply a mathematical artifice and postulate that the critical pressure gradient is a function of the component

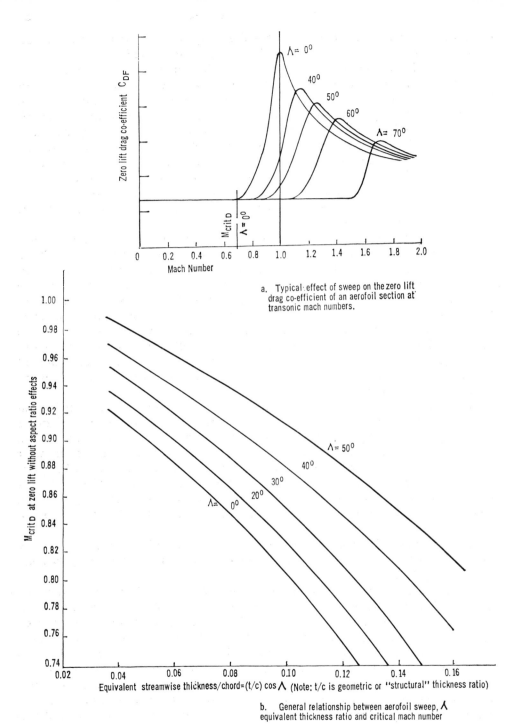

a. Typical effect of sweep on the zero lift drag co-efficient of an aerofoil section at transonic mach numbers.

b. General relationship between aerofoil sweep, Λ equivalent thickness ratio and critical mach number

Fig. 6.4. The effect of aerofoil sweep and thickness on compressibility drag rise

of velocity normal to the isobars—for practical purposes the component across the geometric chord, normal to the quarter-chord axis of the aerofoil.

If an aerofoil is yawed, then the critical velocity component is reduced. In the case of a theoretical infinite aerofoil of parallel chord, the isobars lie parallel to leading and trailing edge. The presence of both fuselage and wing tips alters the isobar pattern and, thus, the effect of sweep along the span. In Fig. 6.3(c) the aircraft is assumed to be flying at M = 0·7 or thereabouts, but the wing root and tip are nearer to their critical Mach numbers for compressibility effects. For this reason we find unusual changes of camber in the vicinity of root and tips of transonic aeroplanes; wing roots with additional sweep, giving the wing a crescent shape and tips with increasing curvature from leading to trailing edge that, in effect, progressively increases sweep outboard (these are called streamwise tips): all for the purpose of achieving constant isobar sweep (see Fig. 6.19).

The unpleasant effects of compressibility are rapid drag-rise, loss of lift, breakdown of local airflows (shock stalling) and buffeting that may be damaging to the airframe and destabilizing from its effect upon control and tail surfaces. These are caused by the air reaching supersonic speeds at some point on the surface of an aerofoil. The deceleration back again to subsonic conditions takes place in a very short distance, through a shock wave (measured in parts of one thousandth of an inch), so called because of the violent increase in static pressure. The increase in static pressure is high enough to cause boundary layer separation, with effects similar to the low-speed stall. Fig. 6.4(a) shows the general effect of sweepback on the drag of an aerofoil at transonic Mach numbers (i.e., the relative airflow is still subsonic at some point on the surface of the airframe).

The flight Mach number—in wind-tunnel terms the free-stream Mach number—at which the relative airflow reaches the speed of sound at some point on the airframe is called M_{crit}. Below M_{crit} the condition of the relative airflow is said to be subcritical, above M_{crit}, supercritical. The situation is hard to determine because one can never be sure of the state of the flow everywhere at once. A more precise value, $M_{crit\ D}$, is used corresponding with an arbitary increase in the subsonic drag coefficient of 0·002 or thereabouts, at constant angle of attack. It will be seen that $M_{crit\ D}$ (which almost corresponds with the steep rise of drag coefficient in Fig. 6.4(a).) is increased by sweep.

The general relationship between equivalent thickness ratio (a function of $c\ sec\ \wedge$ in Fig. 6.3) and sweep, $\wedge$, is shown in Fig. 6.4(b). The thinner and more highly swept the aerofoil, the higher the $M_{crit\ D}$.

The second, more recent, feature of transonic aeroplanes is the use of waisting and area distribution, grouped collectively under area-ruling. We saw in the last chapter that there is an optimum area distribution for any design point with which a body generates the minimum wave drag at zero lift. Instead of a solid of revolution, consider an aeroplane within an imaginary reference cylinder, as in Fig. 5.14. It is possible so to shape the fuselage cross-sections that the bulge in cross-sectional area caused by the wings and tail are faired more smoothly into a profile giving lower wave drag. Paradoxically, area-ruling may cause a growth in local cross-sectional area by the presence of fat bulges between wing and tail, or the growth of carrot-like shock-bodies at the trailing edges of the wings (Kuchemann Carrots'). Area-ruling is shown dotted in Fig. 6.5(a). Fig. 6.5(b) and (c) show, in a slightly different way, how the waisted fuselage generates expansions and compressions that cancel the effects of the wing compressions and expansions. It will be remembered that shock waves and

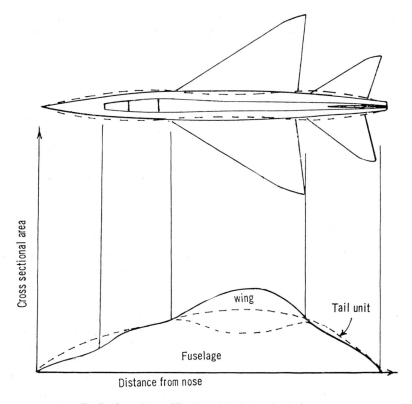

a. Area distribution with modification (dotted) to reduce wing-
fuselage interference.

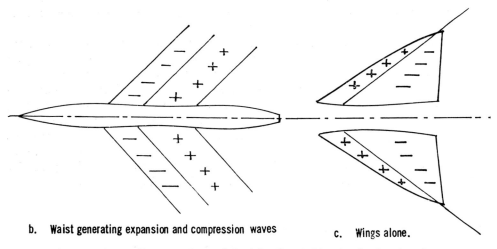

b. Waist generating expansion and compression waves

c. Wings alone.

Fig. 6.5. Area-ruling as a means of obtaining favourable wing-fuselage interference

similar compression phenomena are caused when the air is squeezed into a smaller volume. Conversely, expansion waves are the result of the air being free to expand into a larger volume.

6.1.2 Design for Supersonic Flight

The design of a supersonic aeroplane is simplified by the flow being of one type only: by the time an aeroplane has reached $M = 1.5$ or 1.6 it is unlikely that any significant transonic region will be found over the surface of the airframe.

Design for minimum wave drag is of paramount importance. Wings are thin, around 3 or 5 per cent thickness ratio, fuselages are long and slender, and may feature camber to achieve more favourable lift/drag interference with the lifting surfaces. Wing spans are short—to reduce wave drag by confining the surfaces within the Mach cone, Fig. 6.6—and aspect ratios are low, so low in fact that the spanwise pressure-distribution approximates to that around a pair of wing tips joined together in the middle. The proportions of the aeroplane are determined by the need to keep as much of the airframe as possible within the Mach cone shed from the nose, Fig. 6.6, which illustrates the reason for the appearance of the integrated slender-delta configuration as a more efficient alternative to the classical for economic operations.

The slender-delta has more wing area than a 'straight-winged' classical aeroplane and, therefore, a lower wing loading. The additional area is needed to compensate for the lower lift coefficient. It follows that such an aeroplane should be able to achieve lower landing speeds without recourse to expensive and heavy high-lift devices—as long as low speed instability can be overcome. It should be noted, however, that in Fig. 6.4 the straight (classical) wing has a lower drag coefficient than the swept wing at high Mach numbers. That is one reason why supersonic fighters and research aircraft have tended to classical rather than integrated layouts. When flying off-design the classical straight wing generates the highest drag in the region of mixed sub and supersonic flows. Of the two layouts the one using acute sweep is theoretically preferable.

Another significant feature of the supersonic classical configuration is that the wing and tail tips only affect the spanwise pressure distribution within a region bounded by Mach cones shed from the tip of each leading edge. At subsonic speeds it will be remembered that the tips influence the whole span. The inefficient portion of the wing or tail tip is therefore cropped away at the semi angle of the Mach cone, thus saving some weight. This feature tends to appear on missiles and aircraft intended for continuous flight at one design point, for example, bomber, reconnaissance and supersonic transport aircraft. Cropped surfaces are shown in Fig. 6.7. It will be seen that the disturbance zone caused by the Mach cone shed from the kinked leading edge of the wing above is removed by the presence of a favourably shaped body.

'Non-classical' Aerodynamics and the Slender-Delta

It will be of some assistance to the student if the 'non-classical' concept of the aerodynamics of the slender-delta is explained, for such aerodynamics differ radically from the 'classical' aerodynamics discussed in chapter 5. Such aerodynamics account for certain unusual features of the slender-delta planform, which is by no means simply triangular.

The essential feature of classical subsonic aerodynamics is the generation of an unseparated lifting vortex system around a wing, more or less normal to the direction of motion. Separated flow signifies a loss of circulation and lift while a sudden spread

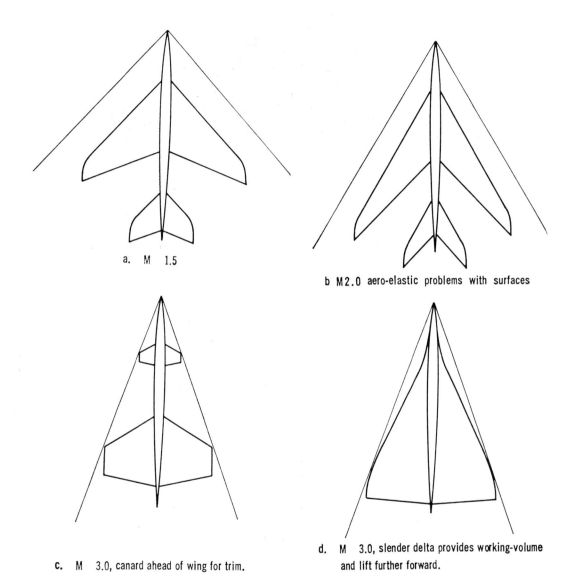

a.   M   1.5

b M2.0 aero-elastic problems with surfaces

c.   M   3.0, canard ahead of wing for trim.

d.   M   3.0, slender delta provides working-volume and lift further forward.

Fig. 6.6.   Enforced slenderness and decreased aspect ratio for low wave-drag in the supersonic regime

marks the stall. Around the wing tips air flowing outwards from the higher pressure undersurface, upwards, and then inwards over the upper surface marks the basic motion around the core of the separated airflow of the trailing vortex system. Re-

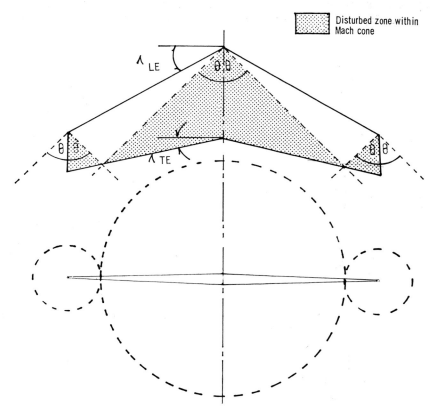

Disturbed zone within
Mach cone

Λ_{LE} θ θ

θ θ Λ_{TE} θ θ

a. Wing alone in supersonic flow showing disturbed zones within Mach cones
   shed from tips and wing junction leading-edge.

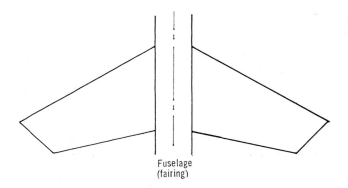

Fuselage
(fairing)

b. Cropped wing, centre section disturbed zone eliminated by favourable body.

Fig. 6.7.   Wing with inefficient portions of surface removed by cropping and fairing

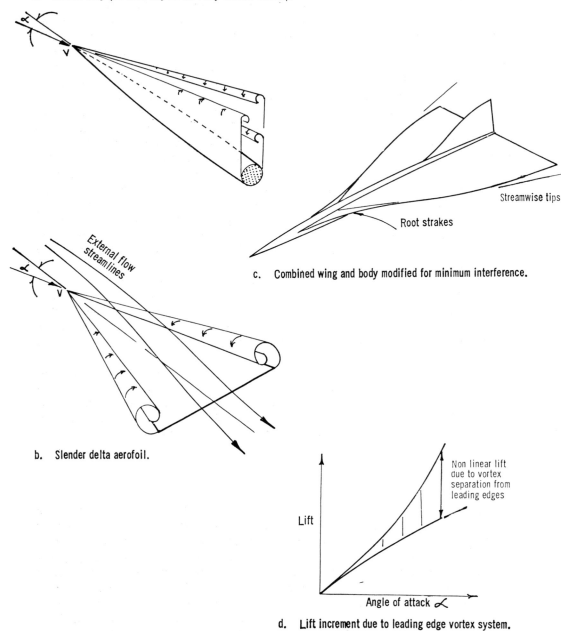

a. Slender body (vortices may be unevenly shed as shown).

c. Combined wing and body modified for minimum interference.

Streamwise tips

Root strakes

External flow streamlines

b. Slender delta aerofoil.

Lift

Non linear lift due to vortex separation from leading edges

Angle of attack α

d. Lift increment due to leading edge vortex system.

Fig. 6.8.   Lifting vortices generated by a separated flow at low speed

moval of the trailing vortices by the substitution of endplates, or by an increase of aspect ratio towards infinity reduces the lift-dependent vortex drag.

The slender-delta, being in effect two large wing tips joined at the centre-line makes use of the separated vortex flow shed from what are now the leading edges of the wings to generate large, non-linear lift increments as shown in Fig. 6.8. The non-linear lift increments are accompanied, however, by the high price of large non-linear drag.

The leading edges of the slender aerofoil are sharp instead of rounded, the sharp edge forcing the relative airflow to separate by causing a large change of momentum and a correspondingly large pressure gradient across the leading edge. For the vortices to form, however, the component of flow normal to the leading edge must be sub-sonic. Looking again at Fig. 6.7 we see that if a Mach line (a line marking the inter-section of a Mach cone with a plane) sweeps backwards more than the leading edge, then the leading edge of the wing experiences a supersonic component of flow. If the same argument is applied to the trailing edge, then part of the trailing edge lying outside (or forward of) a Mach line also lies in a region of supersonic flow. The leading and trailing edges are described as: subsonic, sonic, or supersonic, depending whether their relevant angles of sweep, $\wedge_{LE}$, $\wedge_{TE}$, are: more than, equal to, or less than $(90 - \theta)$. The wing in Fig. 6.7(b) has supersonic leading and trailing edges, and the cropped tips are sonic. The wing in Fig. 6.8(c) is said to have subsonic leading edges and a supersonic trailing edge.

The sharp leading edge strakes at the root of the wings are placed there to force even vortex shedding, because the body forward of the wing may shed vortices unevenly as shown at large angles of attack. As the vortices have a powerful effect upon the lift, by delaying final separation of the flow from the rear part of the wing, any irregularity in their formation affects stability by causing pitching, rolling and yawing.

While the generation of such lifting vortices by separation at low speeds delays the stall in the classical sense, so that a wing may reach very large angles of attack (40° or more), the lift is accompanied by very high drag and low lift/drag ratios. Furthermore, although the wing may still be working at a large angle of attack, instability of various kinds makes it impossible for the lift to be used on take off and landing.

Compression Lift

Beyond $M = 3$ the shape of the aeroplane is dictated by the need to make use of grossly unfavourable features of the violently disturbed airflow. Shock waves are the predominant feature of the relative airflow and, as they cannot be avoided, they may be used to generate compression-lift and (in theory) thrust-producing regions (when combined with surface-burning of fuel: i.e., fuel is burnt in the airstream over a rearward-facing surface and the resulting increase in local pressure produces thrust). The shapes of such aircraft are determined by the need to produce favourable inter-actions between the relatively high-pressure regions behind shock waves and the adjacent airframe surfaces. The simplest example is shown in Fig. 6.9, in which an ogive, shedding a complete ogival Mach-cone, is split longitudinally and fitted with wings. The semi-ogive sheds a semi-Mach-cone and the wings trap the pressure between the body and their sonic leading edges.

The American B-70, which first flew in May 1964, was designed to generate compression lift. Fig. 6.9(c) shows a typical curve of compression lift/drag compared

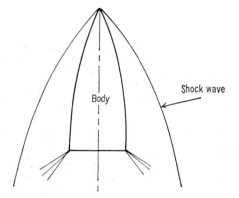

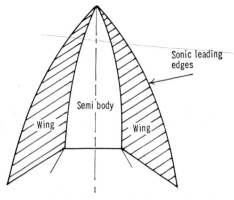

a. Ogival solid of revolution with symmetrical compression region.

b. Semi-ogive with asymmetrical compression region bounded by wings.

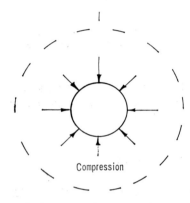

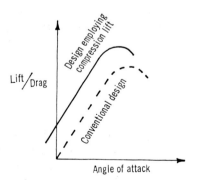

c. Improvement of lift/drag by generation of compression lift.

Fig. 6.9.   The generation of compression lift at high Mach numbers

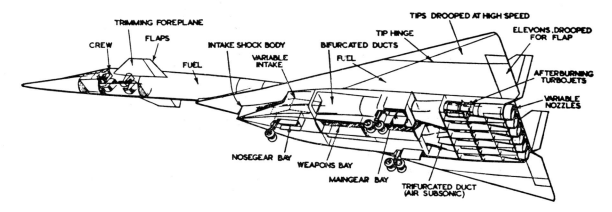

Fig. 6.10 The North American B-70 showing salient features that are typical of current aeronautical practice. Compare the shape of the engine-box and wing combination with Fig. 6.9

with the lift/drag of a conventional design. The salient features of the B-70 are shown in Fig. 6.10. The engine-box beneath the delta wing performs a similar function in compressing the airflow to the semi-ogive shown in Fig. 6.9(*b*).

6.2 Variable Geometry—Changing the Effective Airflow in Flight

Variable geometry is, in various ways, the means of so changing the effective configuration of the lifting surfaces in flight, that the aerodynamic efficiency of the aeroplane is improved in extreme off-design conditions. Variable geometry appears in two forms: polymorphism, in which the planform and, hence, the aspect ratio of a wing is altered; and variable camber, in which for example flaps are lowered to increase lift at low speeds. Certain aircraft, notably those for naval operations, may feature variable incidence wings: a way of altering the angle of attack without altering the fuselage attitude to the flight path.

6.2.1 The Polymorph

A truly polymorphous wing configuration has already been shown in Fig. 2.4, but polymorphism can take many forms, as shown in Fig. 6.11. The Fowler flap, which increases the area of the wing (as well as the camber) increases the lift and reduces the landing speed. Tip droop, used on the B-70, moves the aerodynamic centre forward at high speeds and decreases the nose-down pitching moment and trim drag: it also increases the effective fin-area and increases the compression lift. Both a telescopic and a variable sweep wing reduce the wave drag at high speed and achieve high lift/drag ratios at low EAS. The improved cruising efficiency resulting from variable sweep is shown in Fig. 6.12.

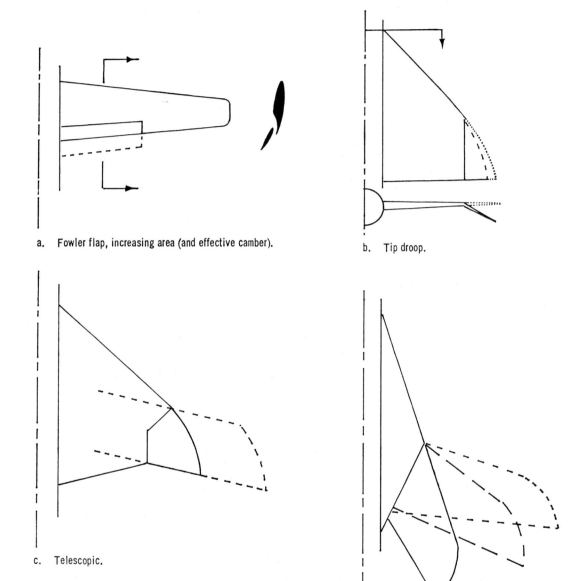

a. Fowler flap, increasing area (and effective camber).

b. Tip droop.

c. Telescopic.

d. Variable sweep.

Fig. 6.11.   Polymorphous variable geometry

Table 6.1 has been included to show the typical benefits that might be obtained from the use of variable sweep for a specific, though hypothetical, bomber like the fighter in Fig. 5.1. The variable sweep wing is heavier than a fixed wing, because of the weight of moving parts and locally increased strength of members. The reduced

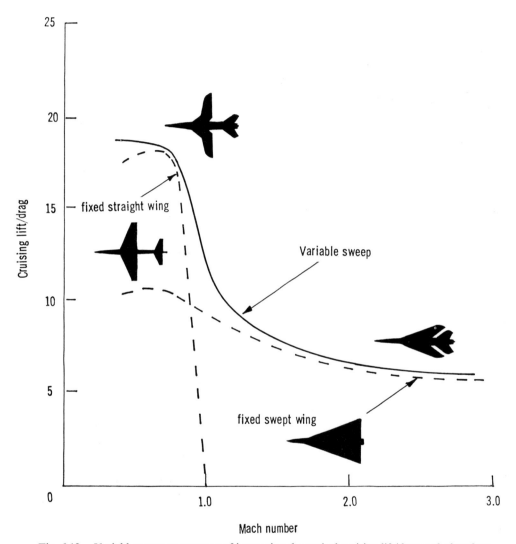

Fig. 6.12. Variable sweep as a means of improving theoretical cruising lift/drag and, therefore, reducing the fuel required for range

drag, however, enables a less powerful and lighter engine to be used. Less fuel is therefore needed, because the engine is less thirsty and, the fuel system can be made lighter. The payload is constant, but this appears as a different percentage of the all-up weight of each aeroplane.

It will be seen from Table 6.1 that of the two designs the aeroplane with the variable sweep wing will be the lighter and, hence, the cheaper of the two. But

TABLE 6.1

Specification

Range: 1,600 nm at range speed and height
: 200 nm at M = 0·9 at sea level
Endurance: loiter for 4 hours
: Supersonic dash to M = 2 for 5 minutes
Payload: 7,500 lb

Item	Percentage All-up Weight	
	Fixed Sweep	Variable Sweep
Structure	30·2	33·2
Power Plant	13·8	12·2
Services (hydraulic etc.)	7·4	8·0
Fuel	37·9	28·5
Payload	8·9	16·5
Total	100	100
Take-off (all-up weight) $\dfrac{7,500 \times 100}{\text{payload } \% \text{ weight}}$	$\dfrac{7,500 \times 100}{8\cdot9} = 84,000$ lb	$\dfrac{7,500 \times 100}{16\cdot5} = 45,500$ lb

broadly speaking variable sweep offers its main advantages over fixed sweep when the required performance involves the need to fly efficiently over a large part of the flight envelope—for example: combining supersonic dash with STOL and subsonic loiter.

6.2.2 Devices which change the Effective Camber of Sections

We saw earlier that the camber of an aerofoil section alters the curvature over the upper and lower surfaces and, therefore, the displacement of the air being affected by each. Positive camber increases the curvature of the upper surface and decreases that of the lower, so that there is a net increase in the lifting circulation imparted to the air. It follows that the greater the positive camber the greater the nose-down pitching moment, and *vice versa*.

Thinking in general terms of altering the curvature of a lifting surface to alter the circulation leads to a collection of devices such as those shown in Fig. 6.13, for controlling lift and drag at low speed. The control of section lift and drag involves control of the boundary layer. Shaping aerofoils by variations of camber, thickness distribution, slots, slats and flaps and, as we shall see, vortex generators, are all ways of inducing the boundary layer to develop and behave in a controlled manner. The term boundary layer control is reserved in practice for mechanical control of the boundary layer by the application of power.

We have seen that for efficiency aerodynamic surfaces must not gather up air any more than is necessary. Intense suction and steep pressure gradients behind suction peaks indicate that the air is being gathered more swiftly than it should be. Slots of various kinds, both fixed and variable, are ways of slackening the pressure gradient. The slot with air blowing from it can be regarded as a means of 'washing away' the air being borne along and tending to cling to the airframe, by the introduction of a sheet of relatively high velocity air tangential to the surface. The slot prolongs the lift

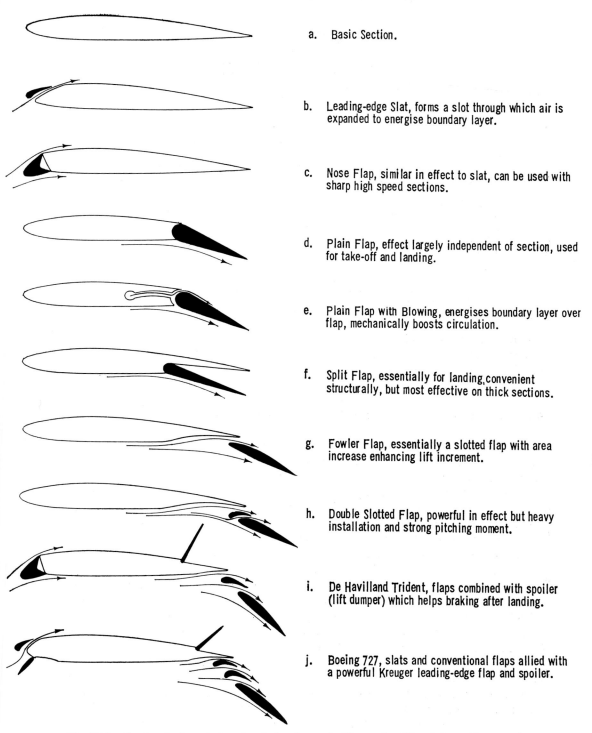

a. Basic Section.

b. Leading-edge Slat, forms a slot through which air is expanded to energise boundary layer.

c. Nose Flap, similar in effect to slat, can be used with sharp high speed sections.

d. Plain Flap, effect largely independent of section, used for take-off and landing.

e. Plain Flap with Blowing, energises boundary layer over flap, mechanically boosts circulation.

f. Split Flap, essentially for landing, convenient structurally, but most effective on thick sections.

g. Fowler Flap, essentially a slotted flap with area increase enhancing lift increment.

h. Double Slotted Flap, powerful in effect but heavy installation and strong pitching moment.

i. De Havilland Trident, flaps combined with spoiler (lift dumper) which helps braking after landing.

j. Boeing 727, slats and conventional flaps allied with a powerful Kreuger leading-edge flap and spoiler.

Fig. 6.13. Camber (and area) changing devices for controlling section lift and drag at low speed

curve by increasing the angle of attack at which the stall occurs. A leading edge flap reduces the suction peak just behind the leading edge, produces a thinner boundary layer and increases the stalling angle in a similar way.

The choice between a slat and a flap at the leading edge is usually based upon mechanical and structural convenience rather than aerodynamic merit. Thin high speed sections with sharp leading edges derive more benefit from nose flaps.

The plain flap is the basis of all conventional control surfaces. When moved downwards lift is increased: upwards, lift is decreased (*i.e.*, it is increased in the opposite direction). The advantage of the trailing edge flap over leading edge slats or flaps is that the attitude of the aeroplane on the glidepath is more nose-down, with improved vision for the pilot.

6.2.3 Mechanical Control of the Boundary Layer

There are three basic ways of controlling the development of the boundary layer and, hence, the lift and drag of a lifting surface by the use of external power:

(*a*) Boundary Layer Control proper, in which power is applied to control separation and the stall of the basic surface, while achieving lower drag at higher speeds.

(*b*) Circulation Control using blowing or suction over flaps and near the trailing edge to increase the circulation and lift at a given angle of attack.

(*c*) Directed Slipstream from jet or propeller efflux over flap surfaces.

Boundary layer control by the use of suction over a large part of an aerofoil surface has been experimented with for many years as a way of achieving laminar flow, notably by Arado in Germany, Handley Page in the United Kingdom and

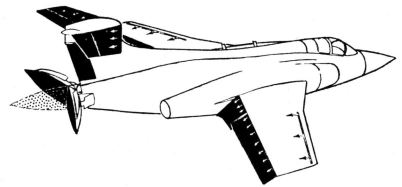

Fig. 6.14.   The Blackburn Buccaneer which employs blowing front and rear on the wings and from the leading edge of the tailplane

Northrop in the U.S.A. Results suggest that wing zero-lift drag may be reduced to one fifth normal values. A Northrop X-21A is claimed to have flown with suction for four hours on fuel enough for something like two and a half hours in the unsucked condition.

Circulation control: the use of blowing to generate supercirculation is most conveniently achieved by the tapping of air from engine compressors of many high performance jet aeroplanes. This is done with the naval Blackburn Buccaneer shown in Fig. 6.14, which employs blown flaps, ailerons and tailplane. The use of super-circulation enables smaller lifting surfaces to be used, with a saving in weight that compensates for the increased weight of the power system. The reduction in lifting surface area achieved in a specific case is shown in Fig. 6.15, where an early Blackburn design study leading to the Buccaneer is compared with a later Buccaneer. Generalized lift improvements from flaps, slats and mechanical control of the boundary layer are shown in Fig. 6.16.

6.2.4 Air Brakes and Drag Chutes

Drag is controlled crudely but effectively by the use of airbrakes and spoilers. Air brakes are often used at low speed, as well as for deceleration from high speed, to increase the zero lift drag on the approach. By so doing the overall drag is increased, but the speed for minimum drag is decreased, Fig. 6.22(a). In this way the delta aeroplane, for example, can maintain speed stability at lower approach speeds.

Speed stability is not an entirely satisfactory term to use, but there is no better alternative for describing what should happen when the attitude (and hence speed) changes transiently at constant power. Beyond the minimum drag speed a decrease of speed is accompanied by a decrease in drag, and vice versa. At constant power a decrease of speed is automatically compensated by an acceleration, because thrust is then greater than drag, while a transient increase of speed results in a deceleration, without intercession by the pilot. Below the minimum drag speed one is operating on the 'backside of the power curve', and a decrease of speed is accompanied by increasing drag and further decreasing speed. On the backside of the power curve there is no speed stability.

Many modern aeroplanes use drag chutes to decrease landing runs and to augment the effectiveness of the wheel brakes. Drag chutes are sometimes used as anti-spin parachutes, to augment the power of the control surfaces and prevent autorotation.

6.3 Fixed Modification to Improve Local Airflows

No matter how carefully the basic shape of an aeroplane may be combined with variable geometry to maintain high aerodynamic efficiency, there are inevitable local regions of interference that cause the airflow to break down under certain conditions. Sometimes the effects are small enough to be ignored, or lived with, at other times the effects may be of critical importance. For our purposes we shall divide the fixed modifications to the geometry of the aeroplane into: palliatives, in the main designed to improve airflow over the lifting surfaces; and the design of wing-body junctions. Palliatives, such as vortex generators, may be found extensively around fuselages as well as wings and tails, so one should not think of them as being exclusive to the lifting surfaces.

6.3.1 Some Aerodynamic Palliatives

Swept wings are particularly prone to misbehaviour of the relative airflow, because of the third component of motion, $V \sin \wedge$ (Fig. 6.3(b)) towards the tips. When shock

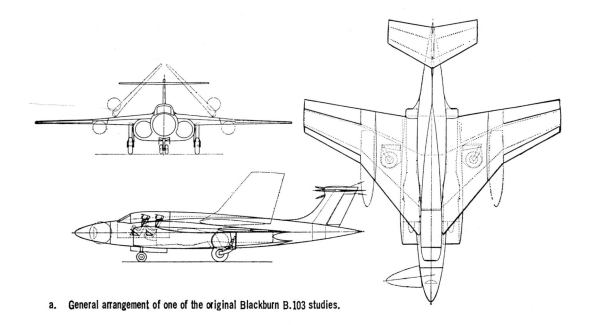

a.   General arrangement of one of the original Blackburn B.103 studies.

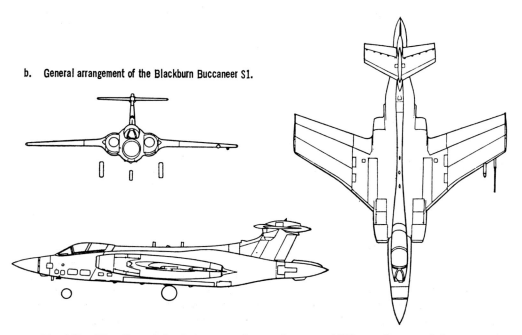

b.   General arrangement of the Blackburn Buccaneer S1.

Fig. 6.15.   The effect of circulation control upon the areas of lifting surfaces needed to meet a requirement

waves also form severe loss of stability may result from an apparently small disturbance spreading rapidly along a wing. The spanwise component of motion causes a drift of the boundary layer towards the tips with thickening of the layer and proneness to separation. The various palliatives are designed to delay separation, or to at least

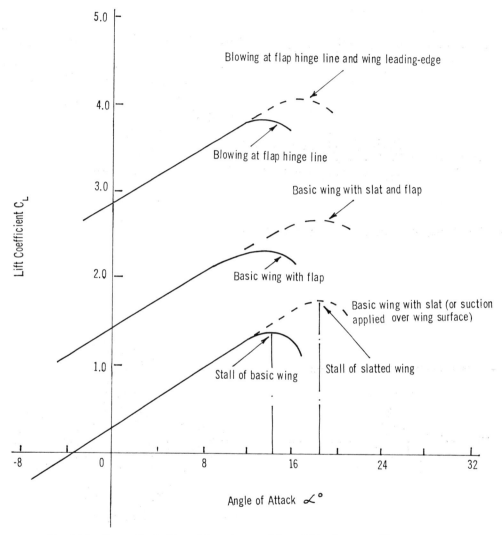

Fig. 6.16. Generalized effect of flap, slat, suction and blowing upon lift of basic wing

make separation predictable. Some use a forced vortex to break down an adverse pressure gradient, others employ camber for the same purpose. The vortex generators, fence, and notched leading edge, all induce a chordwise vortex over part of the wing, the flow around the vortex inhibiting the spanwise drift of the boundary layer.

The cambered and dog-toothed leading edges reduce the peak pressure and proneness to separation of the flow from the wing behind. Conic-camber, in which the camber is formed by part of the surface of a cone, has been used to modify some high speed wings for better operation off-design. The notched leading edge is particularly useful on highly swept wings which shed large leading edge vortices at high angles of attack, for the notch stabilizes the spanwise position of the shed vortex. By preventing the vortex wandering aimlessly up and down the leading edge stability and lateral control can be kept within acceptable limits. Vortex generators are in effect small aerofoils which, in protruding through the boundary layer, generate relatively powerful vortices from their tips. The flow around each tip vortex draws air from beyond the boundary layer and, by mixing close to the wing surface, increases the relative airflow within the boundary layer. In this way the adverse pressure gradient is reduced and the stagnating boundary layer is washed away into the wake.

Each palliative increases the drag over the theoretical minimum that might ideally be achieved with the basic shape of the aeroplane, but the increment of drag is less than the drag rise caused in practice without them. Examples, which belong predominantly to the leading edges, are shown in Fig. 6.17, along with a thin section having a slab trailing edge, (g). It will be seen that the slab trailing edge decreases the slope of the aerofoil surfaces behind the point of maximum thickness thus decreasing the adverse pressure gradients. If the surfaces were continued rearwards to meet beyond the trailing edge the resultant section would be much finer aerodynamically than the section used. Apart from local turbulence behind the slab, the air is unable to detect that no surface remains beyond the trailing edge.

6.3.2   Junctions: Curing Interference

The design of an aeroplane involves detailed treatment of the aerodynamic (and structural) properties of the individual parts, in temporary isolation from the rest. Design data sheets enable broad approximations to be made of the lift, drag and pitching moments of items such as mainplanes, tail surfaces, and bodies of various kinds. But the sum total of the individual drags is usually much less than that of the whole, while lift too is usually less. Pitching moments may be unpredictably, increased or decreased. The cause lies in the interference between adjacent aerodynamic surfaces. The airflows around wing and body junctions usually interacting in such a way as to spoil the simple clean flows experienced in isolation.

The effects of such interference are manifold, the commonest being airframe buffeting, premature stalling of one wing before the other, poor acceleration and reduced airspeeds. Interference effects all arise from decreased velocities in local relative airflows, which cause adverse pressure gradients and premature separation of the boundary layer.

Subsonic Airflows

At subsonic speeds any increase in the cross-sectional area of a flow results in decreased velocity and increased static pressure. When a wing-body junction is right angled there is no marked interference. But if a high or low wing is mated with a curved body cross-section, then the cross-sectional area available to the relative airflow increases towards the leading and trailing edges of the wings as the angle between

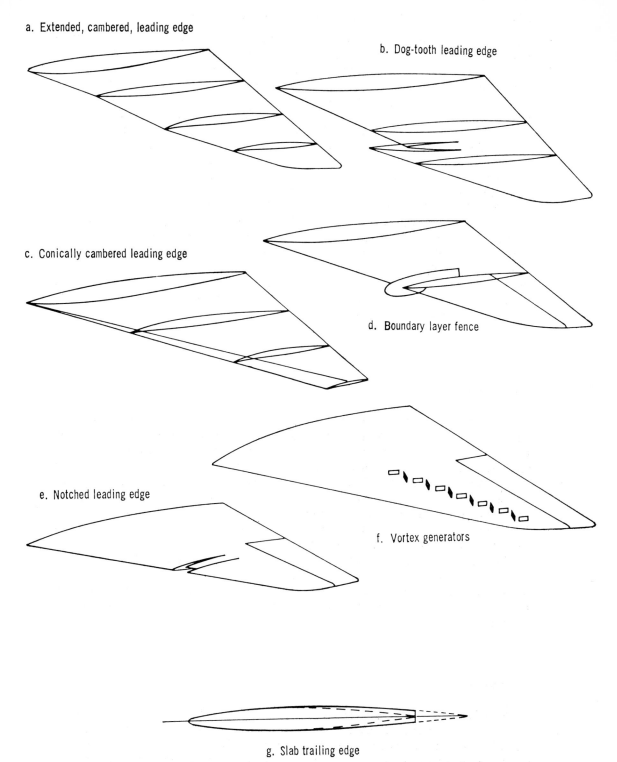

a. Extended, cambered, leading edge

b. Dog-tooth leading edge

c. Conically cambered leading edge

d. Boundary layer fence

e. Notched leading edge

f. Vortex generators

g. Slab trailing edge

Fig. 6.17.   Aerodynamic palliatives for improving local airflows over wings

101

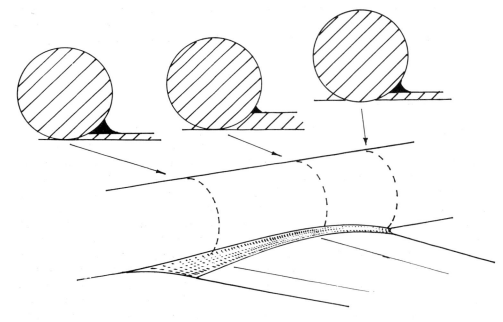

a. Typical fillet at a low wing body junction.

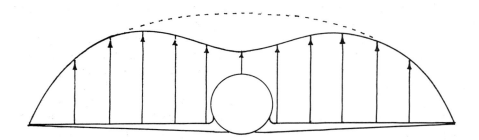

b. Loss of lift due to presence of a body.

Fig. 6.18. The subsonic wing-body junction

body and wing surface becomes increasingly acute. Fillets must then be fitted where surfaces meet at acute angles to maintain smooth airflows.

The relative airflow along the side of a body is usually less than that over the crest of an aerofoil surface, because body curvature is less. There is, therefore, a decrease in the airflow velocity over a wing at the root and a loss of lift. Fillets reduce the amount of lift lost by reducing velocity grddients between wing and body, see Fig. 6.18.

Sonic and Supersonic Airflows

In sonic and supersonic airflows it is necessary to control shock formation as far as possible, because the sharp adverse pressure-gradient through a shock wave causes boundary layer separation. A shock forming in the vicinity of the crest of an aerofoil surface can cause complete disruption of the lifting pressure-distribution behind it. The buffeting and sharp loss of lift (Shockstall) caused by compressibility gave rise to the early misconception of a 'sound-barrier', beyond which man might not fly.

We have already seen that most important component of the relative airflow over a surface is that normal to the local isobars. When two swept aerofoil surfaces are joined in isolation from a body, the airflow over each wing affects the other, giving rise to centre-line effects of a reduction in isobar sweep. Effects similar to those occurring at a centre-line are caused at a junction where an aerofoil is cranked in planform: *i.e.*, where there is a change of sweep. For example, the M-wing was suggested some years ago as a possible transonic-cruise planform that avoided aero-isoclinic distortion (the nose-down twisting of a swept wing towards the tip, caused by bending due to lift) and centre-line effects would therefore have been present at three places across the span: at the two cranks and at the centre-line. The addition of a properly shaped body straightens the isobars at the root, or junction.

A delta wing and part of an M-wing are shown in Fig. 6.19. The initial curvature of the isobars across the span is shown to be altered by the addition of a fuselage and, in the case of the M-wing, by the addition of engine nacelles at the crank of each wing. The bodies are indented in accordance with area-rule theory. Streamwise tips have been added to straighten the isobars at the wing tips.

For tractable handling characteristics at the onset of compressibility many recent high-subsonic transport aircraft have featured negative camber at wing roots to locally straighten the isobars, and revised wing-body fairings that are quite unlike that shown in Fig. 6.18. A typical root section and body fairing is shown in Fig. 6.20.

The negative camber is only the root-end of several possible changes of camber across the span which, when allied with wash-in and wash-out (increase and decrease in wing incidence—the angle at which the wing is rigged and, hence, angle of attack) of different parts of the wing, serve to make every part of the wing work at the same lift coefficient. In so doing the root is made to stall at the same time as the tip.

The fairing is seen to be, in effect, a slab-sided distension of the fuselage which the wings meet almost at right angles. In this way the local flow is least altered between the leading and trailing edges of the wings, while the additional volume usefully increases the stowage-volume, which is always in demand. Such a bulge beneath a wing is less critical than above, because the relative velocity of the airflow below is not so near M_{crit}. It should be noted that many high speed jet aircraft now feature slab-sided body fairings, with rounded corners, at wing and tail junctions.

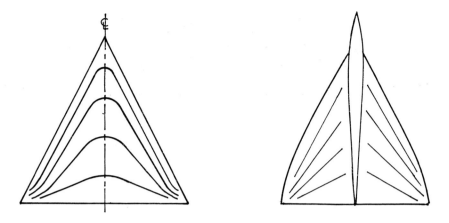

a.   Isobar sweep on a delta wing before and after addition of body.

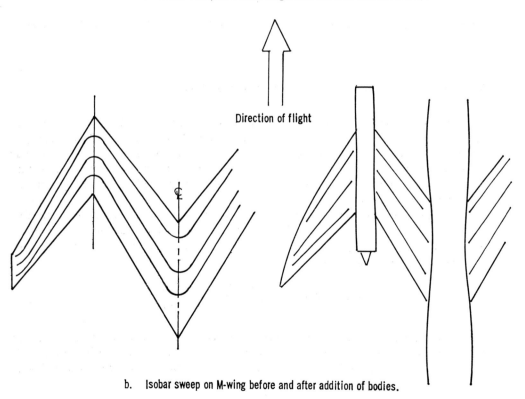

Direction of flight

b.   Isobar sweep on M-wing before and after addition of bodies.

Fig. 6.19.   The effect of favourable junctions and streamwise tips on isobar sweep at the design point

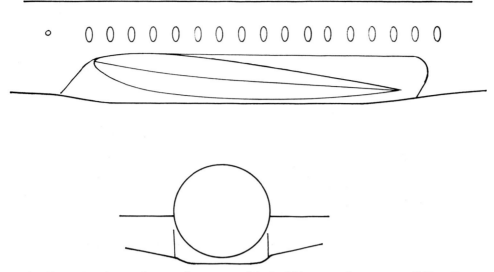

Fig. 6.20. Negative camber at wing root, and body-fairing to reduce compressibility effects

6.4 Design for Optimum Lift/Drag when Range Flying

In being able to control lift and drag and, under certain conditions, to vary both at will beyond the range of values achievable with the basic shape of an aeroplane, we are able to extend the efficiency over a much wider part of the flight envelope. The aerodynamic efficiency is measured in terms of lift/drag, and one of the most important aspects of performance is that an aeroplane should be able to fly as far as possible on a given quantity of fuel.

Although the range-flying efficiency of an aeroplane depends, aerodynamically, upon the attainment of high lift/drag in practice the maximum value is not used. The actual value, $(L/D)_R$, is within a few per cent of the maximum. Using this value, Eq. (4–11) can be restated as:

$$\text{Range varies as } \left(\frac{L}{D}\right)_R \left(\frac{M}{c'}\right) \log_e\left(\frac{W_O}{W_O - W_F}\right)$$

All of the terms do not have the same influence upon the equation and to understand why they must be recombined. In the recombination the propulsive term, $(1/c')$, which is the reciprocal of the thrust specific fuel consumption, must be considered with:

$$\log_e\left(\frac{W_O}{W_O - W_F}\right)$$

the structure weight term. The faster the design cruising speed the greater the drag and the thrust required from the engines. The higher the thrust, the thirstier the engines, and the more the fuel needed to fly a given distance.

Jet aeroplanes cruise at speeds of M = 0·6 upwards. Fortuitously, throughout the whole range of speeds where air-breathing engines can be used, which is up to M = 10, the product:

$$\left(\frac{1}{c'}\right) \log_e \left(\frac{W_O}{W_O - W_F}\right)$$

is very nearly 1. In fact it rises to 2 at high Mach numbers, but even then the effect of the product upon the whole equation is much less than that of the rest, which varies more widely. Therefore we may say that, for simple practical purposes:

$$\text{Range varies as } M \left(\frac{L}{D}\right)_R$$

As the range is specified we see that as the cruising Mach number is increased by the requirements, the cruising lift/drag may be allowed to fall. It is this fact that has enabled a fruitful search to be made for supersonic cruising shapes with apparently low lift/drag ratios.

The cruising Mach number is directly proportional to range. One may consider flying the Atlantic at M = 2, but it would be uneconomical to consider flying only 500 nml at the same speed, simply because the large value of M does not have enough time to affect the block speed, upon which economy depends (see Fig. D.1.1). The 4,000 nml or more to the west coast of America may be flown with reasonable economy from European airports at M = 3 before very long. Various design studies have yielded the following formula for calculating 'good' values of $(L/D)_R$ for trans-atlantic distances of around 3,000 nml:

$$R = 4(M+3) \tag{6-1}$$

so that:

$$M\left(\frac{L}{D}\right)_R = 4(M+3)$$

i.e.,

$$\left(\frac{L}{D}\right)_R = 4\left(1+\frac{3}{M}\right) \tag{6-2}$$

Evaluation of this equation results in a band of state-of-the-art values as shown in Fig. 6.21, that falls asymptotically from around 20 at M = 0·5 to 5, around M = 4. The shape of the figure should be compared with Fig. 6.12.

6.4.1   The Effect of Aspect Ratio

Imagine that an aeroplane is cruising at constant weight, and therefore lift: how exactly does the drag vary with airspeed? We saw from Fig. 5.18, that the total drag has two terms: drag at zero lift, and lift-dependent drag, i.e.:

$$D = D_F + D_L \tag{6-3}$$

and:

$$C_D = C_{DF} + C_{DL} \tag{6-4}$$

where C_D is the drag coefficient used in Eq. (5–9).

As long as flight is at a subcritical Mach number there is no wave drag and C_{DF} remains sensibly constant with airspeed. When flight is at a supercritical Mach number C_{DF} is increased by wave drag components. The vortex drag, on the other

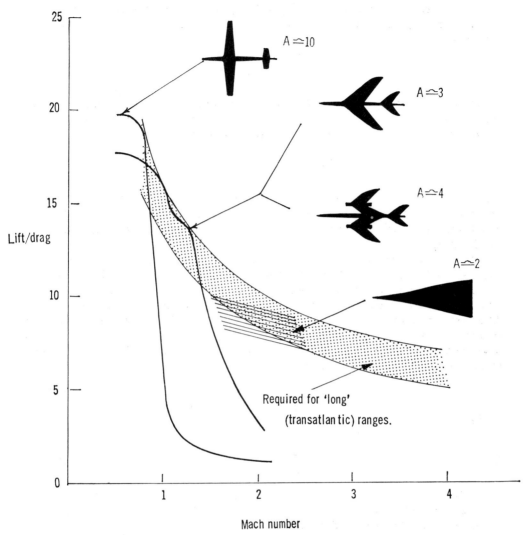

Fig. 6.21. Shape trends giving 'good' lift/drag ratios for typical long ranges of transatlantic order (3000 nml)

hand, must decrease with speed, because the wing flies at a smaller angle of attack, and the circulation causing the vortex system varies directly with angle of attack. In fact, at subcritical speeds the lift-dependent drag coefficient is given by:

$$C_{DL} = \frac{KC_L^2}{\pi A} \qquad (6-5)$$

where π, C_L and A have their conventional meanings and K is a factor measuring the efficiency of the planform. When the planform and lift distribution are elliptical C_{DL} is a minimum, *i.e.* $K = 1$. For 'normal' planforms K varies between 1·1 and 1·3. In fact K might reasonably be called the 'inefficiency factor' of the planform.

The total drag may be plotted as shown in Fig. 6.22(*a*), which is similar to

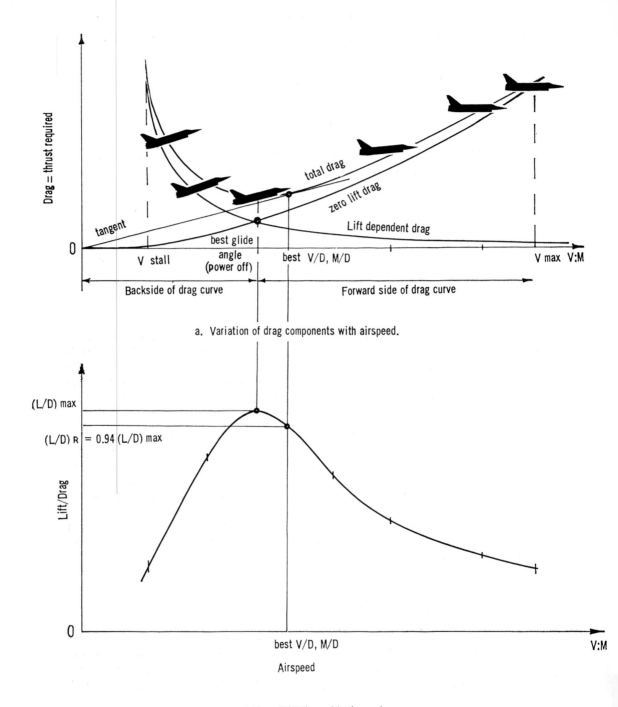

a. Variation of drag components with airspeed.

b. Variation of lift/drag with airspeed.

Fig. 6.22.   Variation of drag and lift/drag with airspeed at constant weight

Fig. 4.9. The minimum drag, corresponding with maximum lift/drag, occurs where $C_{DF} = C_{DL}$, i.e.:

$$C_{Dmin} = \frac{2KC_L^2}{\pi A} \tag{6–6}$$

and,

$$C_L = \sqrt{\left(\frac{C_{DF}\,\pi A}{K}\right)} \tag{6–7}$$

Now, the best lift/drag corresponds with C_L/C_{Dmin} at the design point in question, so that from Eq. (6–6) and (6–7), the maximum L/D is given by:

$$\left(\frac{L}{D}\right)_{max} = \frac{1}{2}\sqrt{\left(\frac{\pi A}{C_{DF}\,K}\right)} \tag{6–8}$$

The speed for best speed/drag, i.e., M/D, at constant lift is, in fact, the speed for best $M(L/D)_R$. It may be seen from Fig. 6.22(b) that $(L/D)_R$ is about 0·94 $(L/D)_{max}$, from which we obtain the relationship:

$$A = \frac{9}{2\pi}KC_{DF}\left(\frac{L}{D}\right)_R^2 \tag{6–9}$$

The aspect ratio, planform efficiency factor and zero-lift drag coefficient all lie within the control of the designer. If a particular planform is chosen to match the design point: wing-sweep for Mach-characteristics, section for both Mach-characteristics and stowage volume, then the essentially constant terms can be evaluated with the aid of wind-tunnel tests to leave the relationship that aspect ratio:

$$A \text{ varies as } C_{DF}\left(\frac{L}{D}\right)_R^2$$

The planforms shown in Fig. 6.21 have aspect ratios and shapes that give 'good' cruising lift/drag values at their design points. Note that the classical subsonic aeroplane has an aspect ratio around 10, while the slender delta, with an aspect ratio around 2, satisfies the transatlantic range requirements from M = 2 onwards. When Fig. 6.22 is compared with Fig. 6.12 the efficiency of variable geometry is made doubly apparent: provided one is willing to pay the price of mechanical complexity and increased first cost.

6.4.2 The Effect of Wetted Area

The calculation of $(L/D)_{max}$ can be approached in another way, although it is one that involves making a broad assumption that the zero lift drag depends more upon skin friction than upon pressure effects. This is reasonable because the highest lift/drag is achieved in subsonic (subcritical) flight, where pressure usually has a much smaller effect than friction upon the zero lift/drag.

We saw from Eq. (6–6) that C_{Dmin} occurs where $C_{DF} = C_{DL}$, and assuming that C_{DF} depends upon friction alone in subcritical flight, where:

$$C_{DF} = \frac{A_w}{S}C_{Dfric} \tag{6–10}$$

we may therefore write:

$$C_{D\min} = 2C_{DF}$$

$$= 2\frac{A_w}{S}C_{D\text{fric}} \qquad (6\text{–}11)$$

This should be compared with Eq. (6–6), while variation in $\frac{A_w}{S}$ can be seen in Fig. 6.2.

Now, drag at zero lift in subcritical flight can be written as:

$$C_{DF} = \frac{f}{S} \qquad (6\text{–}12)$$

where f is a term, called the 'equivalent parasite area' of an aircraft: the sum of every increment of surface area times the $C_{D\text{fric}}$ of each element. In subcritical flight $C_{D\text{fric}} \simeq C_{DF}$. The $C_{D\text{fric}}$ of each element depends upon the surface roughness and the degree of turbulence in the boundary layer. The slipstream from propellers increases the C_{DF} of an aircraft by about 33 per cent over that of an equivalent machine powered by turbojets.

Values of $C_{D\text{fric}}$ vary between different parts of the airframe. Typical values are: 0·003 for the wing, 0·0024 for the fuselage, 0·006 the engine nacelles, 0·0025 the stabilizers, to all of which is added a further 5 per cent for interference. An American formula, which is said to have an accuracy within 3 per cent, calculates f on the basis:

$$f = 1·10 + 0·128\,N_p + 0·007\,S + 0·0021\,N_e(F_e)^{0·7} \qquad (6\text{–}13)$$

where, Np = number of passengers
            S = wing area   (1·10 represents the
            N_e = number of engines   area of nose and tail
            F_e = static sea level thrust per engine.   of the fuselage)

The wetted area of an aircraft is the area of surface exposed to the air. In calculating values of wetted area certain components are blanketed by others. The wing and tail, for example, have not the same gross areas used for calculation of aspect ratio—instead the net area lying outside the fuselage and engine nacelles must be used. Similarly, areas of fin, nacelles and fuselage, where wing and tail join to body, must be subtracted from the total area.

The wetted area of a wing is a little more than twice the net area—a reasonable estimate is to add about $\frac{1}{3}$ of the thickness ratio of the section. A wing with a t/c ratio of 12 per cent would have, therefore, a wetted area $(2 + 0·12/3)$, or 2·04 times the net wing area. The surface area of a body can reasonably be approximated to a gross solid of revolution and the wetted area calculated by multiplying the area in side view by π.

Returning to the condition for $C_{D\min}$ we see from Eq. (6–6) and Eq. (6–11) that:

$$\frac{KC_L^2}{\pi A} = \frac{A_w}{S}C_{D\text{fric}}$$

whence:

$$C_L = \sqrt{\left(\pi \frac{b^2}{S^2}\frac{A_w}{K}C_{D\text{fric}}\right)} \qquad (6\text{–}14)$$

Using Eq. (5–11) we may rewrite Eq. (6–8) as:

$$\left(\frac{L}{D}\right)_{\max} = \frac{\sqrt{\pi}}{2}\sqrt{\left(\frac{b^2}{C_{DF}\,SK}\right)}$$

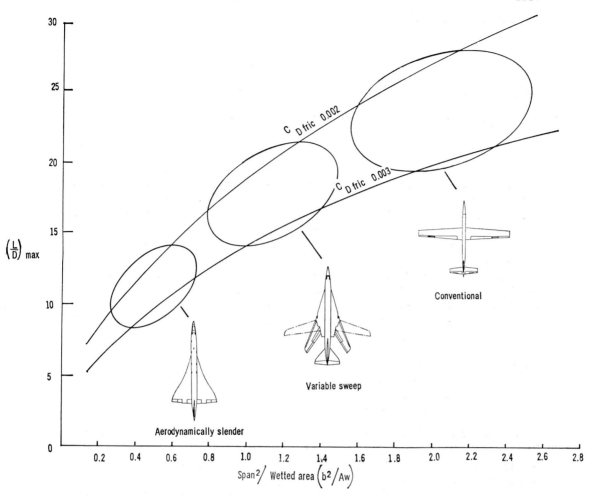

Fig. 6.23.   Subsonic (subcritical) cruise relationship between span, wetted area and frictional
drag coefficient

we may then substitute for $C_{DF}S$ by transposing Eq. (6–10) to give:

$$\left(\frac{L}{D}\right)_{max} = \frac{\sqrt{\pi}}{2}\sqrt{\left(\left[\frac{b^2}{A_w}\right]\frac{1}{KC_{Dfric}}\right)} \qquad (6\text{–}15)$$

from which $(L/D)_R$ may be obtained as before.

The term (b^2/A_w) is the span^2/wetted area, a relative of the aspect ratio, (b^2/S). Some idea of the range of values may be deduced from a consideration of Fig. 6.2. Typical values of C_{Dfric} vary from 0·002 to 0·003, and taking account of the variation in K for 'normal' planforms, Fig. 6.23 may be drawn. This shows the importance of wing span in the design of aircraft for high aerodynamic efficiency in the subsonic regime. It also gives some idea of the need for high quality surface finish, and of the likely benefits accruing from the use of boundary layer control. If, as results suggest, the zero-lift drag may be reduced to $\frac{1}{5}$ normal values by the use of distributed suction, then Eq. (6–15) shows that $(L/D)_{max}$ might at least be effectively doubled.

6.4.3   The Importance of Low Span Loading

It was said in 5.2.5 that once the planform of a wing is fixed the lift dependent (vortex) drag depends upon span loading (and not upon aspect ratio) for the span loading is a measure of the average pressure difference between the upper and lower surfaces. The lower the span loading, the lower the pressure difference, and the lower the pressure difference the further away is the wing operating from those conditions where separation becomes critical.

The argument can be shown mathematically as follows:

$$D_L = C_{DL} q S \qquad\qquad (6\text{–}3a)$$

where,
$$C_{DL} = \frac{K C_L^2}{\pi A} \qquad\qquad (6\text{–}5)$$

and
$$q = \tfrac{1}{2}\rho V^2 \qquad\qquad (1\text{–}5)$$

In level flight $L = W$ and, from Eq. (5–8):

$$C_L = \frac{W}{qS} \qquad\qquad (5\text{–}8a)$$

and,
$$qS = \frac{W}{C_L} \qquad\qquad (5\text{–}8b)$$

Therefore:
$$D_L = C_{DL} \frac{W}{C_L}$$

and, as
$$A = \frac{b^2}{S}$$

from Eq. (5–11), we may restate Eq. (6–3a) using Eq. (6–5), Eq. (5–8a) and (5–8b):

$$D_L = \frac{K}{\pi q}\left(\frac{W}{b}\right)^2 \qquad\qquad (6\text{–}16)$$

Hence, the lift dependent drag at a given speed and height varies as the planform 'efficiency factor', K and the span loading $(W/b)^2$. It follows that the lift dependent drag changes with the weight of the aeroplane, as long as the planform remains unchanged by variable geometry.

CHAPTER 7

Engine-Airframe Matching

The process of matching an engine to an airframe involves the designer in a search for the best compromise between the overall lift/drag ratio, airframe weight, cruising altitude, engine size and weight and overall propulsive efficiency. In its simplest form the problem may amount to no more than bolting the best, or most available, engine onto the nose of a light aeroplane: arranging for adequate cooling and exhaust scavenging by rule-of-thumb methods. In its most complicated form the problem becomes one of structural and aerodynamic integration of engine and airframe. In the case of the supersonic aeroplane, intake design may be the biggest single problem. The cybernetics of the control systems of variable geometry intakes and nozzles affords plenty of scope for engineers in the fields of electronics and servo-mechanism design.

The matching of engine and airframe splits conveniently for our purposes into powerplant installations with propellers and those without. In either case it is instructive to consider what happens to the energy produced from the burning fuel. That part of the thermal energy not used in doing mechanical work is lost as heat through the engine casing and surrounding structure. Some energy is lost through the mere act of heating the air and increasing the kinetic energy of the molecules: for it is impossible to design an installation that does not leave the working-mass of air at a higher temperature than it had to start with. The energy that is used usefully overcomes the frictional and pressure drag: in both cases molecules of air are heated by the aeroplane in its passage. Therefore, from the point of view of converting energy into useful work, powered flight is the result of distributing the heat from the combustion of fuel to the surrounding atmosphere. The lower the temperature generated for a given amount of useful work, the more efficient the process.

7.1 Propulsion Principles

All aeroplanes are propelled by reaction—by the ejection rearwards of a mass of working fluid or series of particles. The working fluid—usually air gathered up in passage—is mixed with fuel and burnt within the aircraft before being ejected rearwards with increased momentum. The momentum is increased by accelerating the air in its passage through the engine (or propeller), while the mass of the exhaust is slightly increased by the addition of fuel products and, of course, the aircraft grows lighter with time as fuel is burnt.

113

Here we are principally concerned with gas turbine engines, in which a mass of air is swallowed by an intake and ejected rearwards as a hot jet through a nozzle. The principle of adding momentum is the same as for a propeller driven aircraft, however, for there is only a difference in technique between accelerating a small mass of air to a high velocity through an engine in a short time, and accelerating a large mass of air to a much lower velocity by using a propeller.

Momentum, which is the product of mass × velocity, may be changed at different rates—the greater the rate of change of momentum, the greater the thrust. The shorter the time in which a change of momentum is required to take place, the greater the heat energy that must be added. Hence, the greater the thrust the higher the fuel consumption. For our purposes we shall assume that specific fuel consumption remains constant with speed of flight and engine rev/min—in fact it does not, but changes in sfc are of second order compared with changes in other factors affecting the range equations, Eq. (4–9) *et seq.*

If a stationary engine imparts a velocity V_J to a mass of air W_a/g every second then the thrust, F, is given by:

$$F = \frac{W_a}{g} V_J = m_a V_J \qquad (7\text{--}1)$$

for a jet engine and:

$$F = m_a w \qquad (7\text{--}1a)$$

for a propeller. The terms V_J and w are called the jet and slipstream velocities respectively.

When the jet engine is in motion relative to the air, the working fluid has an initial velocity V relative to the engine, which alters the equation for the total change of momentum. As the velocity imparted to the exhaust is measured relative to the engine, the total rate of change of momentum and thrust becomes:

$$F = m_a(V_J - V) \qquad (7\text{--}2)$$

The term $m_a V$ is called ram drag by the propulsion engineer and intake momentum drag by the aircraft engineer. Either way it represents a propulsion loss caused by scooping up the air and accelerating it relative to the undisturbed condition, by carrying it along with the aircraft. As we saw earlier when discussing airframe lift and drag, air borne along by the aircraft has kinetic energy added, although the velocity relative to the aircraft is decreased. In the same way air scooped up by the intake causes drag, and the process of adding heat to accelerate the air back again to atmosphere is a way of overcoming the loss of efficiency involved. A positive thrust is only possible if the exhaust velocity is greater than the velocity of flight. In the case of a rocket engine, where the working fluid is contained wholly within the aircraft, ram drag is zero.

The engine converts chemical energy in the fuel to heat energy, the heat energy is then used to accelerate the working fluid and thus do useful work. There are, therefore, two distinct processes involved: one thermal, the other mechanical. Unfortunately all of the energy put into the final exhaust or slipstream cannot be used for propulsion. The fact that the exhaust is hot represents a heat loss, while turbulence left behind in the wake indicates inefficiency of the mechanical process.

7.1.1 Efficiency of a Propulsion System

The efficiency of the overall propulsion process, η_o, is the product of the efficiency of the 'internal' thermal process, η_t, and the efficiency of the mechanical process η_p, i.e.:

$$\eta_0 = \eta_p \eta_t \tag{7-3}$$

$$= \frac{\text{rate at which useful propulsive work is done}}{\text{rate at which energy is applied to the system}}$$

Energy and work have the same dimensions of force × distance through which it is applied. The introduction of a rate of doing work—of applying energy—transforms the statement of efficiency into a statement of power input and output.

Typical values of overall efficiency are shown in Fig. 7.1 for four different kinds of engine. The overall efficiency is also related to the propulsive term in the range equation, Eq. (4–12), for we saw there that the range depends upon obtaining a high value of:

$$\frac{V}{c'} = \frac{\text{range speed}}{\text{specific fuel consumption}}$$

Within the state of the art for a subsonic transport aeroplane this is approximately:

$$\frac{V}{c'} = 4{,}000\ (\eta_p \eta_t)$$

$$= 4{,}000\ \eta_o \tag{7-4}$$

when V is given in ft/sec and thrust sfc, c', in lb/hr/lb (e.g., for a turbojet at M = 0·8, V is about 800 ft/sec, c' about 1·1 lb/hr/lb, η_o about 0·18, and $800/1·1 \times 0·18 = 4{,}030$).

Propulsive efficiency, which is the ratio of the mechanical work involved in pushing the aeroplane through the air and the mechanical work involved in moving the working fluid through the engine, is often given in the ideal form of the Froude efficiency. At the design point thrust equals drag and, for a given flight speed V, jet velocity V_J, and mass flow m_a the thrust is given by:

$$F = m_a (V_J - V)$$

which is the expression for the rate of change of momentum, the correct units (e.g., ft-lb-sec) being used throughout. The rate of performing useful work is:

$$FV = m_a V (V_J - V)$$

But as energy is being added to the working fluid in the form of kinetic energy, the rate of increase of kinetic energy is equal to

$$\tfrac{1}{2} m_a V_J^2 - \tfrac{1}{2} m_a V^2$$

and the ideal Froude efficiency is then given by:

$$\eta_p = \frac{\text{rate of performing useful work}}{\text{rate of increase of kinetic energy}}$$

$$= \frac{m_a V (V_J - V)}{\tfrac{1}{2} m_a (V_J^2 - V^2)}$$

$$= \frac{2V(V_J - V)}{(V_J - V)(V_J + V)}$$

i.e.,

$$\eta_p = \frac{2V}{(V_J + V)} \tag{7-5}$$

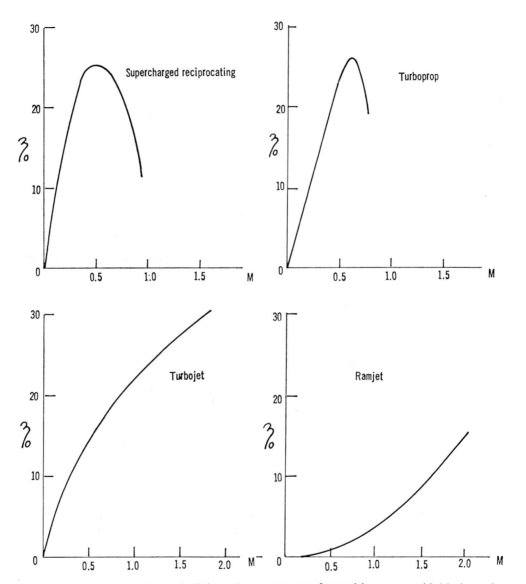

Fig. 7.1. Typical trends of overall efficiency (in percentages) of propulsion system with Mach number

From Eq. (7–5) we see that an aeroplane flying at the tropopause with a TAS of 550 k and a jet velocity relative to the aircraft of probably 1,300 k, has a Froude efficiency of 55 per cent.

Now, it may also be shown that:

$$\eta_p = \frac{2}{1+(V_J/V)}$$

$$= \frac{2}{2+(V_J/V)-1}$$

$$= \frac{2}{2+(V_J-V)/V}$$

i.e.,

$$\eta_p = \frac{2}{2+\left(\dfrac{\text{thrust}}{\text{intake momentum drag}}\right)}$$

$$= \frac{2}{2+\left(\dfrac{F}{m_a V}\right)} \tag{7–5b}$$

We can define arbitrarily an effective propulsive efficiency with pod drag included as:

$$\eta_{p'} = \eta_p\left(1 - \frac{\text{pod drag}}{\text{thrust}}\right)$$

$$= \left[\frac{2}{2+\dfrac{\text{thrust}}{\text{intake momentum drag}}}\right]$$

$$\times \left[1 - \left(\frac{\text{pod drag}}{\text{intake momentum drag}}\right)\left(\frac{\text{intake momentum drag}}{\text{thrust}}\right)\right]$$

$$= \left[\frac{2}{2+\left(\dfrac{F}{m_a V}\right)}\right]\left[1 - \left(\frac{D_{pod}}{m_a V}\right)\left(\frac{m_a V}{F}\right)\right] \tag{7–5c}$$

and this term may then be used in Eq. (7–3) in place of η_p for deriving the overall efficiency. Pod drag is of fundamental importance. If an engine has a propulsive efficiency of 65 per cent on a test bench, but when installed in an airframe the pod drag is 10 per cent of the intake momentum drag, then the effective propulsive efficiency will fall to 55 per cent and the overall by something like 15 per cent.

Thermal efficiency may be improved by improvements in the thermodynamic cycle by, for example, increasing the pressure ratio and the maximum temperature of the process, but there are practical material limitations to what may be obtained at any time. The limiting pressure ratio is around 20/1 for modern engines. With present turbojets η_t is about 35 per cent at $M = 1\cdot0$, rising to 50 per cent at $M = 2\cdot0$, after which it begins to fall slightly, approaching 45 per cent at $M = 3\cdot0$.

A propeller is used to convert the brake horsepower of an engine into propulsive power, but in so doing the brake horsepower of the engine is reduced by propeller losses. Some power is used in overcoming torque, more is lost in the slipstream—which is sometimes called 'propwash' to clarify its nature.

In Eq. (4–8) the power required for flight, P_e, is derived in ft-lb-sec units, while the power of an engine is stated in horsepower (equivalent shaft horsepower, eshp, in the case of a turboprop). The conversion is:

$$\text{one horsepower} = 550 \text{ ft lb/sec}$$

Now, in straight and level flight, where $F = D$:

$$P_e = FV \ ft \ lb/sec$$

and,

$$\frac{P_e}{550} = \frac{FV}{550} \text{ horsepower}$$

$$= \eta P \text{ horsepower} \qquad (7\text{–}6)$$

where η is the propeller efficiency and P the horsepower of the engine. This statement takes no account of altitude, the decreasing air density reducing the power output of the engine in direct proportion to $\sqrt{\sigma}$ where σ is the relative density. For most practical purposes we may write:

$$\frac{P_e}{550}\sqrt{\sigma} = FV_i$$

$$= \eta P \sqrt{\sigma} \qquad (7\text{–}6a)$$

When power loading is used as a measure of merit for comparing different aircraft (W_o/P) lb/hp is used, where W_o is the all-up-weight on take-off and P the sea level horsepower as stated by the engine manufacturer. It should not be confused with the theoretical power-loading (W/P_e), the reciprocal of which is used in Eq. (4–7a) and (4–8).

7.2 Propeller-Engine Installations

There are only two propeller-engine combinations at this time and both are used at relatively low speeds and their intake and exhaust problems are correspondingly smaller than those met with in turbojet installations. Propeller and intake icing problems are more important at lower speeds, however, where kinetic heating is not high enough to prevent large masses of ice forming.

Apart from the need to provide adequate cooling and the protection of the airframe from the effects of hot exhaust gases by efficient ducting, perhaps the most significant effects of the propeller are in the disposition of the engines and the undercarriage arrangement. Two typical propeller-engine installations are shown in Fig. 7.2. Where units are wing-mounted there must be sufficient clearance between propeller tips and adjacent fuselage surfaces to avoid the transmission of fatigue-provoking vibrations. In general there is an attempt to arrange that the plane of a propeller does not lie in the plane of aircrew members or passengers. In this way ice or other materials shed from blades only causes airframe damage without personal injury.

Too much clearance between propeller and fuselage increases asymmetric problems, however, for the asymmetric moment is proportional to the offset of the engine

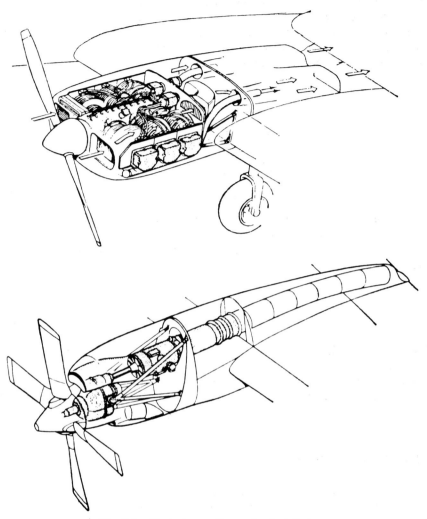

Fig. 7.2.   Typical propeller-engine installations

(*a*) Installation of six-cylinder horizontally-opposed piston-engine in nacelle on port wing. The cooling airflow (white arrows) is augmented by the ejector-effect of the exhaust (black arrows) (Cessna 310, U.S.A., 1953)

(*b*) Turbo-prop installation in port engine nacelle. Note the small space occupied by the engine and gear-box, allowing slender cowling of such units, or adequate room for undercarriage stowage. (Lockheed 188A Electra, U.S.A., 1957)

from the centre of gravity. The larger the moment the bigger the required fin and rudder areas, or the higher the approach and landing speeds.

Although a large diameter propeller with a small number of blades is more efficient than the reverse for converting the brake horsepower of an engine into tractive power, propeller size and undercarriage arrangement are mutually dependent. Propeller tips must not be too close to the ground, because of the danger of sucking up debris, or fouling obstacles (important considerations in bush and outback operations).

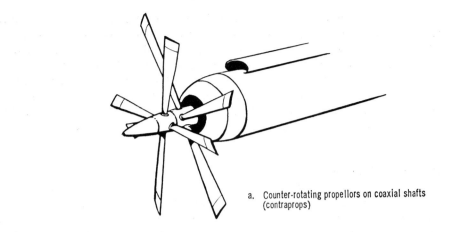

a. Counter-rotating propellors on coaxial shafts
    (contraprops)

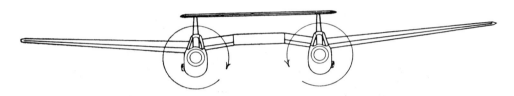

b. Opposite handed propellors

c. Opposite handed propellors fore and aft.

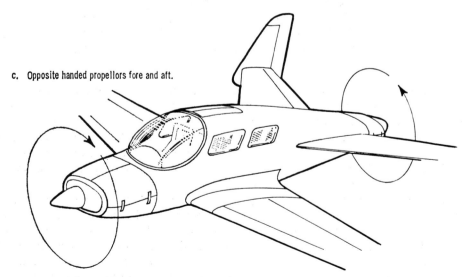

Fig. 7.3.   Torque counteraction using opposite-handed propellers

While excessively long undercarriage units impose unnecessary weight penalties. Smaller ground-clearances are possible with jet aircraft, although the wheel-CG and ground-attitudes on take-off and landing must be maintained if aeroplanes are to be both stable and controllable over a wide range of loading and wind conditions.

The torque of a propeller (the moment reacting rotation) can be dangerous at low airspeeds, where aerodynamic control-surfaces may not be capable of generating powerful enough counter-moments. Counter-rotating propellers, are used to reduce torque to manageable proportions, Fig. 7.3.

7.3 Jet-Engine Installation

In Fig. 7.4 is shown a cut-away view of a typical gas-turbine engine. The aim of engine installation design is to house such a unit within a low-drag cowling, accessible to servicing, with the shortest, straightest intake and exhaust ducting possible. Ducting introduces frictional losses, while curvature that changes the direction of the relative airflow, suffers a reaction to the change of momentum, called momentum-drag.

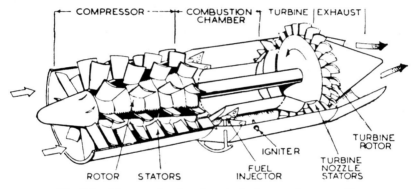

Fig. 7.4. Diagram showing the principal parts of a gas turbine

At subsonic speeds the intake and exhaust system is little more than two simple pipes. The intake consists of a hole taking ram air to the engine compressor: such is called a pitot-intake. The exhaust gases are ducted away to the propelling-nozzle down a cylindrical jet-pipe. For flight at supersonic speeds considerable variable geometry is required in both intake and exhaust systems to ensure that the compression of the swallowed air and its expansion back to ambient conditions, when finished with, takes place with the greatest efficiency.

In order that an engine may be kept as light as possible compressors are designed to operate on air reaching the first stage of blading (referred to as the compressor face) at a relative airspeed of $M = 0.4$, or thereabouts. It follows that an aeroplane flying at speeds in excess of $M = 0.4$ must have the relative airflow decelerated between the intake and the compressor face, *i.e.*, the air is gathered up and accelerated relative to its undisturbed position in space. The function of the compressor is to increase the pressure of the swallowed air by a process of diffusion, before fuel is mixed with it in the combustion chambers. Burning the air-fuel mixture increases the thermal-energy of the mass. The thermal energy is converted to mechanical work by expanding the

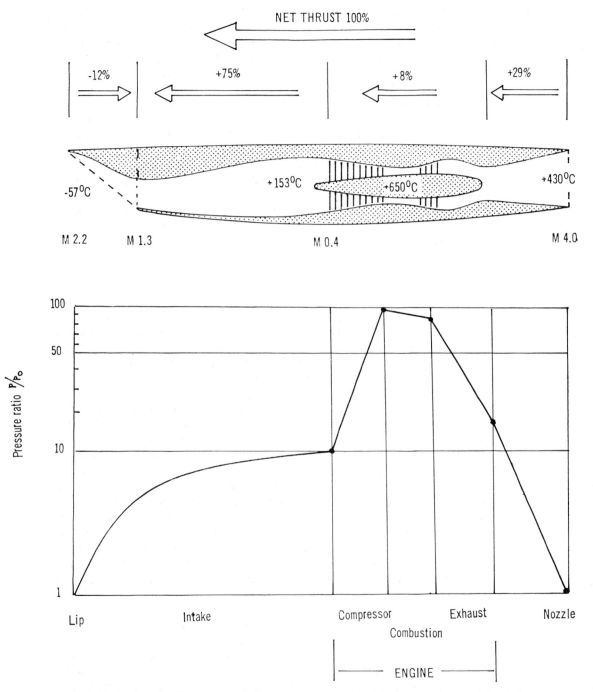

Fig. 7.5. Typical conditions through a supersonic engine installation in flight at $M = 2 \cdot 2$

122

exhaust gases rearwards: decreasing their pressure while increasing their relative velocity on the way to the propelling nozzle. In fact the exhaust velocity is higher than the relative airspeed, but the pressure of the exhaust gas is nearly that of the surrounding atmosphere on leaving the nozzle. With a turbojet the exhaust gases are expanded through a turbine that transmits mechanical work, through shafting, to the compressor.

At high speeds the temperature of the air is raised so much during compression by the intake and diffusion in the intake ducting, that the compressor (and turbine) is redundant. An engine without compressor and turbine is called an aerothermodynamic duct, or ramjet for short. The modern trend is towards symbiosis: mounting a turbojet within a ramjet duct, forming a turbo-ramjet. In this way the turbojet produces thrust at low speeds, but is shut down at high speeds.

The whole process of compressing and expanding the air in its passage through a turbojet installation is shown in Fig. 7.5, which represents the very general conditions in flight at $M = 2.0$. The pressure-ratio through the installation is plotted beneath the section, on which is shown the relative airflow, temperature, and thrust increments as a percentage of the net thrust.

7.3.1 Intake Geometry

The function of the air intake is to deliver the correct mass-flow of air to the compressor face to generate the required thrust. The design point for the intake is the cruising speed for a long-range aeroplane. A short-endurance fighter on the other hand may well have the design point of the intake in the transonic regime, where high thrust is needed to accelerate through the transonic drag-rise.

An allied function of the intake is to deliver an even distribution of air across the compressor face over a wide range of angles of attack. If the airflow is uneven then the compressor blades may stall and cause surging, a phenomenon varying between an unpleasant rumbling and a sharp report, followed by flame extinction.

In supersonic flight the deceleration in the relative airflow from the intake lip to $M = 0.4$ at the compressor face must take place through one or more shock waves. It will be remembered that supersonic compression takes place when air is squeezed into a smaller space. Such compression is achieved by the presence of a spiked centre-body set in an axi-symmetric intake, or by a wedge when an intake is rectangular. In Fig. 7.5 the wedge protrudes downwards to form a throat. An oblique shock is thrown from the leading-edge of the wedge to impinge upon the lower lip. A normal shock lies between the lower lip and the wedge, directly across the throat.

The efficiency of an intake is measured by the pressure-recovery at the compressor face of that part of the total static pressure head at the intake, p_o, expressed in terms of p_1/p_o. The more supersonic the aeroplane the greater the number of shocks needed to achieve smooth compression and high efficiency. This is shown in Fig. 7.6 which applies broadly to both axi-symmetric and rectangular intakes.

It follows that for off-design operation the Mach-angle of a shock must be controllable, and to achieve this the centre-body must move in some way, so that the shock can be arranged to impinge upon the intake lip. If a shock does not impinge upon the lip, but lies outside it, pressure escapes and reduces the recovery at the compressor. The Mach-angle of a shock may be altered by moving a spiked centre-body fore and aft to alter the angle subtended at the intake lip, or by altering the angle of a wedge.

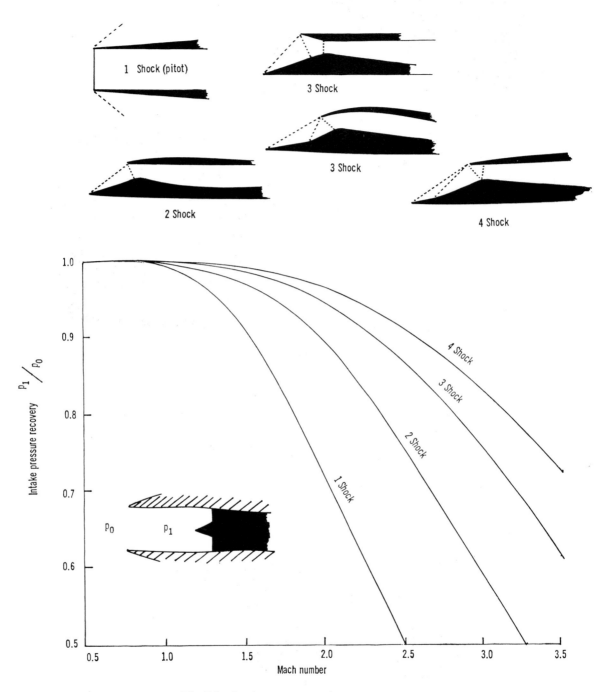

Fig. 7.6. Intake geometry and pressure recovery

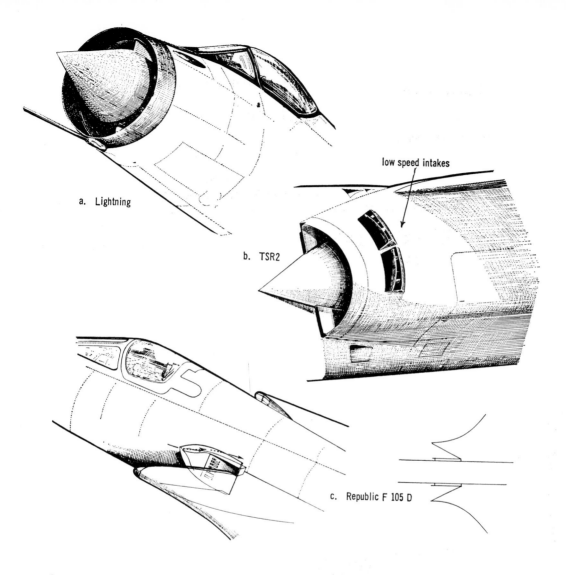

a. Lightning

low speed intakes

b. TSR2

c. Republic F 105 D

d. General Dynamics F 111 A

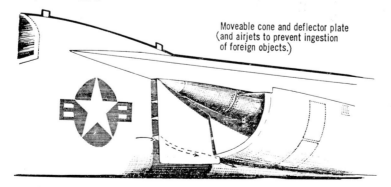

Moveable cone and deflector plate
(and airjets to prevent ingestion
of foreign objects.)

Fig. 7.7. Various intakes

Several air intakes are shown in Fig. 7.7. Note that in two examples there is a channel formed by a gap between the intake and the fuselage. The gap is a boundary-layer bleed for draining away the stagnating boundary layer that would otherwise reduce the pressure recovery and distribution of ram air across the compressor face.

It should be noted that the conical centre-body is used conveniently on many fighter aircraft as a housing for attack and fire-control radar.

7.3.2 Propelling Nozzles

The faster an aircraft flies the greater the difference between the relative airspeeds of the flow through the combustion chambers of the engine and the undisturbed ambient conditions outside. Hence, the more rapid is the required acceleration of the burnt gases through the engine if they are to be exhausted back to ambient conditions with the minimum loss of propulsive efficiency.

If flight is at subsonic speed then the expansion of the gases back to ambient conditions takes place with a change of speed less than $M = 1.0$. It follows, therefore, that to achieve such a change of airspeed the acceleration must take place through a convergent duct.

In supersonic flight, however, the exhaust must be accelerated through a change of airspeed greater than $M = 1.0$. As we saw earlier, a supersonic acceleration takes place through a divergent duct. And if the aeroplane is flying a little more than $M = 1.0$, the required expansion of the exhaust can be achieved through a duct of constant cross-sectional area.

In order to attain optimum performance over a wide range of airspeeds it is necessary to fit supersonic aeroplanes with variable nozzles. The nozzle is formed by an eyelid that can be closed down to a convergent form for subsonic flight, yet which can be opened up to divergent form for supersonic flight. Such a nozzle having convergent-divergent capability, called a con-di nozzle, has many forms, some of which are shown in Fig. 7.8.

Reheat or Afterburning

The thrust of a turbojet is frequently augmented by burning additional fuel in the jetpipe, thus utilizing unburnt air. The technique is called reheating in the U.K. and afterburning in the U.S.A. The diameter of the jetpipe is increased over the reheat section, which terminates at the propelling nozzle. The nozzle eyelid is opened when reheat is used, to cause a rapid supersonic acceleration of the exhaust: and to cope with the lower density (increased volume) of the superheated mass flow. Thrust augmentation comes with the increased rate of change of momentum of the exhaust.

Thrust Reversal

Thrust reversal is a relatively recent technique, used when on the ground to reduce the energy input to the wheel brakes. All deflectors incorporate cascades: curved blades or plates: which turn the exhaust gases through more than 90°. The retarding force is, therefore, merely momentum drag caused by a violent change in direction of

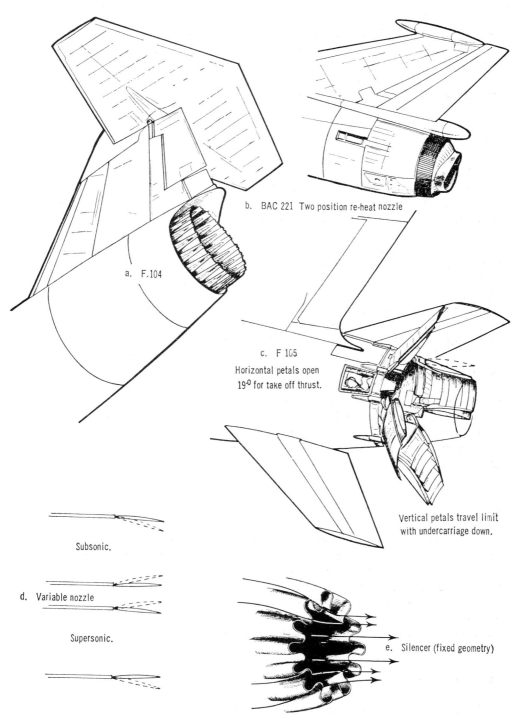

a. F.104

b. BAC 221 Two position re-heat nozzle

c. F 105
Horizontal petals open
19·⁰ for take off thrust.

Vertical petals travel limit
with undercarriage down.

Subsonic.

d. Variable nozzle

Supersonic.

e. Silencer (fixed geometry)

Fig. 7.8. Various nozzles

the exhaust. In some installations the cascades are set in the side of the jetpipe, and a central deflector in the core of the pipe is then opened to split the jet, causing it to impinge upon the cascades, which turn the gases through the required angle. Another form is to move two large curved blades, of bucket shape, from housings at the side of the jetpipe into the exhaust stream. As the buckets close the exhaust is forced away through slots uncovered in the sides of the jetpipe.

Thrust reversal by jet-deflection is only one aspect of the use of thrust for more than propulsion. Clearly, vectored-thrust can be used on take-off and landing, as we shall see. A proposal by Rolls-Royce is the switch-in deflector based upon a thrust-reverser designed by that company. The thrust-switching device consists of a pair of clamshell doors (or eyelids) which form part of the jetpipe wall. When deflected thrust is required the eyelids are swung rearwards to blank of the nozzle, at the same time uncovering two apertures in the jetpipe wall. The apertures lead to cascades, mounted in nozzles that can be rotated by the pilot. In that way the thrust can be deflected in any direction from forward to aft, thereby generating an infinitely variable range of lift, thrust and drag components.

Silencing

Jet noise on take-off and landing is a considerable problem, especially as many cities are served by airfields set in or near built-up areas. Noise is a function of the jet's shear velocity and is roughly proportional to $(V_J-V)^7$. Noise suppression is achieved by fitting special nozzles that mix ambient air into the free surface of the jet, thereby weakening the sharp surface of discontinuity between the jet and the relatively undisturbed ambient air. Corrugated nozzles of various kinds are used for such mixing, a typical example being shown in Fig. 7.8(e).

7.4 Installation Problems

The purpose of an aircraft dictates the size and number of engines required. Aircraft of short duration usually have compact internal payloads and modest fuel requirements: additional fuel being carried in external overload tanks. In the event they are usually small and lack room for installing engines within the wings. Jet engines are usually fuselage-mounted. Wing tips are an attractive position for podded units, from the point of view of providing bending-relief (lighter wing-structure) and aerodynamic endplate effects (reducing the strength of the tip vortices and, hence, lift-dependent drag) but the position poses severe problems in asymmetric flight.

Long-range aircraft are large and heavy and invariably have several wing-mounted units. In recent years it has become fashionable to cluster engines in and around the rear fuselage. There are signs, however, that the fashion may be short-lived.

7.4.1 Rear-Mounted Engines

Broadly speaking the arguments for rear-mounted engines are:

(a) Aerodynamic cleanliness of wings.
(b) Small asymmetric moments.
(c) Reduced cabin noise-levels.

Against which advantages must be levelled the disadvantages of:

(d) Heavier wing structures to compensate for lost bending-relief.

(e) Centres of gravity lying further aft, necessitating larger and heavier tail surfaces to provide adequate stability and control. However, it should be noted that horizontally-mounted nacelles act as lifting bodies and as such they augment the stabilizing moment of the tailplane, so that not quite such a large tailplane would be needed as might at first be thought.

(f) Proneness of configurations with long slender fore-bodies, wings set well aft and high-mounted tailplanes to problems associated with the deepstall, or superstall.

(g) The possibility that in the event of a crash hot, heavy, engines may be mixed with passengers and cargo.

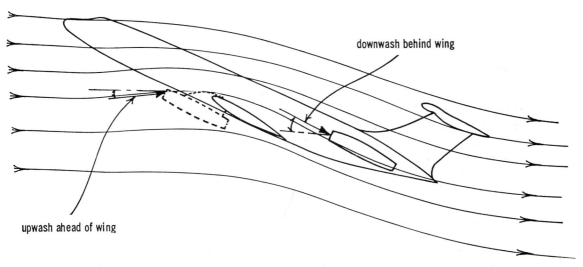

Fig. 7.9.   Flow pattern before and behind wing, showing angle of attack at intake of podded (dotted) and rear-mounted engine

The downwash behind the wings changes with aircraft attitude and thus reduces the angle of attack at the intakes, and it is argued by proponents that rear-mounted engines maintain high efficiencies throughout the flight envelope. Podded engines and other engines with intakes forward of the wings suffer larger changes of angle of attack with attitude. The forward and aft positions are compared in Fig. 7.9.

7.4.2   Wing-Mounted Pods and Engine-Boxes

There are two basic wing-mounted installations: one with engines buried within the wing structure (largely favoured in Europe): the other (favoured in the U.S.A.) being the suspension of engines in pods.

Related to the podded unit is the externally-mounted engine-box, a feature of many projected supersonic transports. The North American B-70, shown in Fig. 6.10, was the first aeroplane to fly with boxed units.

To achieve some perspective in the arguments for each installation consider the area of intake compared with aircraft frontal area needed to meet the engine requirements at different level speeds. Fig. 7.10, which is taken from a paper by Nicholson (Royal Aircraft Establishment), shows diagramatically a front elevation of an aircraft and the minimum intake area needed for level flight. Clearly, around M = 1·0 both engine and intake may be incorporated in either a buried or podded installation. As the design speed is increased the intake grows larger, so large in fact that it must appear outside the main airframe. Therefore, boxed and podded units become the natural installations for highly supersonic flight.

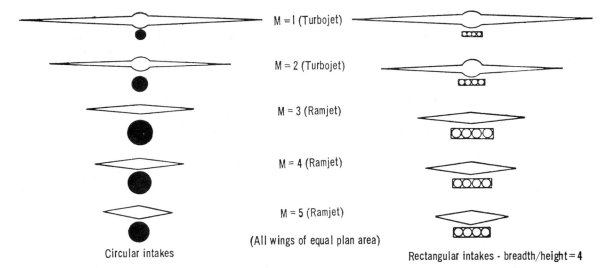

Fig. 7.10.   Comparison of intake and aircraft frontal area with increasing design level speed

Podded units can be positioned for maximum bending-relief; to produce favourable area-distributions, and as dynamic mass-balances to counter destructive cyclic fluttering of thin wing surfaces. The engines, being separated, are less prone to sympathetic failures of more than one unit.

The installed drag of pods is higher than with buried units, although they can be so positioned as to decrease the total drag of an aeroplane. Thinner wings can be used, but at subsonic speeds the interference between relative airflows round the nacelle and wing surfaces is such a large part of the total drag that pods have to be displaced well away from the supporting wing. When pods are low-slung they often introduce ground-clearance problems: a mishandled crosswind landing resulting in a unit being left behind on the runway.

Boxes may be mounted above or below wings, usually near the trailing edge where they create the least unfavourable interference.

Low-mounted boxes attain the highest pressure-recoveries, because the intakes work in the region of relatively high pressure beneath the wings. Also, the isobars beneath the wings are in a less critical state than those above, and interference between the engine-box and wing is likely to be the least unfavourable. However, intakes beneath the wings are more prone to the risk of debris-ingestion.

Boxes mounted on the upper wing surfaces have been suggested for several earlier

SST projects, but all appear to have been shelved at the time of writing. It should be noted that the upper surfaces of the wings of an aircraft with a slender planform are worth considering from the aerodynamic point of view of engine mounting. Although pressures are generally lower than those over the lower surfaces, the leading edge vortices sweep a healthy supply of ram air down towards the trailing edges up to quite large angles of attack, as shown in Fig. 6.8(b). On the other hand, engines mounted above the wings are not as readily accessible for servicing as those below.

7.4.3 Buried units

Engines mounted within the wings are the oldest installations for jet aeroplanes discussed so far. The arrangement was convenient aerodynamically because the aeroplanes being designed some twenty years ago employed sections with much larger thickness-ratios than are now used.

Failures of engines buried inside wings are more likely to affect the surrounding structure when, for example, turbine-blades are shed. Engine changing can be more of a problem too. The buried installation is perhaps the cleanest of all aerodynamically.

Several current engine installations are shown in Fig. 7.11 in which the maritime Comet, (d), is a project utilizing a number of well tried components from the original De Havilland Comet family.

7.5 Interference in General

The degree of interference between the external and internal aerodynamics of an aeroplane is hard to calculate with certainty. The combinations of speed, normal acceleration, height and ambient temperature (all of which add up to attitude to the flight path: the angle of attack), and Reynold's number, that result in flow instabilities are almost impossible to predict. The engine-installation is one of the most thoroughly explored problems in all wind-tunnel testing. Yet it is one of the most thoroughly misrepresented—simply because of the difficulties besetting accurate representation.

The installed drag of an installation is made up of several isolated parts:

$$\text{Installed drag} = f \text{ (isolated drag)} \qquad (7\text{--}7)$$

$$\begin{aligned} \text{Isolated drag} = &\text{ (nacelle wave drag)} + \text{(nacelle skin friction)} \\ &+ \text{(intake drag)} + \text{(nozzle drag)} \end{aligned} \qquad (7\text{--}8)$$

The essential problem is the evaluation of f. If $f = 1\cdot0$, then the installed drag is simply the sum of the isolated parts. If the engines can be placed in aerodynamically favourable positions around the airframe, without sacrificing handling performance and structural integrity, then f might be made less than $1\cdot0$. If, however, f is greater than $1\cdot0$ the implication is that there is unfavourable interference between airframe and installation aerodynamics.

In an effort to maintain flexibility of performance of very high speed aeroplanes over a wide part of the flight envelope, increasing use is being made of symbiosis in powerplant design. Simply, composite powerplants are used, the parts of which are mutually dependent one upon the other. A straightforward and obvious example of

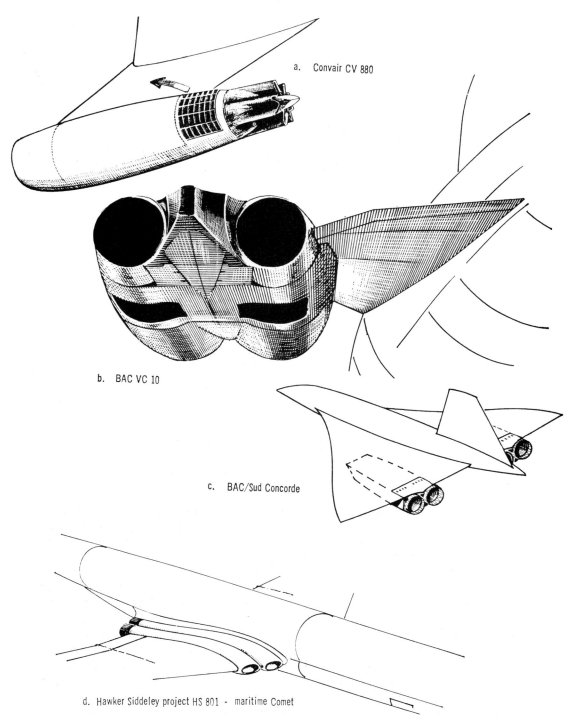

a. Convair CV 880

b. BAC VC 10

c. BAC/Sud Concorde

d. Hawker Siddeley project HS 801 - maritime Comet

Fig. 7.11. Current engine installations

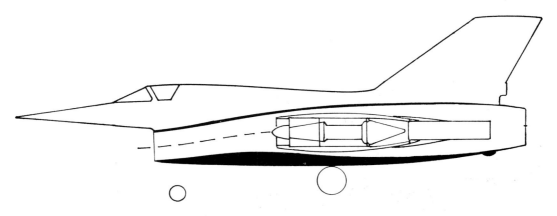

a. Turboramjet in Nord Griffon 02, France.

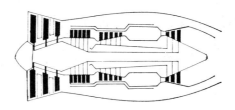

b. Hypothetical twin-shaft turbofan (bypass) engine with
    a front fan.

Fig. 7.12.   Symbiosis, the composite power-unit

symbiosis is the turboramjet combination of a turbojet working in a ramjet duct: A less obvious example is the turbofan engine, which consists of a turbojet engine driving a larger diameter fan (rather like an enlarged compressor stage or even a propeller) inside a duct. Both are shown in Fig. 7.12.

Symbiosis results in larger diameter powerplant units and, consequently, the greater likelihood of interference. Of the two preceding examples the turbofan engine is the commonest. The turbofan handles a greater mass flow of air than an equivalent turbojet. In so doing it is possible to reduce the thrust specific fuel consumption and fuel carried for a given mission. One manufacturer has claimed typical sfcs some 15 per cent lower than an equivalent turbojet, resulting in an aircraft 20 to 30 per cent lighter, burning 30 to 40 per cent less fuel for a given range and cruising speed.

Turbofan engines are described as having a certain bypass ratio, which is defined as the ratio of the total mass of air swallowed to that passing through the combustion chambers. For example, a bypass engine in the 40,000 lb static thrust class might have a total mass flow at sea level of 1,300 lb/sec and a bypass ratio of 8:1—achieved by burning 165 lb/sec of air in the combustion chambers.

Interference between the aerodynamics of the airframe and the propulsion system

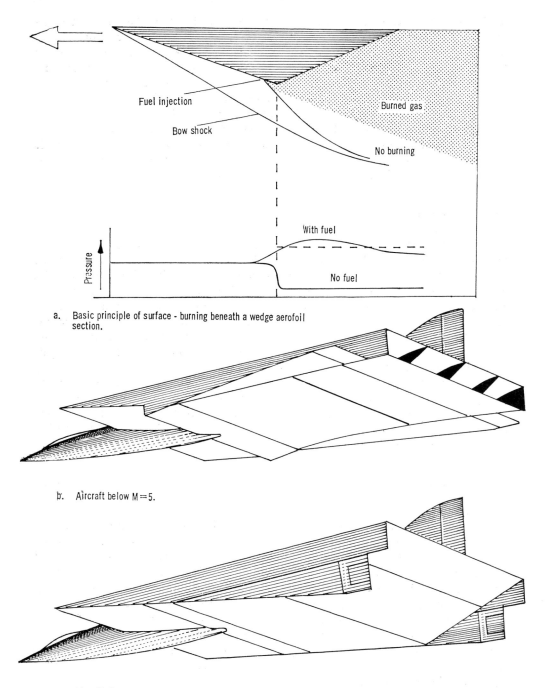

a. Basic principle of surface - burning beneath a wedge aerofoil section.

b. Aircraft below M = 5.

c. Aircraft above M = 5.

Fig. 7.13. Rolls Royce proposal for a surface-burning hypersonic aeroplane

has been turned to theoretical advantage for hypersonic flight, by the study of the uses of surface-burning: combustion on the surface of the airframe. Thrust and lift may be generated if the pressure behind a shock wave is increased by injecting fuel into the compression region and burning it. The adjacent surface is shaped to produce thrust and lift components, as shown in Fig. 7.13, a Rolls-Royce design study. Two configurations are shown: one in flight before and the other about M = 5.

Such an aircraft might be expected to climb at constant EAS of about 400 k, until the speed corresponded with M = 5 around 100,000 ft. External fuel injection would then begin as the shape was changed to a double wedge. The internal engines would be shut down as the intakes and nozzles were blanked off. The hypersonic cruising condition might be about M = 15 around 200,000 ft.

7.6 Powered Lift

Powered lift, the augmentation of aerodynamic lift by a thrust component, is used to achieve vertical take-off and landing (VTOL), or at least short take-off and landing (STOL), and thus make aircraft as independent of prepared airfields as possible. The penalties incurred by carrying special lifting engines or devices for vectoring thrust and additional fuel for low-speed flight, are compensated for in certain cases by smaller wing surfaces and lower structure weights. To achieve maximum economy with a VTOL aircraft one must equate power required for take-off and landing with that required in cruising flight. This is hard to do with anything other than highly supersonic aircraft with low cruising lift/drag.

There are some fifteen ways of using power to generate lift, and these are shown in Fig. 7.14, after the original diagram by Campbell of NASA. All are governed by the same principles as for propulsive thrust: namely that the lifting thrust is the product of mass flow and jet (or slipstream) velocity, while the power required is a function of the square of the jet (or slipstream) velocity:

$$P = \tfrac{1}{2}m_a V_J^2 \qquad (7\text{–}9)$$

for a jet, and:

$$P = \tfrac{1}{2}m_a w^2 \qquad (7\text{–}10)$$

for a propeller.

The most efficient way of generating powered lift is by a large rotor moving a mass of air at low velocity. But rotor-craft are limited to relatively low airspeeds (unless the rotor can be retracted or housed in forward flight) and they are not compact. A jet engine is the least efficient of all, as may be deduced from the power equations when typical values of 50 ft/sec and 2,000 ft/sec are inserted for the rotor and jet respectively. Jet-lift results in compact installations, helped by the modern ability to build very small, light, units generating high thrust/weight. The ducted fan can be regarded as a compromise between the rotor and jet. The fan is smaller in diameter than a rotor, but tip-losses are reduced by enclosing the fan within an annular duct, possibly fitted with cascades. The total lift is that developed by the fan and an increment contributed by the relative airflow over the ducting.

Disc loading is a term describing the amount of weight, or lift, borne per unit area of rotor supporting it. If the area of the compressor face is taken as the rotor area, in the case of a jet engine, then a three-dimensional plot of lift generated/unit horsepower can be made against disc loading for the family of aircraft already illustrated. This is done in Fig. 7.15.

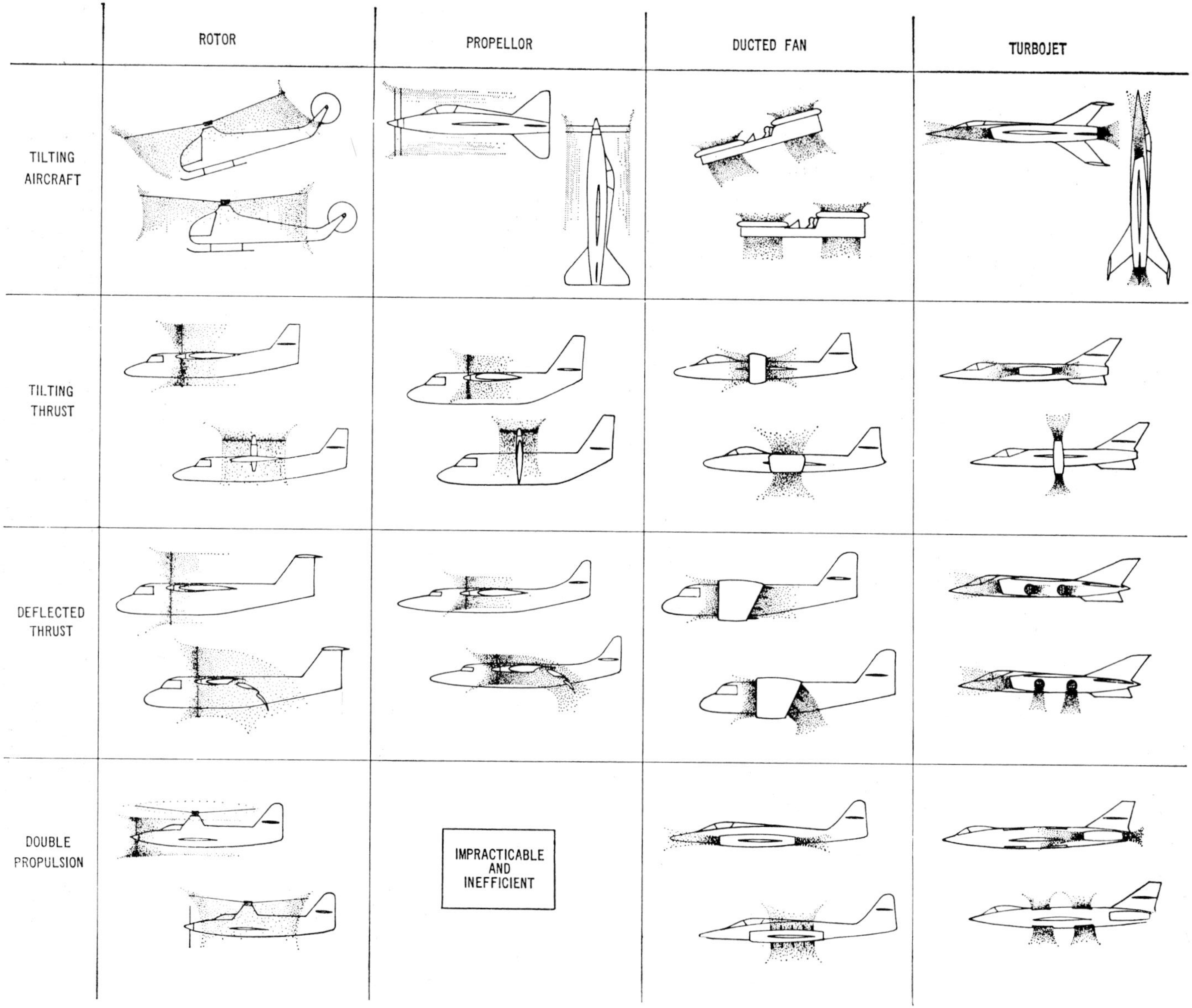

Fig. 7.14. The VTOL family of aircraft

136

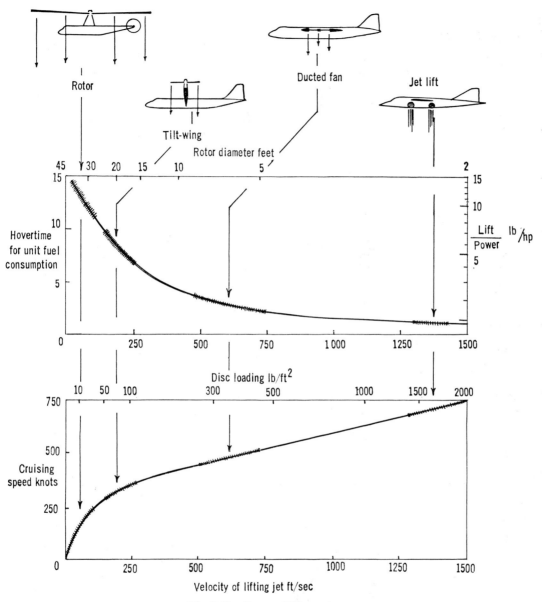

Fig. 7.15. Powered lift spectrum

There has been controversy about the best way of employing jet-lift: one school of thought advocating the use of vectored-thrust; the other the use of separate, small, engines that are shut down in forward flight. No hard and fast conclusions can so far be drawn, the relative advantages and disadvantages of each system depend upon a specific application. Suffice it to say that a large propulsion engine with vectored thrust appears to be the most efficient for a small aircraft, such as might be used for fighter-strike, while separate lifting and propulsion engines can be most gainfully employed with longer range transport aircraft. In the latter case lifting engines can be neatly stowed in slender pods fitted to the wings. The pods often appear to be little larger than overload fuel tanks.

In hovering flight high power is used to fly nowhere. The thrust/weight required for control, lift and manoeuvring while hovering is around 1·4, while the lift/drag in cruising flight may be around 10, say (*i.e.*, the equivalent cruising thrust/weight = 0·1). Such an aeroplane would use fourteen times as much fuel hovering as cruising for the same interval of time. Every minute wasted hovering would reduce the range of an aeroplane flying at M = 1·2 by something like 11 n ml. It follows that there is a close correlation between hovering time, range and disposable load. Considerable fuel saving can be effected by even a short take-off run.

CHAPTER 8

Balancing the Aerodynamic Sum

So far we have looked in some detail at the various aerodynamic portions of an aeroplane and seen how each is intended to play a part in making flight as efficient as possible. When the aeroplane is seen as a whole, in motion through the air, then one realizes that we are dealing no longer with a mere piece of hardware, but with a machine that in many ways responds to its environment as if it had a life of its own. The same near-live response to environment is part of the nature of a ship, in fact there are strong similarities between both in their responses to the elements in which they move.

Look at an aeroplane in the air: how it is stabilized and controlled? Are the stabilizers before or behind the wing? Are control surfaces large and prominent, or are they small and apparently insignificant to the eye? Is there a marked inclination of the wings from root to tip (dihedral), or do the wings seem to droop downwards towards the tips? If they are set with the tips in a lower plane than the root (anhedral) then are the wings also swept backwards? The answers to such questions are to be found in the study of stability and control: the way the aerodynamic sum has been balanced.

In the early days the art of flying was said to lie in keeping the aeroplane 'in such an attitude that the air pressure is always directly in the pilot's face' (H. Barber, 1916). Although pilots of modern aeroplanes probably spend their lives without feeling the pressure of air on their faces at all, the principles are still the same. Stability is possessed by an aeroplane if it responds to a small disturbance in such a way as to oppose the disturbance and return to its original state, without intercession by the pilot. Control may be thought of as disturbance of equilibrium by the pilot, and maintenance of the disturbed equilibrium against the basic stability of the aeroplane. Stability is measurable numerically in terms of derivatives: the rates of change of forces and moments in pitch, roll and yaw, with changes of airspeed, angles of attack and rates of rotation about various axes. Controls alter the value of the stability derivatives.

Whenever a pilot wishes to manoeuvre an aeroplane he alters the positions of the various control surfaces. Conventional surfaces are basically simple flaps, hinged portions of wing and tail trailing edges. Movement of the surfaces alters the local pressure-distributions and resultant aerodynamic forces. Reactions, in effect hinge-moments, are felt by the pilot as a feedback through the control system. The feedback may be direct (but reduced by the mechanical advantage of the system) or, if hinge-moments are too high to be handled efficiently, artificial forces may be transmitted through the stick and rudder-pedals by an artificial feel-system. Ideally, control forces should increase with airspeed, angle of attack (and normal acceleration), and with increasing control deflection: as a safeguard against the pilot inadvertently breaking the aeroplane.

8.1 Reference Axes

There are three sets of reference axes that are significant in the measurement of stability and control: the body axes, the wind (or stability) axis, and the inertia axes. The body axes have their origin at the centre of gravity, O, and are denoted positive with OX forwards, OY sideways to the right (starboard) and OZ downwards. It follows that the XZ-plane splits the aeroplane symmetrically along the centre-line. As the CG varies with disposable load and airborne time, an arbitary value fixes O relative to the designers datum point which lies inside the outline of the aeroplane as laid out on the drawing board.

8.1.1 The Wind Axis, or Stability Axis

The direction of flight at a particular moment is the axis along which the relative wind (relative airflow when local effects are ignored) is assumed to blow. If, however, a transient gust appears the wind axis is changed while the momentum of the aircraft along the flight path remains sensibly unaltered, so that the coincidence of wind axis and flight path is not immutable.

The wind axis before a disturbance is thought of as remaining fixed relative to the body axes, and in this way it serves as a datum for measuring subsequent changes in flight path. Fig. 8.1 illustrates an extreme example of the difference between wind and body axes, such as might be experienced during a spin. The relative wind is seen to have three components: one fore and aft, one vertically upwards and one from the side. Any change in the wind axis is, therefore, accompanied by a change in the airspeed indicated in the cockpit, the angle of attack of the aircraft in the pitching (XZ) plane, and the angle of attack in the yawing (XY) plane.

8.1.2 Inertia Axes

All masses are said to possess inertia, and the distribution of mass throughout the airframe is extremely important. Pitching, yawing and rolling takes place about the CG and the moments of inertia about the CG are an indication of how swiftly such motions may build up (or be brought about by control movements); and of how much aerodynamic effort will be needed to stop them when they have become established.

Moment of inertia, I, about an axis is defined as:

$$I = \Sigma_0^M \, mr^2 \qquad\qquad (8\text{--}1)$$

$$= Mk^2 \qquad\qquad (8\text{--}1a)$$

where M is the total mass (W/g), m is the mass of a small component of the whole, r is the distance of the component (*i.e.*, the radius of its rotation) about the axis in question, and k is the radius of gyration of the total mass.

The moment of inertia in roll about the OX-axis is denoted A; that in pitch about the OY-axis, B; and that in yaw about the OZ-axis, C. There is, however, a principal inertia axis, passing through the CG and lying in the plane of symmetry which may be found to lie at an acute angle to the body axis, Fig. 8.2, which dominates the subse-

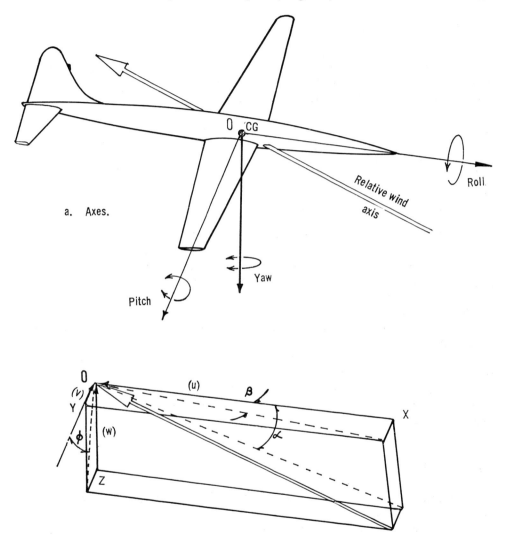

a. Axes.

b. Resolution of relative wind into components of velocity and angle of attack.

Fig. 8.1. Relationship between the body and wind axes at a particular instant

quent motion of long slender aeroplanes having large ratios of pitching inertia to inertia in roll. The motion of any aeroplane disturbed by either the pilot or the environment depends upon the outcome of a battle between the aerodynamic stability and the inertias in pitch, roll and yaw. At subsonic speeds aeroplanes have wings of high aspect ratio and spans that are much the same order as the lengths of their fuselages, and the principal inertia axes are almost coincident with the body axes.

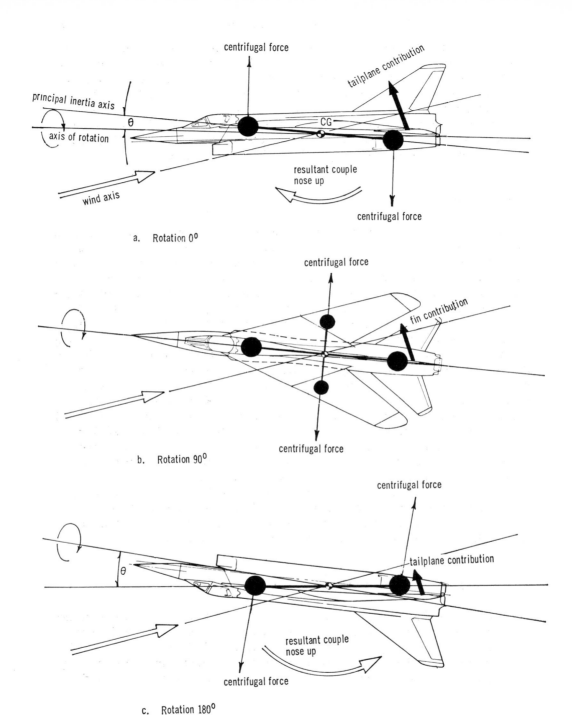

a. Rotation 0°

b. Rotation 90°

c. Rotation 180°

Fig. 8.2. Inertia coupling during roll. The aircraft mass can be represented by a system of 'dumbell masses': note divergence in pitch (θ increasing) through action of centrifugal forces

The response of such aircraft to basic stability and movements of the control surfaces is dominated by the aerodynamic forces involved. Aircraft designed for supersonic flight have low aspect ratios and much smaller inertias in roll than in pitch and yaw. Although in this case initial motion in roll takes place about the wind axis when the ailerons are deflected, subsequent motion tends to take place about a resultant axis near the principal inertia axis, because this represents the way of least resistance. Before rotation about the resultant axis can be established, however, inertia-coupling may have taken place and catastrophically broken the aeroplane.

Inertia Coupling

The more stable the aeroplane the more nearly will motion take place about the wind axis (and pitch and yaw axes at right angles to it). The less stable the aeroplane, and the larger the inertia in pitch and yaw, the more nearly will motion take place about the principal inertia axis. If the roll axis, is inclined to the flight path (and, hence, the wind axis) there will be a cyclic interchange of angle of attack and sideslip (angle of attack in the XY-plane). Such a cyclic interchange is shown in Fig. 8.2 for 180° of roll. The figure also shows how divergence in pitch is caused by the centrifugal pitching moments overcoming aerodynamic moments. The result of inertia coupling for the hypothetical aeroplane shown would be failure of the fin, or wings or tailplane, through reaching too high an angle of attack or sideslip. The pilot would have to be warned of the danger of combining high rates of roll with low EAS at height with an aeroplane having such dynamic configuration. The significance of speed and height is that aerodynamic damping is reduced at high altitudes, so that response to control deflection is much more lively. Low EAS and high TAS result in the aircraft flying at large angle of attack at high Mach number. At large angles of attack the radii of gyration of the fore and aft masses about the axis of rotation are increased and, therefore, the centrifugal forces generated by a given rate of roll.

The figure also shows that the fin and tailplane forces provide correcting moments that would point the nose of the aeroplane into the relative wind, if they were strong enough. Before considering the function and positioning of the various stabilizers, let us consider what factors affect the efficiency of an aerofoil surface.

8.2   Factors Affecting the Efficiency of an Aerofoil Surface

Stabilizing surfaces, like wings, are designed with the same aerodynamic principles in mind, although they may not have the same geometry. Most stabilizers have lower aspect ratios than the wings with which they are combined. Three main factors affect their efficiency as lifting surfaces: aspect ratio, compressibility and TAS—although local interference and wake-shedding from other parts of the airframe are also important.

8.2.1   Aspect Ratio

At a given angle of attack a low aspect ratio aerofoil does not generate as much lift as one having a higher aspect ratio. At very large angles of attack the trailing (and

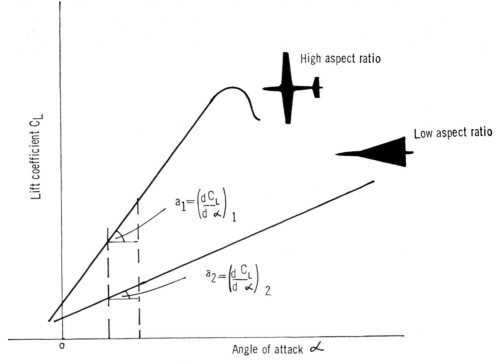

Fig. 8.3.   Effect of aspect ratio on slope of lift curve *a*, of an aerofoil surface (applicable to wing or stabilizer) when unaffected by compressibility

leading) edge vortices maintain useable lift from a low aspect ratio aerofoil long after an aerofoil of higher aspect ratio has stalled. However, the drag is very high. It follows from Fig. 8.3 that, for a given change in angle of attack a high aspect ratio aerofoil generates a larger lift increment than one of low aspect ratio. But if tail surfaces have lower aspect ratios than the wings with which they are combined, then the wing will advantageously stall before the tail, and the resultant nose-down pitching moment will tend to unstall the aircraft.

For the very same reason fighter aircraft, especially those used during and after the First World War, had very low aspect ratio fins and rudders. Pilots could then manoeuvre using large angles of sideslip when necessary for evasion, or bringing guns to bear on targets, without danger of a fin-stall.

8.2.2   Compressibility

Compressibility produces two important effects. The first is that the aerodynamic centre moves rearwards from somewhere near the quarter chord point to the half chord point, and this causes a nose-down moment that must be trimmed out in some way if the aircraft is not to dive into the ground. The second is that the lift coefficient obtainable at a given angle of attack changes with Mach number, as shown in Fig. 8.4(a). The variation in lift, $C_L M^2$, is shown in (b).

The significance of these curves is that they show that the rate of response of an aircraft to control displacement, or to a disturbance, does not increase as V^2 (or M^2). In fact, if the aerodynamic force flattens out enough at high speeds, and the aerofoil surface is affected by the wake of surfaces ahead of it, then the stability and control

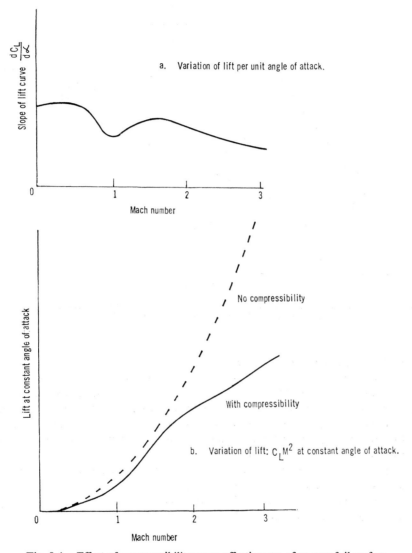

Fig. 8.4.   Effect of compressibility upon effectiveness of an aerofoil surface

of the aeroplane may well diminish as speed is further increased. A topical example is the way in which some very high speed aircraft 'run out of fin area' at high speeds: *i.e.*, they require even larger fins than those fitted. Many supersonic fighters have grown additional fin area (and keel-strakes) as they have been developed with time.

The loss of aerodynamic effectiveness with increasing speed is caused by the aerofoil surfaces increasingly compressing and expanding the air, *i.e.*, merely changing the proximity of the molecules, without a corresponding increase in their useful rate of displacement, the measure of their capacity for useful work.

Shift of Aerodynamic Centre

At angles less than the stalling angle of an aerofoil, the lift increases with increasing angle of attack, but the pressure distributions do not remain similar throughout. At small angles of attack the centre of pressure of the distribution (in effect the point at which the lift acts) is further behind the leading edge than at larger angles. As angle of attack increases the centre of pressure moves forwards to a position limited by the stall, whence it moves back to around the $0\cdot5\ \bar{c}$ point. The aerodynamic centre, or ac, is the point about which the moment of the aerodynamic force, caused by the pressure distribution, remains constant. It follows that at small angles of attack the lift coefficient is small, but the moment arm about the aerodynamic centre is large. At large angles the C_L is large, but the moment arm about the ac is small. The product of C_L and moment arm remains constant about the aerodynamic centre. One should hasten to add that in using C_L alone the picture has been grossly simplified, because the drag component has been neglected and this too has a moment about the aerodynamic centre. It has been neglected, however, because the drag is usually much less than the lift in steady flight.

At subsonic speeds the bulk of the lift is provided by the forward portions of an aerofoil; in fact the lift acts somewhere around $0\cdot25$ to $0\cdot3\ \bar{c}$. At supersonic speeds the whole of the surface behind the crest of an aerofoil causes expansion of the relative airflow. The accompanying suction over the upper surface contributes far more to the total lift than at lower speeds, and the resultant lift acts much further aft (around the $0\cdot5\ \bar{c}$ point). If the centre of gravity is at $0\cdot25\ \bar{c}$, then the supersonic, nose-down, pitching moment must be trimmed out by the use of controls, or the CG must be shifted (e.g., by pumping fuel rearwards).

A simplified picture, in which the pitching moment about the aerodynamic centre has been deliberately omitted, is shown in Fig. 8.5(a), illustrating displacement of the CG, which helps to eliminate trim-drag. Fig. 8.5(b) shows the possible arrangement of the variable geometry of an aircraft like the fighter in Fig. E.2.1, where the aerodynamic centre with the wing extended for low speed flight lies between the aerodynamic centres in sub and supersonic flight.

The North American B-70, shown in Fig. 6.10, compensates for the rearward shift of the aerodynamic centre by turning the wing-tips downwards in supersonic flight, thus removing some of the area aft of the CG. The increment in effective fin area from the turned down tips compensates for any loss of fin effect due to compressibility; for the fins, like any other aerofoil surface, suffer in the same way as shown in Fig. 8.4.

8.2.3   Aerodynamic Damping: the Effect of True Airspeed

It was said early in the book that the true airspeed and equivalent airspeed, used in actual aerodynamic calculations, are only identical at sea level in the standard atmosphere. Throughout the book forces have been shown in the form:

$$L = C_L \tfrac{1}{2}\rho V^2 S \qquad\qquad (5\text{--}8)$$

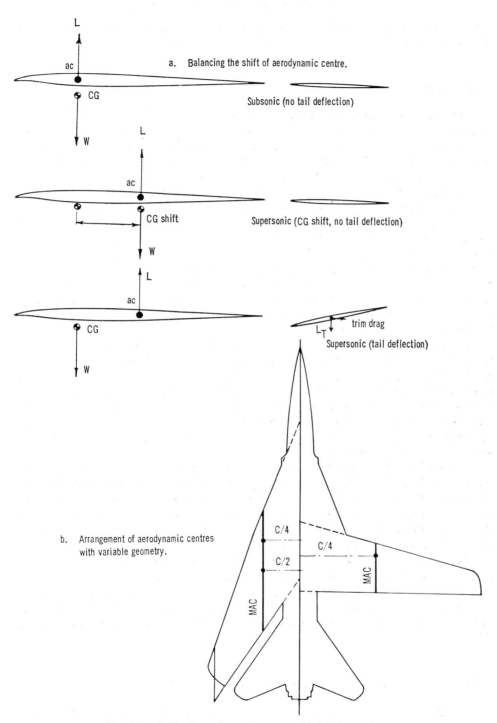

a. Balancing the shift of aerodynamic centre.

Subsonic (no tail deflection)

Supersonic (CG shift, no tail deflection)

Supersonic (tail deflection)

b. Arrangement of aerodynamic centres with variable geometry.

Fig. 8.5.   Shift of aerodynamic centre with Mach number

in which ρ is the density of the air at the height in question and V the TAS. The equation would have been written by an aerodynamicist as:

$$L = C_L \tfrac{1}{2} \rho_0 V_i^2 S$$

from the relationship implied by Eq. (1–6), *i.e.*,:

$$\rho V^2 = \rho_0 V_i^2$$

If the EAS is maintained constant during a climb to height, then all aerodynamic forces remain constant (in the absence of compressibility effects) along with angle of attack and the angle of displacement of a control surface to generate a constant force. But the true airspeed increases. Now, when an aircraft pitches, rolls or yaws it does so about the CG. The relative airflow (in effect the relative wind) felt by a surface is altered by a component due to rotation. For example a constant rolling moment from the ailerons will at low altitude rotate the aeroplane at a given rate. The rate will depend upon inertia and the forces generated by the altered relative airflows over the whole airframe. At high altitude the rolling moment and inertias remain the same, but the angle through which the relative airflow changes is decreased, because the TAS component is increased, as shown in Fig. 8.6. The forces due to changed angle of attack are therefore less and the initial response of the aircraft to the applied control is much faster than at low altitude, *i.e.*, aerodynamic damping of the motion is reduced.

8.3 Longitudinal Stability: Balancing an Aeroplane in Pitch

When it comes to analysing longitudinal stability there are two aspects normally taken into separate account: the static stability, and the dynamic stability. Closely related to the static stability is the study of longitudinal manoeuvrability and control: the effect of altering the static stability by the deflection of the stabilizing and control surfaces. The measure of static stability and longitudinal manoeuvrability and control are academically convenient steps towards understanding reality: that an aeroplane in flight is in a dynamic state. Whenever static cases are considered the dynamic reality behind them must be constantly borne in mind.

8.3.1 Static Balance

An aeroplane is longitudinally stable if, after a disturbance in pitch (conventionally, a gust) it returns to the undisturbed condition. Such a disturbance increases the angle of attack of both wing and stabilizer and, consequently, the lift generated by these surfaces. The aeroplane is statically stable if the resultant moment about the CG decreases the angle of attack. In responding to the disturbance the dynamic situation inevitably appears, for it is rarely that the response is 'dead-beat', *i.e.*, that the aeroplane adjusts its angle of attack without the slightest trace of an oscillation in pitch about the CG. If the oscillations die away with time (their amplitude decreases) then the machine is dynamically stable. If the oscillations increase their amplitude with time, then the aircraft is dynamically unstable, but statically stable. If a disturbance results in further divergence of the aircraft from the flight path, then it is statically (and dynamically) unstable.

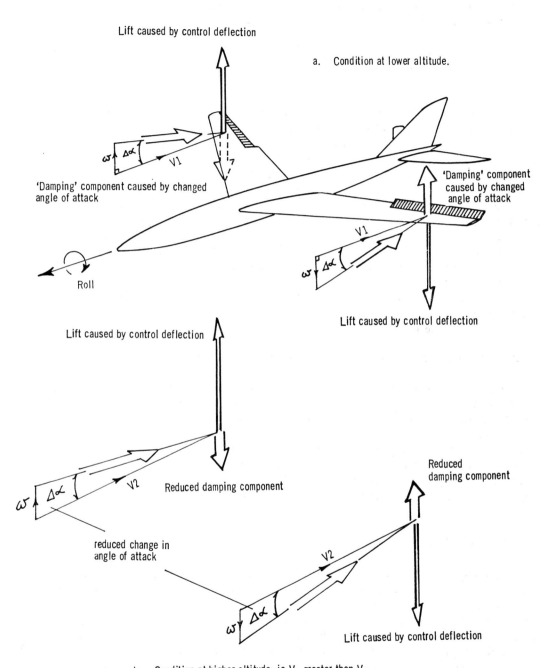

Lift caused by control deflection

a.   Condition at lower altitude.

'Damping' component caused by changed angle of attack

$V1$

'Damping' component caused by changed angle of attack

$V1$

Lift caused by control deflection

Roll

Lift caused by control deflection

$V2$

Reduced damping component

reduced change in angle of attack

Reduced damping component

$V2$

Lift caused by control deflection

b.   Condition at higher altitude, ie V_2 greater than V_1.

Fig. 8.6.   Change of aerodynamic 'damping' component with altitude at constant equivalent airspeed

An aeroplane is trimmed when the moments of all forces about the CG are zero, *i.e.*, the machine can be flown 'hands off' by the pilot. Of course, it does not follow that if the aeroplane can be trimmed for insignificant disturbances it can also be trimmed for larger varieties. Trim can be defined with mathematical precision, but in reality it becomes purely relative.

The condition shown in Fig. 8.7 represents a tailed aeroplane encountering a 'sharp-edged gust', which alters the wind axis momentarily. For the aeroplane to be stable, *i.e.*, to pitch nose-down into the relative wind the moment of the tail-lift about the CG must be greater than the sum of the wing-lift moment and the moment about the aerodynamic centre of the wing. Reducing all forces and moments to dimensionless coefficients, and remembering that, for many purposes, the slope of the lift curve is constant below the stall, a family of curves of C_{Mcg} may be drawn against C_L for a variety of CG positions. The aeroplane is said to be in trim when the C_{Mcg} is zero.

Centre of Gravity Margin and Tail Volume

Inspection of Fig. 8.7(*a*) shows that if the CG could be moved forward in flight: by pumping fuel from rear tanks to tanks further forward: the moment of the tail would increase in the nose-down sense. Moving the CG rearwards would decrease the moment of the tail, while increasing the destabilizing moment of the wing. The moment about the CG is stabilizing when −ve, *i.e.*, the convention assumes that a −ve moment causes a reduction in total lift. Conversely a +ve moment increases lift.

The larger the surface of the tail the larger the tail moment, and the further aft the CG might be arranged to lie without the aeroplane becoming neutrally stable. The distance through which the CG might be arranged to move before the neutral point is reached is called the static margin. The product of the tailplane area and moment arm about the CG is called the tail-volume. The larger the tail-volume the larger the permissible CG margin. Transport aeroplanes, which must be reasonably flexible when it comes to loading, have large tail-volumes. Tail-volume is expressed as a coefficient in terms of tail area, S_T, wing area, S, wing mean chord, $\bar{c}$, and tail moment arm, l_t:

$$\bar{V} = \frac{l_t S_T}{\bar{c} S} \qquad (8-2)$$

TABLE 8.1

Power and Flap Combination (i.e. slipstream and circulation)	Horizontal Tail Volume $\bar{V}$		
	Fighter	Transport and Bomber	All-moving (Slab) Tail
Propeller-driven, high-lift flaps	rare	0·85–1·2	not used
Propeller-driven, simple flaps	0·35–0·6	0·5–0·9	not used
Jet, high-lift flaps	0·3–0·4	0·3–0·65	about 0·3
Jet, simple flaps	0·2–0·55	0·4–0·6	0·2–0·4

If the elevator is deflected downwards, then the stabilizing moment of the tail is increased, if deflection is upwards, then *vice versa*. It follows that control surface

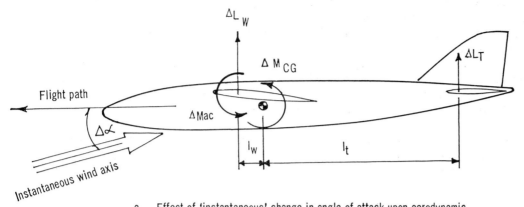

a. Effect of 'instantaneous' change in angle of attack upon aerodynamic
    forces and moments (drag and pitching moment about aerodynamic centre
    of stabiliser neglected).

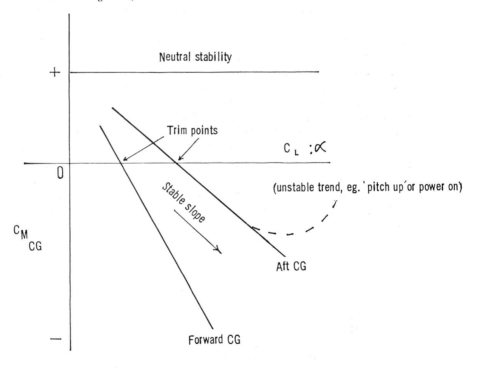

b. Pitching moment curves taken about the centre of gravity.

Fig. 8.7. Static longitudinal stability

position (either elevator or all-moving tail) directly affects the CG margin. Controls are aerodynamically balanced: to make them easier for the pilot to move, and to make them trail in the right sense if the aircraft is disturbed when being flown 'hands-off'. There are, therefore, other CG margins to be taken into account in practice: the static margins stick-fixed and stick-free, and the manoeuvre margins stick-fixed and free. They will not be considered here.

8.3.2   Conventional or Canard Stabilizers

It is very easy to imagine that a stabilizing surface behind a wing is somehow different from one in front. The distinction becomes less pronounced if we forget wings and stabilizers for a moment and group them all collectively as aerofoil surfaces. The distinction between the leading and following surface depends then upon relative size alone.

We have already seen that the wing, in its position as the leading surface, generates a destabilizing moment about the CG, while the tail, as following, is stabilizing. It is easy to see that a forward stabilizer, a canard, is destabilizing, when compared with a conventional stabilizer. However, as we have seen from Fig. 6.6(c) there are times when one is forced to use a canard, if only for reasons of economizing on structure weight. The destabilizing effect of a canard is not in itself significant, for a proper positioning of the CG takes care of over-all stability.

The attraction of a canard is that it lies clear of the wing-wake and, when high lift devices are used on a wing (causing strong nose-down moments) the canard generates an upload that increases the overall lift. At supersonic speeds the rearward shift of the aerodynamic centre causes a strong nose-down moment and the upload of the canard used to trim out the moment contributes again to the overall lift, whereas a conventional surface must generate a download. The overall lift/drag of a canard aircraft can therefore be maintained more efficiently in supersonic flight.

Fig. 8.8 shows the relationship between the leading and following surfaces and the CG. Note how the CG must be placed further aft as the following surface grows and the leader diminishes. Note too how the area (and therefore weight) of the fin surfaces grow with rearward CG position.

In some cases the use of a canard foreplane for trim and a rear tailplane for control looks attractive. The canard would trim both the aft shift of the aerodynamic centre at supersonic speeds, and the strong nose-down moment from the high lift devices at low speed with an uplift: important in both cases. At the same time control would be kept in a favourable aft position. When not in use the canard could be arranged to float, *i.e.*, trail in the relative airflow at the angle of zero-lift, generating minimum drag.

Vertical Displacement of Surfaces

The aerofoil surfaces shed vortex systems that trail downstream parallel, more or less, with the relative wind. The conventional stabilizer, being smaller than the wing, has the relative airflow dominated by the wing vortices and operates in a large region of downwash. The canard, being smaller than the wing, has a much smaller vortex system. But the smaller system still affects the airflow over the wings: when the aircraft is yawed, for example, the vortices may sweep across the span asymmetrically,

Fig. 8.9. Extreme adjustment of tailplane position to clear adverse wing wake at large angles of attack, thus improving control at pitch-up. McDonnell F-4 Phantom (U.S.A., 1955)

(*By permission of* Flight International)

(a) Main leg fully down

(b) Bogie folding almost completed

(c) Bogie starting to retract

(d) Retraction in progress

(e) Leg approaching up-lock

(f) Leg up and locked

Fig. 9.5. Belfast undercarriage retraction cycle

By permission of Short Brothers & Harland Ltd

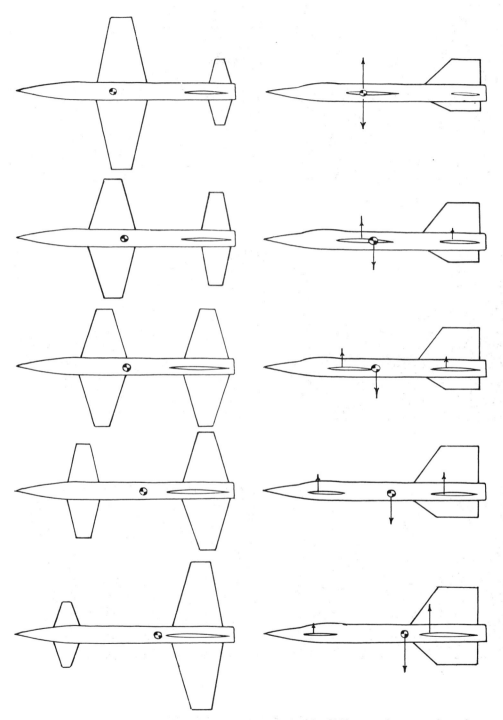

Fig. 8.8. Relationship between the canard, conventional stabilizer, and centre of gravity

153

from one side to the other. The result may be unpredictable rolling moments that vary with airspeed and attitude. Ideally the canard surfaces should lie above the plane of the wings, so that an increase in angle of attack and, hence, the strength of the shed vortices, is countered by a greater displacement between the canard and wing in the vertical plane.

Similar arguments apply to the vertical position of a conventional tail. A tailplane set on top of a fin, as shown in Fig. 7.9, dips deeply into the wake from the wing as angle of attack is increased. The downwash from the wings tends increasingly to reduce any stabilizing upload from the tailplane, so that the slope of the C_{Mcg}/C_L curve becomes shallower and, hence, increasingly unstable. With a very low aspect ratio wing the shed vortices may generate such a strong downwash that at large angles of attack the aircraft 'pitches up', $i.e.$, increases its angle of attack uncontrollably.

A low-set tailplane becomes increasingly more efficient with increasing angle of attack, for the vertical displacement between surfaces is increased. Pitch-up is a phenomenon affecting backward-swept wings, caused by the tips stalling before the roots and the lift remaining over the inboard portions of the wings (which lie predominantly ahead of the CG) generating an increasingly nose-up moment, which further aggravates the stall. The moment may become so strong that it overcomes the effect of the elevator control surfaces, forcing the pilot to take drastic action to regain control. One such example has been the need to force the stalled aeroplane into a spin, so that it pitched nose-down: spin-recovery technique could then be used to recover level flight.

Many high performance aeroplanes have low-set tailplanes, some have even had tailplanes canted downwards to cure pitch-up: an extreme example is shown in Fig. 8.9, the McDonnell F-4 Phantom of the U.S. Navy. Vortex generators and other devices shown in Fig. 6.17 are used in conjunction with tailplane position to ensure longitudinal stability with many modern high speed configurations.

8.3.3 The Tailless Aeroplane

It has not been common practice to design tailless aeroplanes for flight at low subsonic speeds, although a few experimental machines have been tried in the misguided attempt to reduce drag. In fact such tailless aeroplanes cannot employ high lift devices, because of the short control moment arm, and larger wing areas have been needed to reduce the landing speeds. Such increased wing areas have usually generated more drag than a separate wing-stabilizer combination.

It is apparent from Fig. 8.7(b) that at zero lift a maximum nose-up moment is required of a stable aeroplane. The argument follows from consideration of the relationship between C_L and airspeed, in the figure increasing C_L implies a decrease of speed, whereas decreasing C_L implies an increase of speed. At high speeds, beyond the speed at which the aeroplane is in trim longitudinally, the pitching moment M_{cg} must be +ve to raise the nose, increase the angle of attack and thus decrease speed. At speeds below the trimmed speed a −ve moment is needed to depress the nose and increase speed again. When this is the case the aeroplane may be flown hands-off, but it may hunt with a cyclic motion about the trimmed speed. Such hunting—called a long-period oscillation, or phugoid, is a common phenomenon with all aeroplanes.

The tailless aeroplane requires special wing geometry to replace the effect of a separate stabilizer. Fig. 8.10 shows how reflex camber, sweep and washout are

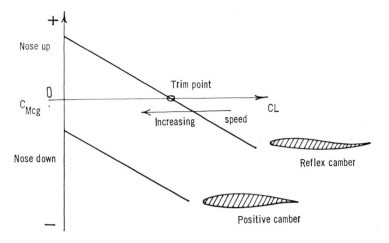

a. Effect of camber upon C_{Mcg} of a regular planform.

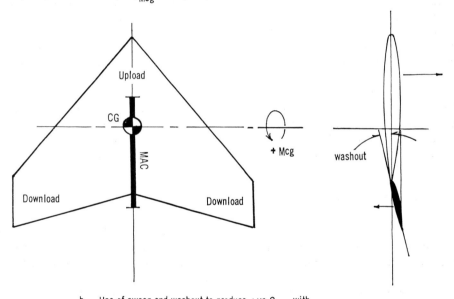

b. Use of sweep and washout to produce +ve C_{Mcg} with
    increasing airspeed.

Fig. 8.10.   Balancing the tailless aeroplane by the use of reflex camber and sweep

employed to generate the required download well behind the CG with increasing airspeed.

The tailless delta has been employed for flight at supersonic speeds in recent years. The attraction of such a planform lies in the geometry: aerodynamically fine wing sections can be used that, because of the long chord, result in adequate spar depth and volume inside the wing. The long chord also results in trailing-edge control surfaces that lie well behind the CG with reasonably large moment arms. Trim drag is reduced by the use of CG shift in a number of cases.

The great spar depth and stowage volume inside the delta and even the swept wing

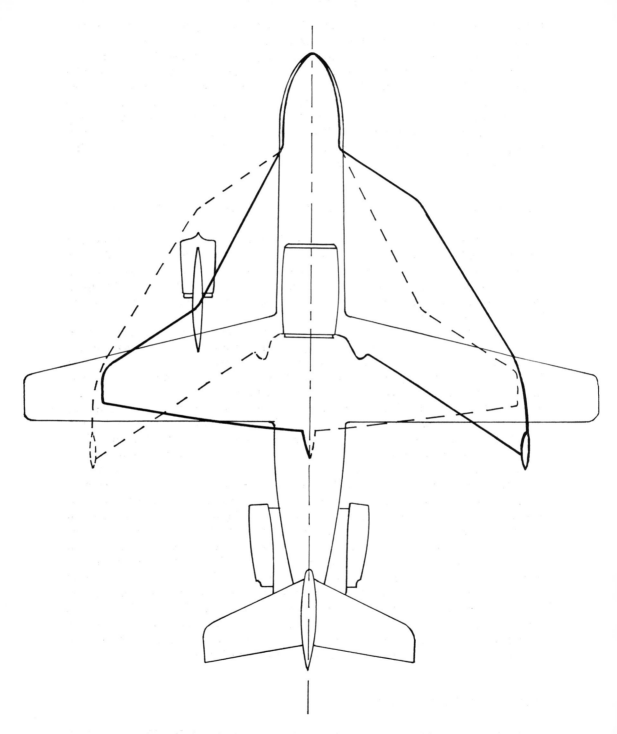

Fig. 8.11. Tailed and tailless aircraft having same payload capacities

has made the flying-wing transport aircraft an attractive proposition again in recent years. A number of design studies have been carried out to determine the optimum configuration for a low-cost air transport. Although nothing has yet been done in the way of building a machine, some idea of the relative sizes of aircraft for a job can be gained from Fig. 8.11, in which two tailless planforms are compared with a conventional classical aeroplane of similar capacity (see Appendix C). By spreading the payload across part of the span, inside a fairly thick aerofoil section, structural bending relief is obtained that is quite impossible when the load is carried inside a compact fuselage that pays only a small bonus in lift. The smaller the aeroplane for a given job the cheaper it is to produce—all else being equal.

8.4   Lateral and Directional Stability: Balancing an Aeroplane in Roll and Yaw

Much of what has been said already in the discussion of longitudinal stability applies to the lateral and directional case. Aerofoil surfaces suffer the same effects of compressibility in whatever plane they lie along the flight path. Lateral and directional stability are two aspects of a mutual and largely inseparable problem: that of keeping the air pressure 'always directly in the pilot's face', by stabilizing motion in a plane lateral to the flight path.

To consider the way in which lateral and directional stability are mutually dependent, imagine an aeroplane to be flying straight and level before meeting a lateral gust. The gust causes a change of angle of attack in the X–Y plane, as shown in Fig. 8.12. The sideforce generated by the fuselage usually acts ahead of the CG and is destabilizing. For the aircraft to possess weathercock stability (an early term for directional stability) the sideforce generated by the fin and rudder acting as one unit must be powerful enough to overcome the yawing moment of the fuselage sideforce.

Ideally the yaw should be corrected in such a way that the heading of the aeroplane is unchanged in space. But if the nose merely swings round to point into the relative wind, then the heading will be altered by an angle roughly equivalent to the angle of yaw. In yawing the outer wing travels faster than the inner wing and generates more lift, so that (in this particular case) yaw is accompanied by roll in the direction of yaw. If the aeroplane is neutrally stable in roll, then a sideslip in the direction of yaw will follow, ending up in a spiral dive: the aeroplane constantly turning into a relative wind caused by perpetual sideslip. If directional stability is weak and the lateral stability is strong, then yaw will be accompanied by a roll away from the direction of yaw: a motion that reduces the sideslip and then reverses it. Resultant motion is an uncomfortable oscillation in roll accompanied by a cyclic yawing: to the pilot the feeling that the aeroplane is slowly wagging its tail from side to side. Dutch roll, as the motion is called, is commonly experienced with aircraft with swept wings. Many such aircraft have grown separate fins beneath the rear fuselage to increase the directional stability and thus reduce the relative power of the lateral stability.

8.4.1   Dihedral and Anhedral

When an aeroplane is viewed from the nose it will be noticed that the wings are set at an angle to the fuselage. If the wings are inclined upwards, the tips being higher than the roots, they are said to have dihedral. If the reverse, with the tip set lower than the root, anhedral. Most low subsonic aircraft have dihedral, while aircraft designed for increasingly higher speeds have less and less dihedral. Many supersonic aeroplanes have anhedral. It is no accident that increasing anhedral is associated with leading edge sweep and decreasing aspect ratio.

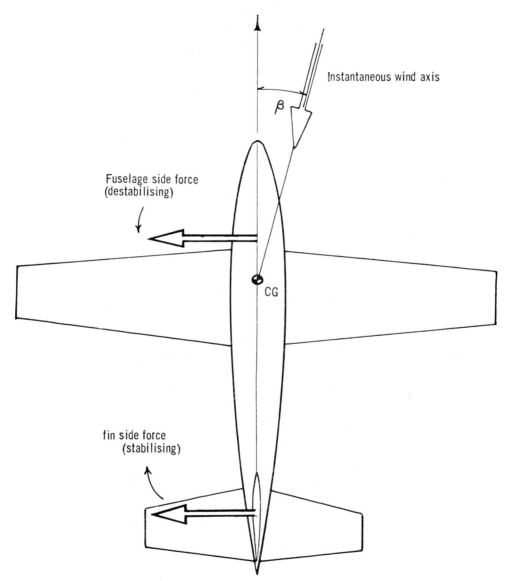

Fig. 8.12.   Stabilizing and destabilizing moments of fin and fuselage in yaw

Fig. 8.13(*a*) shows the simplest case of an aeroplane sideslipping under the influence of a component of weight, $W \sin \phi$, where ϕ is the angle of bank. It may be shown geometrically that if the wing has dihedral, then the wing on the leading side has a larger angle of attack than the other. The result is more lift on the leading wing and a rolling moment away from the direction of slip that reduces the bank. Anhedral

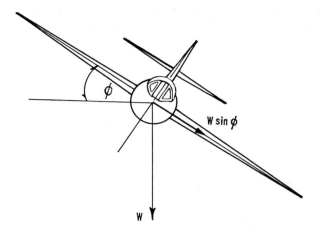

a. Aircraft sideslipping.

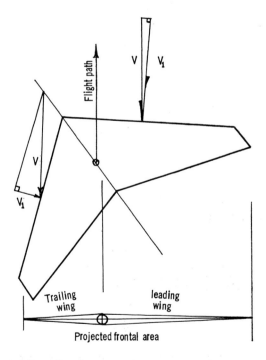

b. Relative airflow normal to leading edges of swept wings
when sideslipping.

Fig. 8.13. Effect of sweepback upon apparent dihedral

results in the leading wing having a smaller angle of attack than the wing on the trailing side, and a rolling moment is produced that tends to increase the angle of bank. It should be noted that low winged aeroplanes have more dihedral (or less anhedral) than the high winged varieties. The reason being that the CG of a high winged machine lies below the aerodynamic centre and, rather like a pendulum, the low-set weight tends to hold the wings level. Put another way, the moments of lift and drag of a high-set wing, in acting above the CG, tend to roll the aeroplane upright.

A swept wing, such as is shown in Fig. 8.13(b), experiences a higher velocity normal airflow past the leading wing than past the trailing wing when sideslipping. The lift of the leading wing is therefore higher than that of the trailing wing, and a strong rolling moment is generated. The greater the sweep or the larger the angle of attack, the more powerful the dihedral effect of a swept wing. For that reason anhedral is used to counter the dihedral effect of sweep. It should be noted, however, that the anhedral on the tailplane in Fig. 8.9 is countered by dihedral outboard on the Phantom wing, even though the wings are swept.

8.4.2 The Vertical Tail

Determination of fin size is not quite such a straightforward problem as might be thought from its apparent simplicity as a surface, because the fin efficiency is affected by an unusually large number of 'dirty flows' from the airframe ahead of it. Fin size and dihedral of both wing and tailplane are correlated. Alteration of one invariably affects the efficiency of the others.

Straight-winged propeller-driven aeroplanes have vertical tail areas around one half to two-thirds of the horizontal tail area. The actual size is determined by the required yawing moment that must be generated when sideslipping, and this in turn depends upon such important factors as asymmetric engine failure and the EAS. There is the further consideration of rolling moment caused by sideslip in relation to the yawing moment. The total rolling moment should be between 0·75 and 1·0 times the yawing moment caused by the same slip, but the fin contributes in turn to the rolling moment, and so does the wing position on the fuselage. A swept wing makes a favourable contribution to the yawing moment due to sideslip, as may be deduced from Fig. 8.13(b).

A high-set fin causes a lateral rolling moment with sideslip that augments the dihedral effect of the wing. But as the angle of attack is increased, by a change of airspeed or change of altitude, the fin is borne deeper into the wake shed by the fuselage, so that the effectiveness of the fin is decreased. Dutch-rolling is most noticeable at height, where the angle of attack is increasing to maintain lift. It is also noticeable during steep climb-outs from airfields in the hotter parts of the world where air density is low. A fin set beneath a fuselage becomes more effective at large angles of attack (and works against dihedral) a fin above the fuselage is less effective.

The modern, clean, high speed aeroplane requires a much larger fin than a slower aeroplane for the same role. Invariably there is not enough fin and, if the situation cannot be improved by the addition of strakes, then artificial stability (automatic rudder or fin deflection) must be introduced.

A fin surmounted by a high tailplane and terminating in a fuselage at its root is effectively borne between two aerodynamic endplates. As such the effective aspect ratio is increased and the fin becomes more powerful as a stabilizer. When the tailplane is set low one of the endplates is removed and the effective aspect ratio of the fin is reduced. Although the sideforce generated by a low aspect ratio fin is less for a given angle of yaw than one of higher aspect ratio, there is less proneness to fin-stalling. As fin-stalling is inevitably catastrophic, fins are usually of lower aspect

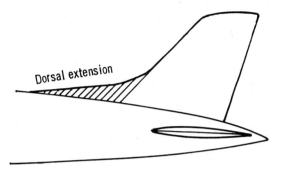

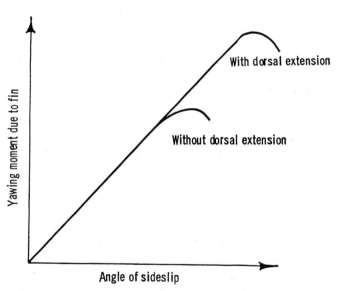

Fig. 8.14. Effect of a dorsal fin on yawing moment

ratio than any other surface. The larger required area is accepted as a justifiable penalty. In many cases aeroplanes grow dorsal fin extensions during later development. The dorsal extension serves to reduce the fin aspect ratio. As shown in Fig. 8.14, it does not improve the effectiveness of the fin very much at small angles of sideslip, but it has very powerful anti-stall and stabilizing properties at large angles.

Aerobatic aeroplanes usually have a large portion of the fin surface lying ahead

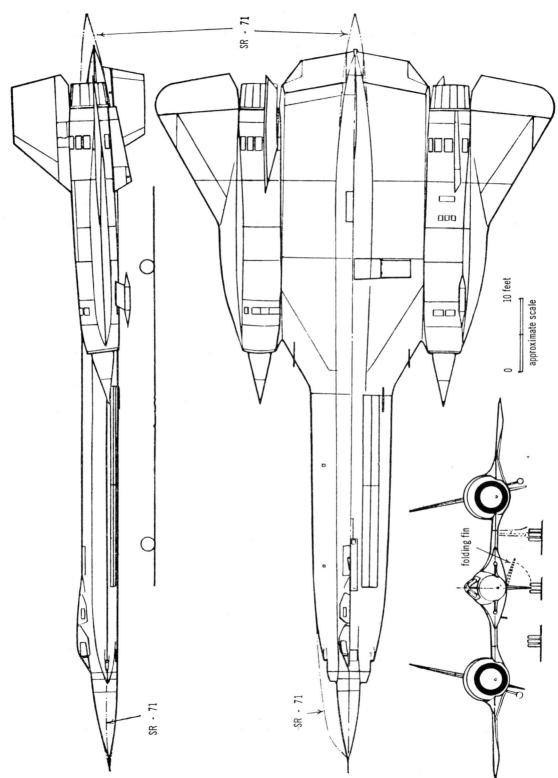

SR - 71

SR - 71

SR - 71

SR - 71

folding fin

10 feet

0

approximate scale

Fig. 8.15. The Lockheed YF–12A (U.S.A., revealed early 1964)

of the tailplane, or a large portion of the fin and rudder lying behind its trailing edge. This arrangement helps to avoid fin and rudder blanketing at large angles of attack during a spin.

One of the most interesting aeroplanes designed for very high performance (around $M = 3\cdot0$ in excess of 70,000 ft), that demonstrates many of the points discussed earlier is the Lockheed YF–12A, Fig. 8.15, first revealed early in 1964. Features that should be noted are: the slender, lifting forebody and nacelles with sharp-edged strakes: the delta wing set well aft: the twin fins and rudders mounted on the engine nacelles, and the additional (folding) fin beneath the rear fuselage. There appears to be marked washout of the wings relative to the lifting fuselage, while outboard sections of the wing leading edges are cambered. If the cruising flight path is more or less normal to the plane of the engine air intakes, the forward fuselage must ride at a markedly high angle of attack. Vertical components of the sideforces from the inclined fins cause destabilizing rolling moments opposing dihedral effects of sweep and high fin position.

8.5 Control

Control is achieved by altering the lift of the aerofoil surfaces; and 'active' or 'fly-by-wire' controls can be used to provide stability artificially. Control in roll, as we have seen, is brought about by making the lift of one wing greater than that of the other, usually by fitting a form of simple flap (called an aileron) at each trailing edge. For flight at comparatively low speeds ailerons are placed well outboard, but as design speeds increase and aerodynamic loads with them, the ailerons are placed further inboard, to reduce the effects of aero-elastic distortion of the wings. At very high speeds spoilers may be used to break down the lift of a wing surface without attendant distortion of the structure.

In a similar way the elevators and rudder for control in pitch and yaw appeared as simple flaps on tailplane and fin, but compressibility has so reduced the efficiency of such camber-changing devices at high speed that all-moving (or slab) tailplanes and fins are now used instead.

Fig. 8.16 shows some types of lateral control. In (a) the F-105 uses conventional ailerons at low speeds, where spoilers are least effective, but relies upon the spoilers at high speeds without recourse to ailerons. The moving wing-tip in (b) has attractive features, for it has the advantages of a slab surface. It tends to be overpowerful at low speeds and, perhaps because of complexity of gearing, has only appeared very intermittently. The tailerons of the BAC–TSR 2, (c), were slab surfaces that moved either together, as pitch controls, or independently for additional control in roll. It should be noted that modern aeroplanes having large tail surfaces and small wings suffer rolling moments from moving fins. Such cross-coupling between control surfaces makes the problems of stability and control more complex than ever before.

8.5.1 Balancing and Harmonizing Controls

With the exception of spoilers, flap and slab surfaces, in altering local lift circulation, experience opposing moments which are fed back to the pilot either directly or indirectly. The feel of a control system is of great importance, for control forces that are too heavy make an aeroplane tiring to fly, while forces that are too light may

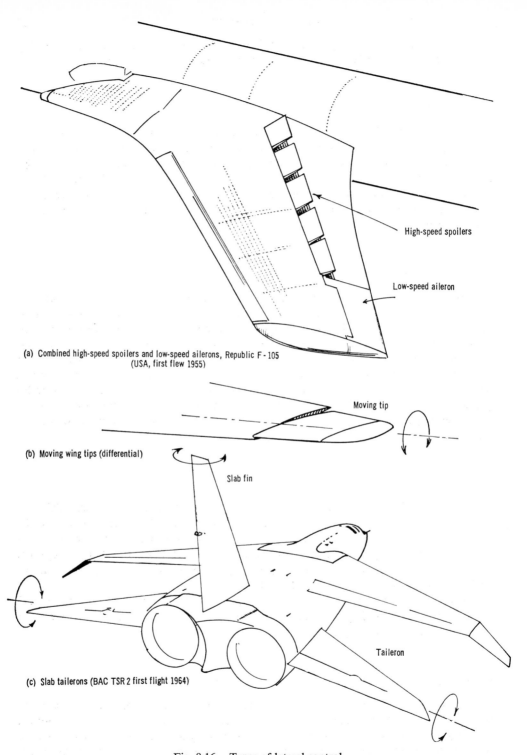

High-speed spoilers

Low-speed aileron

(a) Combined high-speed spoilers and low-speed ailerons, Republic F - 105
(USA, first flew 1955)

Moving tip

(b) Moving wing tips (differential)

Slab fin

Taileron

(c) Slab tailerons (BAC TSR 2 first flight 1964)

Fig. 8.16.   Types of lateral control

result in an aeroplane being broken in flight. The commonest devices for making control surfaces feel right are aerodynamic balances and tabs of various kinds.

Aerodynamic Balance

Aerodynamic balance is achieved by hingeing a control surface some way aft of its leading edge, so that a portion of the control surface area projects forward of the hinge-line. When the surface is deflected, part of the load in acting forward of the hinge introduces a moment opposing the moment caused by the load acting behind. As the moment caused by the load acting behind the hinge opposes control movement, that acting ahead assists the pilot. Too much area ahead of the hinge leads to control overbalance.

Trim Tabs (Balance and Anti-Balance)

Trim tabs are miniature control surfaces set in the trailing-edges of control surfaces. Balance tabs move in opposition to the control itself: depression of a tab causes an upload at the control trailing-edge, which helps the pilot to deflect the control upwards. An anti-balance tab is used when a control surface can be moved too easily. By moving such a tab in the same sense as the parent surface the moment of the surface about the hinge-line is increased. Tabs are moved by gears, to respond immediately when the parent surface is moved, or they can be operated by independent trimming-controls in the cockpit. Trim-tabs are used by the pilot to reduce a control hinge-moment to zero, so that no force has to be tiringly applied by him in steady flight.

Mass Balancing

Control surfaces, in having mass, are affected by accelerations. If the CG of a control surface lies behind the hinge, then a normal acceleration will deflect the control surface relative to the main aerofoil: the control being apparently depressed by an acceleration upwards, and raised by downwards acceleration of the aeroplane. If such movement is not stopped it is possible to break an aeroplane, or at least to suffer dangerous fluttering of control surfaces.

Surfaces are dynamically balanced by weights, either built into horns, or suspended on arms ahead of the hinges. One such mass balance, in the form of a streamlined weight, is shown in Fig. 8.17(*d*).

8.5.2 Flying Control Systems

Mechanical systems for moving the control surfaces are still basically the same as they have always been. Their increasing complexity has arisen from the combined effects of increased speed and size. Fig. 8.18(*a*) and (*b*) compares two control systems, one simple and straightforward, such as might be found in a sailplane or light aeroplane, the other more complicated for a moderately high-speed aeroplane. The second is recognizably similar to the first.

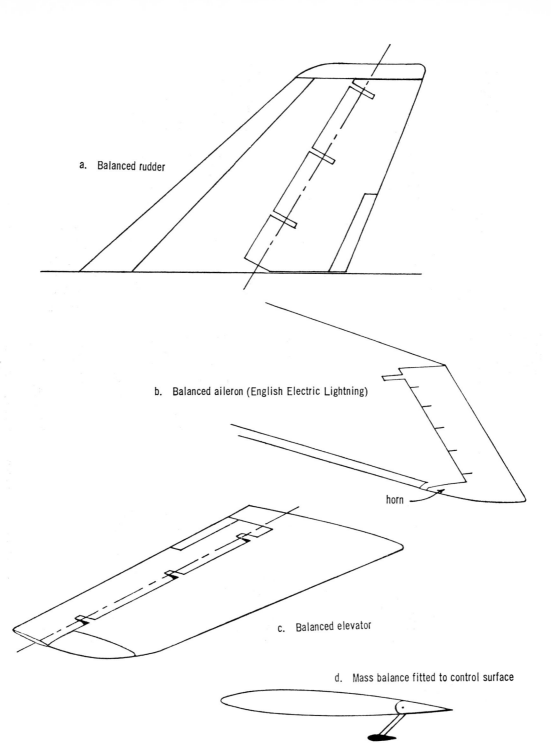

a. Balanced rudder

b. Balanced aileron (English Electric Lightning)

horn

c. Balanced elevator

d. Mass balance fitted to control surface

Fig. 8.17. Forms of control surface balance

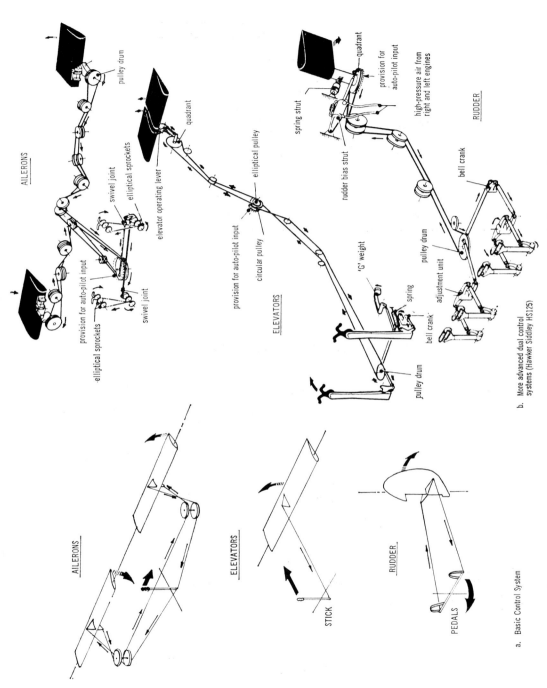

AILERONS

pulley drum

swivel joint

elliptical sprockets

elevator operating lever

quadrant

swivel joint

elliptical sprockets

provision for auto-pilot input

swivel joint

provision for auto-pilot input

circular pulley

elliptical pulley

ELEVATORS

'G' weight

spring

bell crank

pulley drum

quadrant

provision for auto-pilot input

high-pressure air from right and left engines

spring strut

RUDDER

rudder bias strut

bell crank

pulley drum

adjustment unit

pulley drum

AILERONS

ELEVATORS

STICK

RUDDER

PEDALS

a. Basic Control System

b. More advanced dual control systems (Hawker Siddley HS125)

Fig. 8.18.   Flying control systems, arrows indicate direction of travel for left aileron up, elevators up and left rudder

167

A novel feature of the second system (Hawker Siddeley HS 125) is the rudder-bias strut, which is a pneumatic ram with compressed air tapped from the engine compresser deliveries and fed to either side of the piston. Failure of one engine reduces the compressor delivery on the appropriate side of the piston, causing displacement and rudder deflection to counter the asymmetric yawing-moment from the live engine. The feature represents power-assistance in a most rudimentary form.

If manual controls are to be retained for flight at high speeds it is necessary to use a higher degree of aerodynamic balance as aircraft size is increased. As the degree of balance is increased the net hinge-moment becomes more sensitive to manufacturing tolerances. Furthermore, because of the non-static nature of shock-waves, compressibility can vary hinge-moments very rapidly with slight changes of airspeed and control surface deflection. At high speeds it becomes impracticable to use manual controls and fully-powered controls (or at least power-assisted controls) must be fitted.

Powered controls employ rams, or servo-units, to move the surfaces. The control-column and rudder-pedals become power-selectors, moved by the pilot to provide power to one side or other of pistons which, through a system of linkages, in turn deflect the flying-controls. Most power-controls are hydraulic, but work is being done to improve the reliability of electrical systems for advanced aircraft. With such systems it may be possible to save valuable cockpit-space, replacing the traditional stick and rudder-bar with switches on an arm-rest of the seat. Pilots, however, are conservative by nature and several attempts to replace stick and pedals with smaller levers or switches have been vigorously resisted. It should be noted that there is good sense in such conservatism, for some change that might look sensible on a drawing-board could well cost a man his life in the isolation of a cockpit, with several things going wrong at the same time.

It is worth noting that servo systems of all kinds, designed to aid the pilot, introduce instabilities of their own. These are treated as part of the whole stability problem of an aircraft.

8.6   Aero-Elasticity

Aerodynamic and inertia loads are resisted by the airframe structure, which possesses a measure of strength and a measure of stiffness. While it is comparatively easy to build a small aeroplane that is both stiff and strong, large aeroplanes tend to be strong without being stiff enough, they are 'floppy' and much of their structural weight is there to meet the stiffness rather than the strength requirements. The resilience of a structure leads to flutter problems that are discussed in 12.1.1.

All aero-elastic distortion, caused by aerodynamic loads bending the airframe, is destabilizing in its general effect. Swept wings suffer more from aero-elasticity than straight wings, while high aspect ratio surfaces distort more than those with low aspect ratio. Fig. 8.19 shows the aerodynamic twist along the flexural-axis of a swept wing caused by bending alone, that results in a loss of incidence at the tip and aggravation of pitch-up. The effects of aero-elasticity can be delayed, or reduced, by the use of podded engine installations, a common feature of many American airliners and bombers. The engines are, in effect, mass balances for the wings, placed along the span in positions that are the result of compromise between design for asymmetric engine failure and wing stiffness. On the other hand, the unusual 'M-wing', shown in Fig. 6.19(b) is designed to distort in such a way that the increased incidence due to

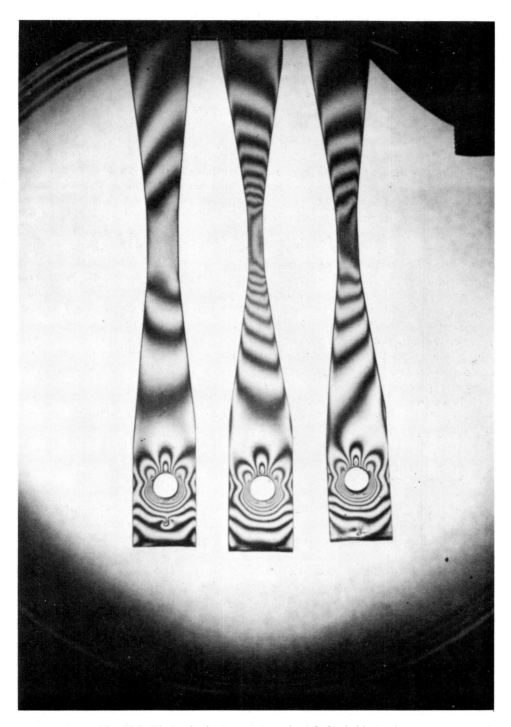

Fig. 11.6   Photo-elastic stress patterns in strip loaded in tension

(By permission of D. H. Division Hawker Siddeley Aviation Ltd.)

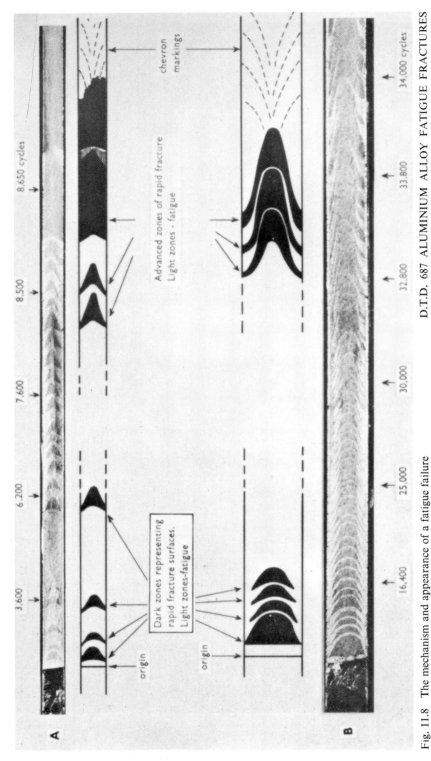

Fig. 11.8 The mechanism and appearance of a fatigue failure

By permission of the Ministry of Aviation

D.T.D. 687 ALUMINIUM ALLOY FATIGUE FRACTURES

A. $\begin{bmatrix} 0.08'' \text{ thick} \\ 4' \times 8' \end{bmatrix}$ Stress $14,000 \pm 4,000$ p.s.i.

B. $\begin{bmatrix} 0.16'' \text{ thick} \\ 4' \times 8' \end{bmatrix}$ Stress $14,000 \pm 2,000$ p.s.i.

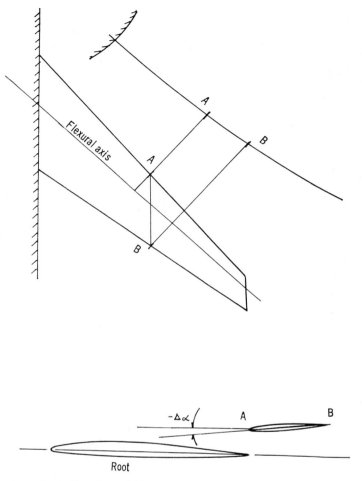

Fig. 8.19. Aero-elastic distortion of thin swept wing under load showing loss of incidence with bending, which decreases lift towards the tip and may lead to pitch-up when manoeuvring

bending of the forward swept portions is equal and opposite to the loss of incidence of backward swept portions of the wings.

If a fuselage is not stiff enough then movement of the elevator bends the fuselage, reducing the angle of attack of the tailplane and, therefore, the effect of the elevator. In a similar way, if a wing is not stiff enough in torsion then the pitching moments from the ailerons twist the wing in the opposite direction to aileron movement, reducing their effect. If the torque applied by the ailerons is strong enough aileron reversal occurs, *i.e.*, the ailerons do not reverse direction, they twist the wing so far that it generates the opposite load to that required.

Aero-elasticity is readily apparent and usually appears early in the life of an aeroplane. However, when a machine is well-worn and has been hard worked all of its life slight tolerances in the joints can lead to effects similar to those described. This has probably been the reason for a number of aeroplanes being called 'rogue': an imprecise term for an aircraft that does not respond to control movements in the way that it should, when others of the same type are perfectly predictable.

PART 4

GROUND AND WATER OPERATIONS

CHAPTER 9

Landplanes

The undercarriage, or landing gear, serves a triple purpose in providing a stable support for an aircraft at rest on the ground, forming a suitable shock-absorbing device during landing, and acting as a rolling chassis for taxying. The undercarriage is dead-weight in flight and much art is needed to retract it in such a way as to cause the least interference with the outboard and inboard profiles. The outboard profile is simply the shape of the airframe surface presented to the relative airflow. The inboard profile is the outline of the volume available for payload and equipment.

A complex retraction mechanism is heavy and there is much skill in making it light and simple, yet strong enough to absorb the shock of moderately heavy landings without breakage or strain of the surrounding structure. The rate of descent on touchdown should ideally be zero, but values up to 25 ft/sec must sometimes be allowed for. Naval aeroplanes present some of the worst problems, for the undercarriage must absorb the shock of a heavy fast aeroplane flying straight onto the deck without checking the rate of descent (flare, or round-out), and the deck may also be rising to meet the aircraft as the ship pitches.

Superimposed on the need to absorb high vertical kinetic energies is the case of drag load caused by the rotational inertia of the wheel (moment of inertia about the axle) during the time of violent spin-up on touch-down. Further drag loads are caused by braking, while side-loads are caused by turning, lateral skidding and cross-winds. In cold weather there is the additional drag of snow and slush. In the worst design case a number of these things are allowed to happen simultaneously.

The number of wheels and tyre sizes are determined by the requirement that an aeroplane should be able to operate at maximum design take-off weight from both rigid and flexible surfaces, having specified load-bearing properties. The size of tyre and its pressure determines the 'footprint' area of contact with the ground. The load applied by a wheel is felt as a stress, a pressure, equal to the wheel loading spread over the footprint area. If a surface is soft or weak the surface-stress must be kept low by increasing the number of wheels bearing the load. A number of small wheels can be stowed more easily than a large wheel having the same total footprint-area, and they tend to be lighter, although no gain may be felt because of the need for more complicated and heavier retraction mechanisms. Current thinking is towards transport aeroplanes weighing more than 700,000 lb, carrying payloads of 200,000 lb (more than 350 and 100 short tons respectively), with anything between 12 and 24 main-wheels, for soft-field operations. A possible design feature for such units will probably be tyres that can be partly deflated and inflated in flight, thus enabling the size of undercarriage-housing to be reduced. Undercarriages of the latter kind are sometimes called 'high-flotation' units.

The criteria in most common use for relating the maximum permissible weight of an aircraft to the size and number of wheels, and the pavement strength of the airfields from which it is to operate, are the load classification number, or LCN, and the equivalent isolated single-wheel load. These are calculated for a particular weight, undercarriage geometry and tyre pressure by the aircraft manufacturer. Most modern airfields have stated maximum LCNs for runways and pavements.

Wheels are disposed either in a tricycle arrangement about the CG, or in tandem as a bicycle arrangement, stabilized by small outriggers. Tricycle units may be either nosewheel or tailwheel variety.

9.1 The Tailwheel Undercarriage

The tailwheel undercarriage is one having two main units forward of the CG and one behind which, in very simple light aircraft, may be only a skid. At rest the aeroplane sits tail-down at an angle of attack slightly less than the stalling angle of the wings with high-lift devices extended. The arrangement allows the aeroplane to be three-pointed onto the ground with power off.

The tail-down attitude allows the pilot to use large aerodynamic drag to assist braking during the landing run, but has the disadvantage of a sloping floor that makes loading heavy objects difficult. The mainwheels lying ahead of the CG make the configuration prone to ground-looping, an uncontrollable spiral motion. The tendency is reduced by placing the mainwheels only a little way ahead of the CG, but there is then the danger of nosing over.

Directional control is by differential braking, or by tailwheel or skid connected to the rudder. The tailwheel undercarriage has lower drag than the nosewheel variety and as such is most convenient for the simplest utilitarian aeroplanes.

9.2 The Nosewheel Undercarriage

The nosewheel undercarriage is the commonest today. Ground-looping and nose-overs are eliminated, while loading is simplified by the level floor. Control is neatly achieved by differential braking with a castoring nosewheel, or by making the nose-wheel steerable. Jet efflux is kept clear of the ground, where it can do the least damage. Nosewheel legs can be made extendable, to set aircraft at a high angle of attack for take-off, but this can only be done when the thrust/weight is large to begin with, for the drag is high. Tail brake-parachutes are easily employed.

The arrangement is shown in Fig. 9.2. Ideally the tail-down attitude should exceed the stalling angle of the wing, but jet aircraft with short undercarriages often require tail-bumpers. The CG position is such as to give a static nosewheel reaction between 6 and 15 per cent of the all-up weight: heavy enough to prevent the aircraft tipping onto its tail, yet light enough for the elevator to rotate the aircraft about the mainwheels on take-off.

Very slender aeroplanes with low aspect ratio wings will be found to employ nosewheel units that are shorter than the main units, giving a slight nose-down ground-attitude. The reason is that low aspect ratio wings cannot be stalled on landing, the stalling angles being well beyond possible aircraft attitudes. Therefore, to prevent dangerous 'ballooning' after touchdown the nose is dropped to give a ground attitude something less than the angle of zero lift. The aircraft is then held down aerodynamically. Rotation on take-off becomes more of a problem, especially

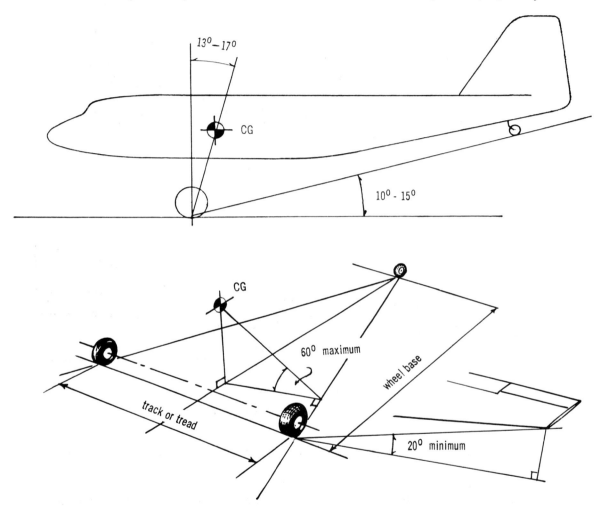

Fig. 9.1.   The tailwheel undercarriage

with trailing edge control surfaces on a wing, the large download required for rotation detracting substantially from the total lift. A canard becomes most attractive as a control surface under such conditions, and the canard plus rear tailplane combination mentioned in 8.3.2.

The slender aeroplane with its large pitching inertia takes longer to respond to elevator than the less slender and 'normal' classical varieties, particularly if the elevator control is aft of the CG. Undercarriage design must, therefore, take into account the effect of a late flare-out on landing that results in very high loads, for the CG is rotating about an instantaneous centre some way ahead of it and there is an added vertical component of velocity to be absorbed by the mainwheels. The situation shown in Fig. 9.3 may result in the pilot having the sensation of rising away from the

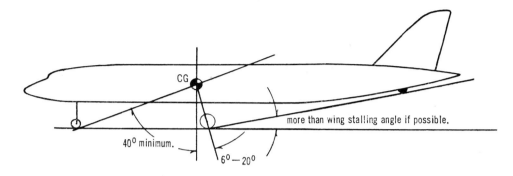

(a) Disposition of nosewheel undercarriage units about CG.

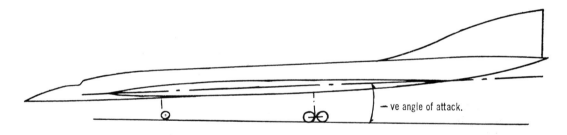

(b) Slender (low aspect ratio) aircraft with −ve ground attitude.

Fig. 9.2. The nosewheel undercarriage

ground as he flares-out, while the tail of the aircraft and main units are being broken off along the runway.

On both types of tricycle undercarriage adequate ground-clearances must be allowed for propeller tips, with shock-absorber units fully compressed. The minimum clearance is about six inches.

9.3   The Bicycle Undercarriage

The bicycle arrangement of mainwheel units in tandem has appeared sporadically in recent years on certain jet bomber, transport and special aeroplanes. The merits of such a layout lie in the low weight and drag of the units. The position of the main wheels allows little margin for variation of landing attitude, and speeds must be maintained within 2 to 3 k. If the aeroplane is landed nose-high, the pitching moment of the CG about the rear wheels forces the nosewheels down with a high risk of

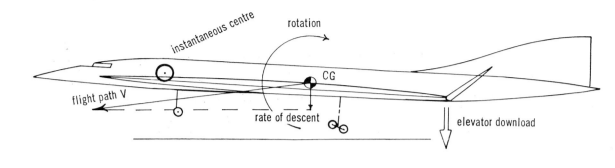

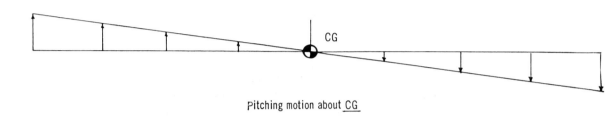

Pitching motion about <u>CG</u>

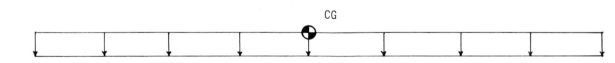

Sink through loss of lift from elevator download

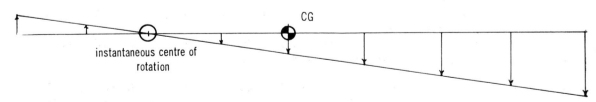

instantaneous centre of
rotation

Resultant of pitching and sinking motions

Fig. 9.3.   Motion caused by flare-out on touch-down

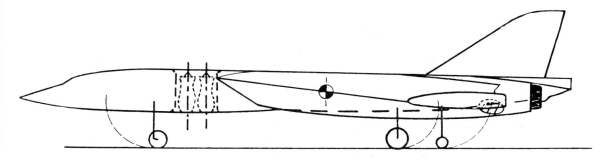

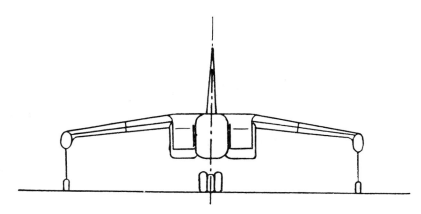

Fig. 9.4. The bicycle undercarriage

bouncing. For equal, optimum, sized units front and rear the wheels should be placed at a distance from the CG equal to the radius of gyration of the fuselage in pitch. But if bouncing is to be avoided, *i.e.*, if the pilot is to be given a reasonable margin of freedom in landing speeds for different weights and crosswind conditions, then the rear wheels must be as close to the CG as possible. The position of the mainwheels depends therefore upon a number of factors:

(1) Role and size of the aeroplane.
(2) Airfields from which it will operate: condition of runways and alignment with prevailing winds.
(3) Stowage available for undercarriage units: the layout is well suited to large aircraft with plenty of under-floor volume.

The bicycle undercarriage is mainly used on large transport and bomber aircraft operating from well prepared airfields, although variations have appeared on the Hawker Siddeley Kestrel VTOL fighter, the single-engined Lockheed U2 reconnaissance aeroplane, and Russian Yakovlev Yak–25 developments.

A bicycle arrangement is shown in Fig. 9.4, in which the outriggers retract into wing-tip housings. As with the mainwheel units, the loads would be equal and a minimum for an outrigger-first landing if they could be placed at the lateral radius of gyration of the aeroplane. In general, if units are placed at a distance less than the radius of gyration the gear touching first has the greater load. If they are placed out-board, or at a distance greater than the radius of gyration, then the gear touching last is the most heavily loaded.

9.4 Mechanical Engineering

The engineering of an undercarriage may involve little more than the arrangement of an uncomplicated rubber shock absorber in a fixed leg at the simplest end of the scale, while at the other may be the design of a complicated mechanism involving retraction movement combined with movement for shock-absorption, and sideways extension of bogies for increasing wheel-track. Shock-absorption methods are many and varied. The simplest involve bungee rubber chord for lashing axles to struts, rubber blocks or coiled springs working in sleeves. The commonest are based upon the oleo, or oleo-pneumatic principle in which a column of oil, or oil and air is trapped in a sealed telescopic strut. Compression of the strut causes a piston to com-press the liquid and pneumatic 'springs'. High performance aeroplanes use hydraulic power for flying-controls and undercarriage operation. Hydraulic fluid may be used for shock absorption in the oleo legs, and leg length can be altered conveniently for different take-off, landing and ground-loading conditions.

9.4.1 Undercarriage Retraction

Stowage of the undercarriage in flight poses some of the most complicated problems for both designer and systems engineer. Most propeller-driven aeroplanes have thick enough wings to house undercarriage units, or engine nacelles with enough volume behind the engine for wheel stowage. Actual movement of legs, wheels and linkages may involve much contortion. An example is shown in Fig. 9.5 which illustrates the retraction cycle of a mainwheel bogie into a blister fairing on the fuselage of the Short Belfast.

Some of the early subsonic jet aeroplanes had thick enough wings for the tradition of wing-stowage to be continued, without much alteration in wheel and tyre size. Faster aeroplanes had much thinner wings, fuselages packed with engines, ducting, fuel and equipment, that necessitated the development of much thinner and smaller wheels with very high pressure tyres.

With the coming of the jet aeroplane propeller-clearance problems largely dis-appeared and undercarriage legs grew shorter and easier to stow. But the slender low aspect ratio planform, with its ability to fly at exaggerated angles of attack without stalling, is now causing the undercarriage leg to grow longer again, to provide adequate ground clearance and long strokes for absorbing the energies involved.

An undercarriage generates considerable drag: with gear down the overall lift/drag of a high performance aeroplane may be reduced by 20 to 25 per cent. On a light aeroplane with a well faired fixed undercarriage the drag may be only 12 to 15 per cent of the total. Partially lowered mainwheels have been used as air-brakes on the Folland Gnat trainer. Lowering an undercarriage often reduces the nose-down pitching moment caused by the flaps, because the disturbance reduces local circulation.

Most aeroplanes employ stressed (load-bearing) skins and the strength of such structures is reduced by cut-outs, so that local stiffening is needed around wheel-wells.

Ideally units are stowed where there is ample space, and stiffening can be introduced with the minimum penalties in structure weight. Wing leading edges, engine nacelles, spaces beneath fuselage floors are used: all places where there are already adjacent spars, booms and frames forming reasonable attachments and stiffening. Special pods and blisters may have to be added to fuselages and wings when the configuration of an aeroplane does not permit the design of economical mechanisms.

9.4.2   Water, Slush and Ice

Heavy rain leaves standing-water on runways and the high ground speeds of modern aeroplanes have brought the problem of aquaplaning to the fore: a phenomenon in which the tyres are lifted hydrodynamically off the ground. Wheel arrangement and tyre size and pressure all affect the problem. A trailing tandem-wheel is less prone to aquaplaning than a leading wheel, because the leading wheel clears some of the water away. A low pressure tyre aquaplanes at a lower speed than a high pressure tyre of the same size, as shown by the empirical formula:

$$V_a = 9\sqrt{p} \qquad\qquad (9\text{--}1)$$

where V_a is the aquaplaning speed in knots, and p the tyre pressure in lb/in.^{2} A motorcar with tyre pressures of 25 lb/in^2 and reasonable tyre treads will aquaplane at 45 k, say 52 mile/h. An aeroplane with a tyre pressure of 120 lb/in^2 will aquaplane at 100 k, or 115 mile/h. If the treads are well worn then the aquaplaning speed is considerably reduced, with a consequent reduction in braking and steering.

Slush is a transient condition between standing-water and snow which drastically increases wheel-drag. The pitching moment of the wheel-drag about the CG may be high enough to prevent the elevator rotating the aircraft for take-off, while the slush drastically reduces the effectiveness of wheel brakes and steering. Bogie wheels in tandem cause less drag than a number of wheels in line abreast.

Braking and steering are consistently poor on ice, while water thrown onto undercarriage mechanisms may freeze hard enough in flight to prevent their operation after letting down from high altitudes. Some aircraft have required special heaters for undercarriage bays. Others merely have the undercarriage cycled up and down several times after take-off, to break up ice and blow away slush and water clinging to the mechanisms.

CHAPTER 10

Seaplanes

It is probably fair to say that the seaplane, in the form of the long-range flying-boat, was in a more advanced state of development than the landplane right up to the beginning of the Second World War. During the war the rapid development of the heavy bomber and the provision of long runways in many parts of the world favoured the development afterwards of civil transports along the same lines. Whether or not the seaplane will reappear again as anything more important than it is at present is a matter for conjecture, but there are many applications in the role of long-range heavy weight-lifting that make the seaplane an attractive proposition. Furthermore, there is public interest being shown in the U.S.A. in a submersible aircraft for a number of military uses. Such an aircraft would be able to fly in the air and underwater and would increase considerably the number of options available for weapon-delivery.

The advantages of the seaplane lie in the argument that seventy-five per cent of the Earth's surface is covered by water, all of it flat and most of it (neglecting storms and shoals) unrestricted for take-off and landing. Flying-boats can be built in larger sizes than landplanes, and they can be operated away from centres of population, so that noise problems would be small. Beriev, in Russia, was rumoured early in the 1960s to be thinking of a 2,000 passenger flying-boat weighing 2,000,000 lb (1,000 short tons) and cruising at 500 k.

The disadvantages are that seaplanes cannot ride out the same rough seas as ships, and scheduled operations would be limited to coastal waters, rivers and lakes. Marine airports with good communications would have to be built. Loading and unloading and servicing pose considerable problems: no passenger wants to fly 4,000 miles to be made wet and seasick in the last 400 yards. Transport systems are geared to landplane operations in all developed countries. Seaplane lift/drag ratios are less than equivalent landplanes.

10.1 Basic Design Requirements

The shape of the seaplane is a compromise to meet the following requirements:

(1) Buoyancy and static stability.
(2) Low water-drag, and the provision of hydrodynamic lift at low speeds to reduce the wetted surface as much as possible.
(3) Spray must be avoided or suppressed from reaching propellers, intakes and other vulnerable parts.

(4) Dynamic stability on the water.

(5) Manoeuvrability and control while taxying.

(6) Adequate performance and versatility.

In meeting the design requirements seaplane shapes have followed two distinctive lines of development. The first, traditional line, was that of adapting a marine hull to the task of transferring the weight of the aircraft from water to air and back again. The basic disadvantage of the traditional seaplane lay in the bad marriage between a displacement hull and a wing. The second approach, that came in recent years but has not been developed, is that of designing a fair aerodynamic blended-hull shape possessing hydrodynamic and hydrostatic properties. The resulting aircraft bear strong similarities to the 'integrated' landplane shapes for supersonic speeds. The form of the latter seaplane has natural lateral stability and the traditional floats and sponsons are no longer necessary.

10.2 The Traditional Seaplane

The traditional and blended-hull forms are governed by the same hydrostatic and hydrodynamic principles, the applications alone differ. The principles are therefore considered for the traditional seaplane, and as such they apply to both floatplane and flying-boat.

10.2.1 Buoyancy and Static Stability

A traditional flying-boat hull is shown in Fig. 10.1, and the most noticeable differences between the hull and an equivalent fuselage are the depth and the shaped ventral surfaces which form a planing-bottom. The buoyancy of the hull is proportional to the volume of water displaced: the weight of water displaced being equal to the weight of the aircraft.

The forces acting on the hull (or floats) at rest are the weight acting at the CG and the buoyancy reacting it at the centre of buoyancy, or CB. The static stability of the system is measureable in terms of the distance between the metacentre, M and the CG. The metacentre is the point of intersection of the line of action of the buoyancy in the plane of symmetry (X–Z plane) of the aircraft. The distance between the metacentre and CG is called the metacentric height. If the CG lies below the metacentre when heeled the metacentric height is +ve and the aircraft is statically stable. If they coincide, or if the metacentre lies below the CG, then the aircraft is either neutrally stable or unstable, and will turn over with the slightest disturbance. The static stability when heeled is shown in Fig. 10.2, in which all three metacentric heights are +ve. It should be noted that a conventional hull, such as that shown in Fig. 10.2(a) is unstable by itself. Wing tip floats must be fitted, or sponsons (buoyant stub wings sprouting from the hull sides). But the latter have high weight and drag and have not been universally favoured.

In a similar way the static longitudinal stability is measureable in terms of the metacentric height of the buoyancy vector intersecting the Y–Z plane through the CG. The significance of the metacentric height may be reasoned from Fig. 10.2, for the greater the +ve distance between M and the CG for a given angle of heel the greater is the righting-moment of the weight and buoyancy couple.

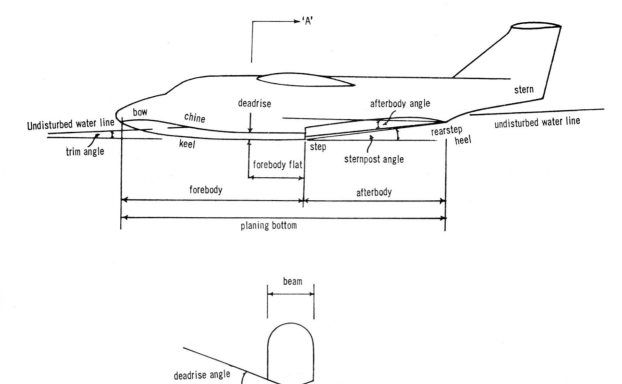

Fig. 10.1.   Parts of a seaplane hull

10.2.2   Hydrodynamic Lift and Drag

A buoyant flat plate immersed in water has static lift when at rest, but generates hydrodynamic lift as well when moved forward at a positive angle of attack. We speak of the displacement-regime as being that in which the lift is predominantly hydrostatic, and of the planing-regime in which hydrodynamic lift provides most of the support.

Early seaplanes had flat-bottomed floats which were, in effect, buoyant hydroskis. But as the speed of take-off and landing increased along with wing loadings flat bottoms were changed to vee-bottoms, with keels and chines, to reduce impact loads and structure weight.

The drag of the water is made up of frictional, normal pressure and wave-making components. In the planing-regime frictional drag is reduced because the hull draught is small. The total resistance, R, is shown in Fig. 10.3, as a ratio of drag/weight, R/W, against unstick-speed ratio, V/V_{us}. Two other curves have been added: the thrust/weight, T/W, and trim-angle. All seaplanes have had marginal performance in the vicinity of the 'hump', where $(T/W - R/W)$ is least.

The change of attitude, represented by the trim-angle, is caused by the increased normal pressure on the forward facing hull surfaces and the suction on the rearward facing surfaces. The conditions are similar to those affecting a convex aerofoil

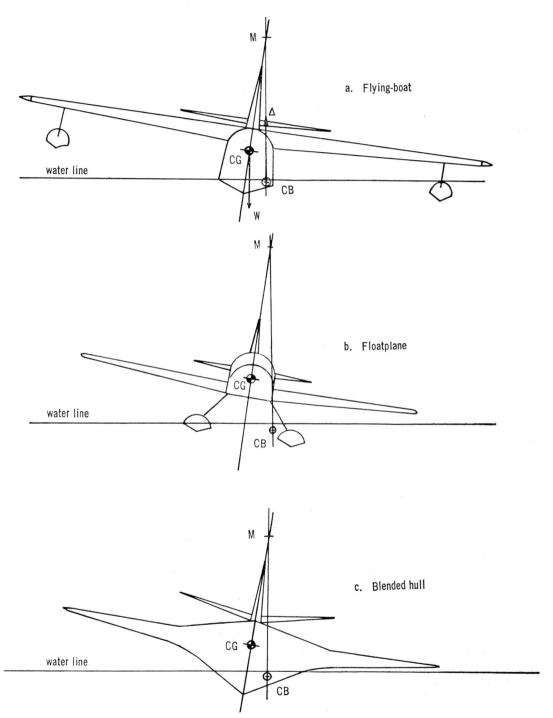

a. Flying-boat

b. Floatplane

c. Blended hull

Fig. 10.2. Static stability when heeled showing required relationship between weight W and buoyancy, Δ, which places the **metacentre**, M, above the centre of gravity

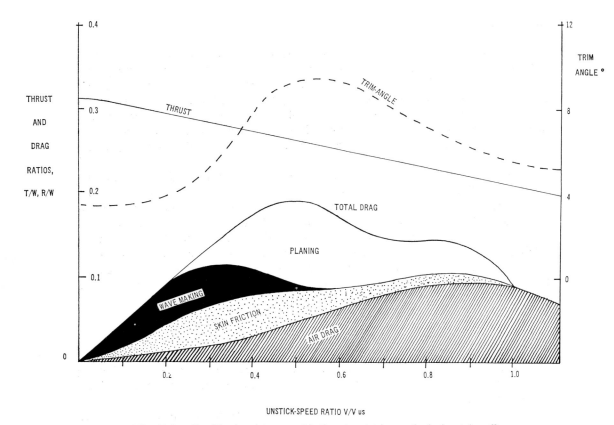

Fig. 10.3.   Combined resistance, with thrust and trim-angle during take-off

surface in supersonic flight. The normal pressure and suction forces cause a nose-up couple that must be countered by elevator deflection to hold the aircraft at the optimum trim-angle.

The suction acting on the afterbody holds the hull down and causes porpoising. To break down the suction it is necessary to ventilate the afterbody by introducing a layer of air between the skin and the water, and this is done by the introduction of a step about half-way along the planing-bottom. Unfortunately steps cause high drag in flight, and various designs have been tried to reduce it. From the simple step cut across the planing-bottom at right angles to the keel, step shapes have changed to elliptical forms, have been made retractable, and have been replaced by slots ducting blown air from engine compressors. The earliest, simplest, steps increased the drag of the basic streamlined body upon which the hull was based by about 48 per cent. An elliptical step has a drag increment around 15 per cent, while the latest seaplane hulls can be built with a total drag increment around 12 per cent, compared with a value of 4 to 5 per cent for an equivalent landplane. Ideally complete ventilation of the hull on the hovercraft principle, by using a cushion of air, would provide the greatest reduction in drag, but the weight penalty of such a mechanical system would be very high. A more practical alternative is the hydrofoil, a highly loaded planing-surface that lifts the hull clear of the water, which can be retracted in flight for a small weight penalty.

10.2.3 Spray

Spray is caused by the peak pressure developed in the area where the planing-bottom enters the water and occurs in two forms. The first, ribbon or velocity spray is flung sideways in a flat trajectory from the line of forward contact of the planing-bottom with the surface of the water. Being light it causes few problems, apart from misting of windscreens. The second kind, called blister spray is heavy and far more damaging. Blister spray is thrown upwards and rearwards by the chine in a heavy cone. The height to which blister spray rises determines the heights of wings, engines and tail-surfaces.

Spray is suppressed by hollowing the forebody from keel to chine, by increasing the forebody fineness (length/beam) and by attaching strips, called spray dams, to the forebody chine. The spray dam must be tangential to the airflow, and for that reason it cannot be fitted to run far along a conventional chine, which has marked curvature. The dam protrudes at right angles to the spray path and derives its effectiveness from mixing air with the spray as it is deflected downwards towards the water. The aerated mass penetrates the free water surface with high velocity and little or no reflection. Spray patterns and the effect of bottom contour and spray dam are shown in Fig. 10.4.

10.2.4 Dynamic Stability on Water

There are three kinds of dynamic longitudinal instability: porpoising, skipping and pattering. Porpoising is the most dangerous and can occur at both small and large angles of trim.

At small trim-angles porpoising is reduced by the use of a flat region of the forebody, called the forebody-flat. The forebody-flat extends 1·5 beam-widths forward of the step and, being flat, sustains more or less constant pressure over the whole surface. Curvature would cause a variation in longitudinal pressure distribution with trim and alter the metacentric height with any disturbance in pitch, so that any motion would be aggravated. Later hulls with refined slender lines, Fig. 10.5, do not have a marked forebody-flat. Instead the deadrise-angle is increased forward of the step, which in effect increases the acute vee at the keel. Increasing the deadrise-angle forward is called forebody-warp. While decreasing the tendency to porpoising it causes the forebody keel to run deeper in the water and decreases the directional stability.

Porpoising at large trim-angles is caused by the afterbody dipping into the water. This is prevented by maintaining large afterbody keel and sternpost angles. Porpoising at high speeds results in skipping, the aeroplane being thrown clear of the water before stalling back again. Porpoising is also caused by the step centroid being too far in front of or behind the CG. Skipping is caused by the step being too shallow and, therefore, insufficient ventilation of the planing-bottom. Tests indicate that the depth of the step should be 6 to 10 per cent of the beam.

10.2.5 Manoeuvrability and Control

Fine hulls, similar to that shown in Fig. 10.5, have long forebodies and deep-running keels that move the centre-of-lateral-area forward relative to the CG,

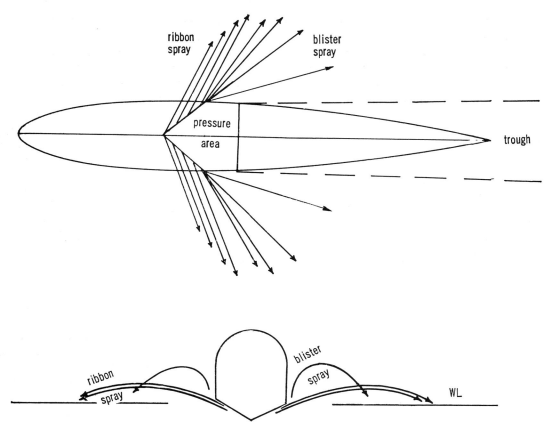

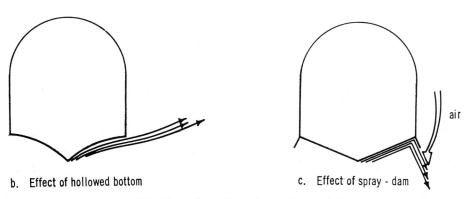

a. Ribbon and blister spray patterns

b. Effect of hollowed bottom

c. Effect of spray - dam

Fig. 10.4. Spray formation and suppression

184

decreasing the directional stability and making the hull prone to ground (water) looping.

The fine hull (with length/beam around 10/1) cannot be used effectively with a small aircraft, because there is not enough beam for stowage of disposable load and equipment. Hull sections must bulge outboard beyond the chines, and the curvature of the hull sides causes yaw if spray strikes one side before the other.

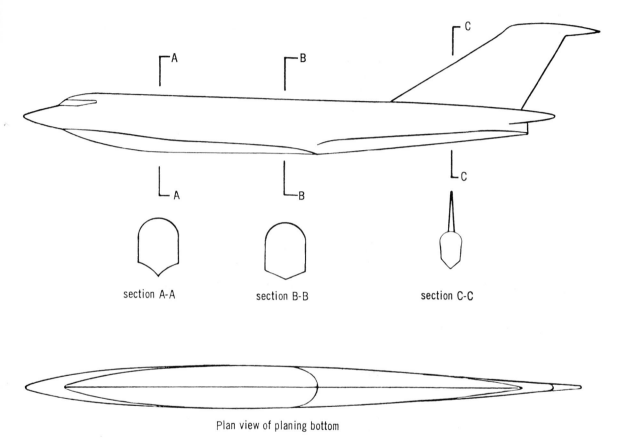

section A-A   section B-B   section C-C

Plan view of planing bottom

Fig. 10.5. Refined hull form with elliptical step and planing-tail

Directional instability may be cured by a skeg, a small fin, protruding into the water from the afterbody keel, but its effectiveness is limited by the range of trim-angles at which it runs in solid water.

Directional control is by water-rudder, or by water-flaps. A rudder usually forms part of the rear-step heel, or the sternpost. Water-flaps, (which can be used in the air as air-brakes) open differentially under water for turning, or together for braking. They are fitted either side of the afterbody keel and are most necessary for jet aircraft that do not have the beneficial effects of propeller slipstream to help with manoeuvre and control.

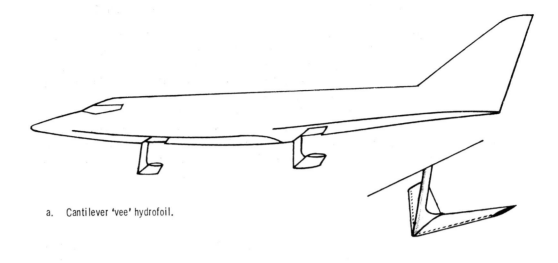

a.   Cantilever 'vee' hydrofoil.

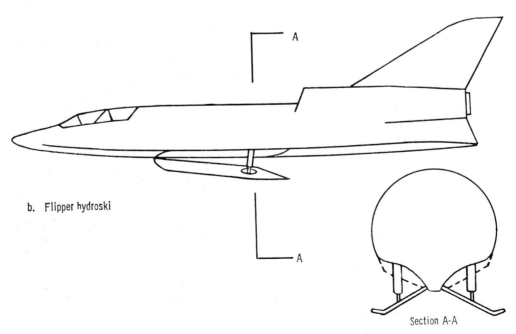

b.   Flipper hydroski

Section A-A

Fig. 10.6.   The generation of hydrodynamic lift using retractable hydrofoil and hydroski arrangements

10.3 Future Seaplanes—the Search for Increased Performance and Versatility

It is always dangerous to forecast the future in aeronautics and there is no intention of forecasting any future for the seaplane here. There were certain lines of development that could be clearly discerned some years ago, that might have led in two definite directions, if seaplane development had not fallen into abeyance. All that we can do here is to look at the threads that are left.

The first line of development away from the traditional hull and float form was in the direction of using separate hydrofoil and hydroski surfaces to provide hydrodynamic lift. The second line was in the direction of the blended-hull: more or less an integrated shape in which the body possessed buoyancy, natural stability, and the ability to generate both hydrodynamic and aerodynamic lift.

10.3.1 Hydrofoils

The hydrofoil is, in effect, a small water-wing that remains completely immersed until lift-off, and which is capable of generating lift/drag ratios around 30/1. The attraction of such an arrangement is that relatively small, retractable, surfaces can be used to lift the hull in the displacement regime. Some attempts have been made to support aeroplanes completely on hydrofoils, but the operating speeds are so high that the suction over the upper surfaces is too intense and the water 'boils', a phenomenon known as cavitation. Cavitation causes an immediate loss of lift/drag and longitudinal instability.

Experiments indicate that the best arrangement is a main lifting foil slightly aft of the CG stabilized by a foreward canard foil. Such an arrangement reduces the hump R/W by about one third, from 0·18 to 0·12. A cantilever 'vee' hydrofoil is shown in Fig. 10.6(a). The hydrofoils would be used to lift the aircraft up to medium speeds then, after cavitation, they would be retracted to leave the aircraft planing on the hull surfaces. The use of spray-dams would allow a shallower hull to be designed.

10.3.2 Hydroskis

It was said earlier that the hydroski was the predecessor of the planing-bottom. Because the ski has a much smaller area it is not as efficient as the planing-bottom and does not generate such high lift/drag; values of R/W are around 75 to 80 per cent higher at the hump than those of a conventional bottom. The ski works at much higher trim-angles than a hydrofoil and it does not cavitate, so that it can be used to support the weight of the aeroplane without transferring a load to the hull surfaces.

The greatest advantage of the hydroski is that it can be retracted easily, in fact it may be formed from part of the hull contour, as shown for the flipper-ski in Fig. 10.6(b). In this way a radical redesign of hull form is possible: the step can be dispensed with and the hull made much shallower.

The high thrust/weight of the jet aircraft makes the hydroski an attractive installation, for the higher hump-drag can be accepted without loss of take-off performance. There is a structural advantage too, for skis reduce the normal pounding accelerations imposed on the aircraft by about two-thirds, so that reduced structure weight compensates for the weight of a ski installation.

10.3.3   Blended-hulls

Undoubtedly the most attractive seaplane development of later years lay in the unorthodox approach of attempting to make an aerodynamically refined shape seaworthy. The blended-hull, an American project, consisted of taking an experimental jet bomber, the Convair XB–46 which first flew in 1947, and modifying it for operation from water. The modification involved the addition of a large wing-hull

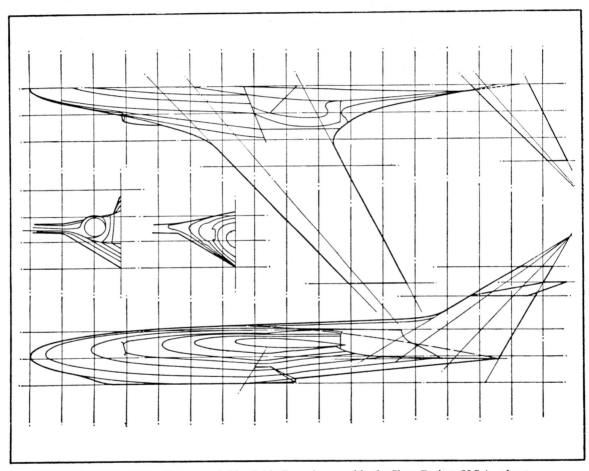

Fig. 10.7.   Lines of a transonic blended-hull seaplane used in the Skate Project, U.S.A., about 1950

fillet, which faired into the bow and stern, giving the hull an aerofoil section when viewed from the side. The increased volume of the hull, brought about by the fillets, eliminated the need for nacelles allowing the engines to be buried in the thick wing roots. Buoyancy was provided by fillet volume, while spray-control was achieved by the use of spray dams. The lateral stability of the new hull form was such that lateral floats were no longer necessary.

From the modifications to the XB–46 a blended-hull form was drawn that satisfied the requirements for transonic flight and elementary flotation. Fig. 10.7 shows a typical set of the blended lines and offsets which formed a starting-point for the particular hydrodynamic research programme. The lines are taken from a paper by Stout, that is mentioned in the bibliography. They have been reproduced here because they show not only the form of an aircraft with a blended-hull, but also the technique of lofting, which is the way of draughting contours of a body by taking the lines of intersection with the body of a number of mutually perpendicular sections.

The lines of such an aircraft, suitably scaled up, allow for a large payload-volume/surface-area. When we couple this with the virtual absence of take-off and landing restrictions on water, it would appear that the blended-hull seaplane represents the most natural form of aircraft for lifting really heavy weights in the foreseeable future. Of course, any major redevelopment of the seaplane will involve the building of large, highly specialized bases with docks and hard slipways. The problems involved are, however, probably much smaller than the problems that will have to be faced with the development of airfields for equally heavyweight landplane operations.

PART 5

STRUCTURAL SHAPE

CHAPTER 11

The Structure

Throughout the book there has been built up the picture of an aeroplane as an essentially aerodynamic shape, an envelope of specially shaped airframe surfaces. Within the envelope lie the masses of payload, fuel, engines and equipment. Outside the envelope lies the supporting air. The reaction of the air to the presence of the aeroplane can be resolved into component pressures which, when related to specific areas of airframe surface, serve to express the various forces making up the total lift and drag. The airframe is, therefore, a means of distributing a loading upon the surrounding air. But in making the air do work the airframe must also protect what it contains. Clearly, to do work on the air while serving a protective function the airframe must be strong and stiff, but economically so, in that the weight of structural materials must be no more than is absolutely necessary otherwise the payload and fuel load will be reduced and the economy jeopardized. Much of the art of aircraft design lies in the creation of economical airframe structures. It follows that the structural engineer cannot produce a good structure if he has not been given an accurate distribution of air-loading by the aerodynamicist and, as we have seen, there is a great deal of difficulty involved in predicting accurately the state of the air at every point on an airframe surface all of the time. Much of the early work of the structural engineer is concerned with picking out the most critical design cases—which often run into thousands—arising from the various combinations of speed, attitude and weight throughout the flight.

While seeking economy of structural shape the structural engineer must also include a capacity for potential development. Many aircraft have been known to increase in all-up weight by fifty per cent or more during a useful life. A future supersonic transport with a payload of only 4 or 5 per cent could have the payload or range critically reduced by a structure only slightly heavier than it might have been. A unit increase in percentage structure weight can increase the all-up weight by as much as 10 per cent, because of the additional power, fuel load and fuel system requirements needed to carry the additional weight a set distance at a given speed. An increase of 10 per cent in all-up weight can increase the take-off distance by more than 20 per cent, and decrease the ceiling and sea-level rate of climb by 10 per cent. Most airframe structures lie between 20 and 40 per cent of the all-up weight, as shown in Fig. 11.1.

While aiming for structural economy it is also necessary to ensure that skins are reasonably smooth and free from large scale wrinkles in 1g flight—a marked difference from smoothness on the ground with wings unloaded. Smoothness at higher normal

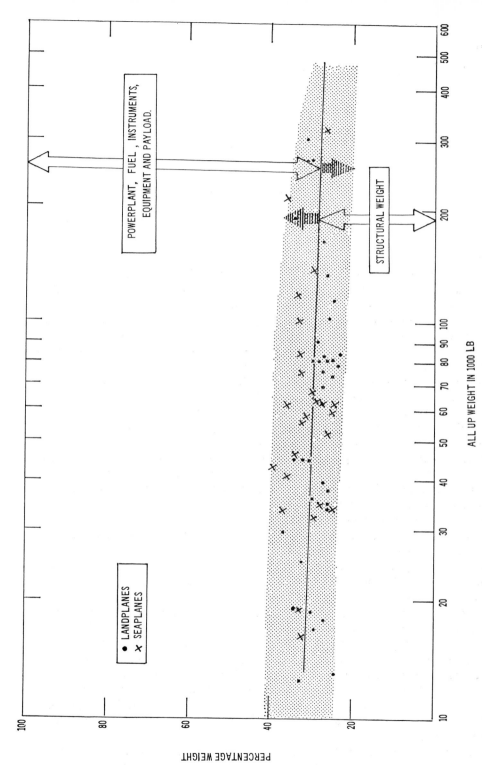

Fig. 11.1 Typical structural weights

191

accelerations is unimportant because of the transience of such conditions. Smoothness requirements with limitations on steps and waviness measured in thousandths of an inch are almost impossibly hard to achieve on a large scale, although modern methods of manufacture are now reducing the magnitude of the original problem. Visualize, for example, the technical effort required to maintain a surface contour of one or two thousandths of an inch over a structural length of 100 ft and more. And yet the structural engineer must aim for such accuracies because the dividends to be gained in speed and range are so great. Boundary layer control allows some of the limitations to be relaxed, but smoothness of a high order is still essential.

Structural design affects the achievable flight envelope, stability and control, the operational role and the development potential of an aeroplane. To understand how such effects come about we must know something of the principles involved.

11.1   Strength of Materials

A wide range of materials is used in the construction of an aeroplane: aluminium alloys, steel, copper wiring, rubber, magnesium, titanium, tungsten and phosphor-bronze, plastics, fabrics, glass, wood, lead. All of the materials have unique mechanical and chemical properties that must be known and used to the best advantage: some materials react electrolytically, for example, certain aluminium alloys and steels and they should not be used in combination. Under some conditions, such as contact with sea-water, the use of certain materials must be considered from the point of view of corrosion. Non-magnetic materials only should be used in the vicinty of magnetic compasses.

The mechanical properties of greatest importance are a high strength/weight, particularly at high temperatures, and high specific stiffness. The strength/weight is sometimes expressed as the specific strength, the ratio of the ultimate strength in tension, or compression, or shear (depending upon what is required), to the density of the material. The specific stiffness is the ratio of Young's Modulus of Elasticity to the density. The modulus of elasticity is the ratio of the stress to strain within a specified working range of a material. To understand the nature of strength and stiffness we must look at stress and strain and their connection with the elasticity of a material.

11.1.1.   Stress, Strain and Elasticity

Stress

A material is said to be stressed when it is loaded in a particular way. It is useless to say that the material is merely 'loaded', because the effect of the load depends upon the way in which it is applied and upon the area over which it is applied. A knife cuts because the load is applied over a very fine area by the cutting edge: skates melt ice to form a lubricating film of water beneath their sharp edges. In both examples the knife and the skate create high intensities of compressive stress over local areas of the surfaces with which they are in contact.

The equal and opposite action and reaction which takes place between two parts of the same body, transmitting forces, constitutes a stress. The intensity of stress at a surface (usually referred to less exactly as merely stress) is estimated by the force transmitted per unit area, in the case of uniform distribution. When a stress distribution is not uniform the stress intensity at a point on the surface is defined as the local force divided by the element of area, when each is decreased indefinitely.

The three basic stress forms are shown in Fig. 11.2. The first, tensile stress, is caused by pure tension distributed across the cross-sectional element at X–X. The tensile force could be in pounds or tons and the intensity of stress expressed in lb/in^2 or ton/in.^{2} The area of the cross-section is a in^2, and the tensile stress:

$$p_t = \frac{P}{a} \qquad\qquad (11\text{–}1)$$

The second, compressive or bearing stress, is the reverse of the tensile stress (a), so that if the compressive load is equal and opposite to the tensile load applied over the same area of cross-section, then:

$$p_c = -p_t \qquad\qquad (11\text{–}2)$$

(for many materials the bearing stress is about 1·5 times the tensile stress required to rupture a material).

The third, shear stress, acts tangentially to the surface of contact as, for example, in the given case of a rivet holding two plates together. The rivet is assumed to have the same area of cross-section as the two specimens of bar, so that the average shear stress is, therefore:

$$q = \frac{P}{a} \qquad\qquad (11\text{–}3)$$

(The shear stress is usually around 2/3 of the tensile stress required to rupture a material.)

Strain

When a material is stressed a change of shape takes place. The change of shape is multi-dimensional: for example, a bar compressed as in Fig. 11.2(*b*) is shortened, but the cross-section expands laterally in all directions if the material is unconstrained. For the purpose of discussion it is enough to consider only the major strain that takes place with stress, and three examples that correspond with Fig. 11.2 are shown in Fig. 11.3. Both tensile and bearing strain are measured as the stretch, or compression, per unit length of the material so that:

$$e_t = \frac{\Delta L}{L} \qquad\qquad (11\text{–}4)$$

and: $\qquad\qquad\qquad\qquad\qquad e_c = -e_t \qquad\qquad (11\text{–}5)$

in the examples given, where ΔL is the change in the original length L.

Shear strain, which is sometimes referred to as 'distortional-strain' is measured as the angular displacement produced by shear stress. If a piece of material is subjected to a pure stress in a certain plane, the change of inclination (in radians) between the plane and a line originally perpendicular to it, is the numerical measure of the resulting shear strain. The example shown in Fig. 11.3(*c*) would be seen if a longitudinal

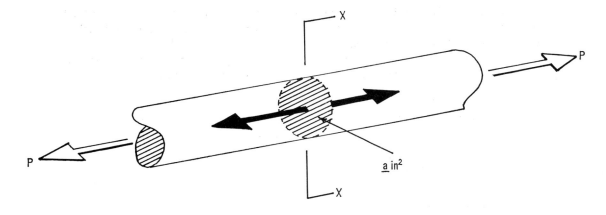

a. Tensile stress

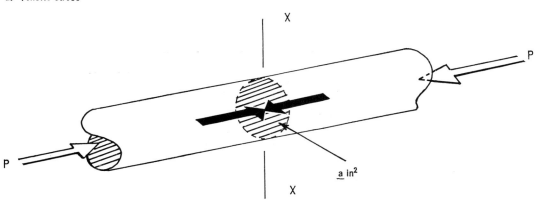

b. Compressive (bearing) stress

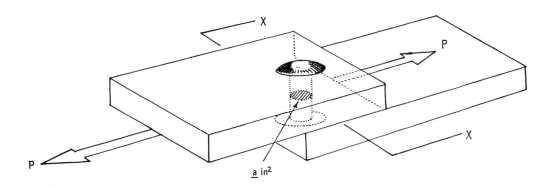

c. Shear stress

Fig. 11.2   The three basic stresses

section through Fig. 11.2(*c*) could be examined under a microscope. The vertical distance between the shear force action and reaction is the result of inevitable tolerances in the mating of the two plates.

When talking of stress and strain we are not talking of an irreversible action and reaction: stress causes strain, but strain also causes stress. A compressed component

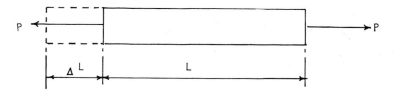

a. Tensile strain

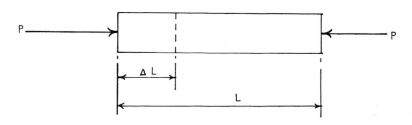

b. Compressive strain

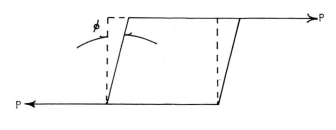

c. Shear strain

Fig. 11.3   The three basic strains

exerts a lateral stress upon other components that constrain it. This is caused thermally as well as mechanically. A modern aircraft flying at high speed is immersed in a boundary layer of heated air which raises the temperature of the aircraft skin, Fig. 11.4. Inside the aircraft the colder air and fuel maintains a lower temperature in the adjacent structure, so that expansion of the skin relative to the inner structure causes strain, and *vice versa*.

Aerodynamic heating is not the only source of heat effects. Military aeroplanes may have to operate in the vicinity of detonating atomic weapons, which generate high thermal radiations. A bomb the size of that dropped on Hiroshima generates about seven times the quantity of heat reaching the stratosphere in one minute from the sun, at all points about one mile from the explosion. The amount of radiant heat absorbed by a structure depends upon the type of material, its reflectivity and the

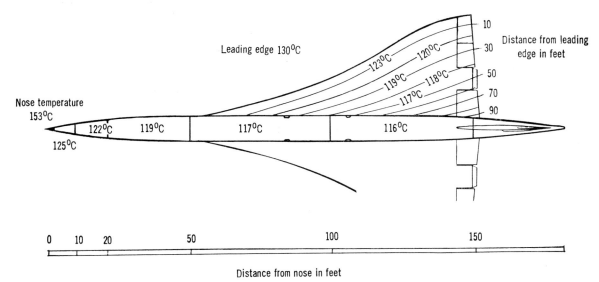

Fig. 11.4 Equilibrium skin temperatures on the upper surfaces of the BAC–Sud Concorde calculated for M = 2·2 cruise at 60,000 ft, ISA

incidence of the rays. Most nuclear strike aircraft have polished, or white surface finishes (on the under-surfaces at least) to counter the effects of such radiation. Many scheduled tests are carried out in the early stages of development of an aircraft when it is necessary to study the combination of aerodynamic forces, inertia, pressurization loading and acoustic effects in a hot environment.

Elasticity

A material is said to be wholly elastic if the strain caused by a stress disappears when the stress is removed. On the other hand plasticity has occurred if the strain does not disappear: the material is said to have a permanent 'set'. Under certain conditions a metal can be made to 'flow' in much the same way as a liquid by stressing it mechanically. The plasticity of a metal is utilized in the manufacture of aluminium pots and pans, when spinning a metal sheet at high speed causes centrifugal stresses to be set up. Other examples are forging and the drawing of wire.

To explain elasticity and plasticity Fig. 11.5 shows a typical stress-strain relationship for a metal specimen. From the origin O to the elastic limit the material will return to its original shape when the stress is removed, and this represents the working range for all practical purposes. Beyond the elastic limit, which marks the limit of proportionality, the material is left with a permanent set. Beyond the hump of the curve the material begins to flow in a plastic state, even though the stress is reduced, until failure occurs at some stress value less than the maximum. A structure is designed so that the working range of any component does not exceed its elastic limit.

It is now possible to study stress-patterns established in structural components by various applied loads. A good example is shown in Fig. 11.6, which shows photo-electric stress-patterns in three test specimens loaded in tension. Models of components are made from transparent plastic materials and, under load, the refractive

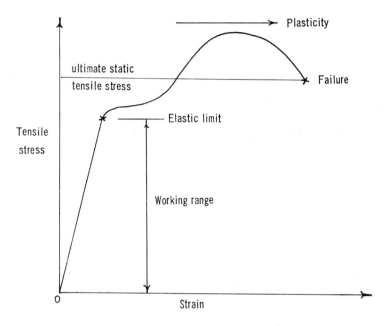

Young's Modulus of Elasticity, E, equals
stress/strain in the working range.

Fig. 11.5   Typical tensile stress-strain relationship for a metal static test specimen
Young's Modulus of Elasticity, E, equals stress/strain in the working range

index is altered by the resulting strain caused by a local stress. The lines are lines of equal stress and, hence, equal refraction.

A useful general law, known as Hooke's Law, states that within the elastic limits of a material the strain produced is proportional to the stress producing it. The law applies to all kinds of stress.

11.1.2   Bending and Torsion

The shape of an aeroplane is such that tension, compression and shear are rarely found in isolation. For economy the various members of a structure must be made to take as much simultaneous stress as possible. An important aid in structural analysis is the Principle of Superposition: that the total strain caused by a load-system may be considered as the sum of the individual strains caused by the various load components, taken in isolation.

The system of stresses applied to the structure of an aeroplane comes mainly from bending and torsion (*i.e.*, twisting). The difference between them is that pure bending alone takes place when a load applied at some point on the flexural axis of a member is reacted at another point along the flexural axis (*i.e.*, the locus of points at which an applied load produces bending only). Torsion accompanies the bending when either the applied load or its reaction is offset from the flexural axis. The conception of a flexural axis is useful and reasonably accurate when thinking of unswept wings, but it becomes inaccurate—though still useful—when applied to swept wings. Looking back to Fig. 8.19 we see that pure bending takes place along the flexural axis of the swept wing, but from the point of view of the aerodynamicist torsion is taking place at right angles to the wing root and section *A–B*.

Imagine a beam fixed at one end and supporting a weight at the other. Between the upper and lower surfaces it is possible to define an imaginary neutral axis which, when the end of the beam is bent downwards relative to the root, forms the boundary between the upper fibres that are stretched in tension and those below that are shortened by compression. In a similar way a neutral axis can be drawn in the skin of a pressurized cabin for, as the pressure causes the skin to bulge outwards, on matter how slightly, the outer surface is placed in tension and the inner in compression. Returning to the beam: if the applied load is *W*, then the load exerts a bending moment at any section *X–X* distance *x* from the point of application. The moment is given by:

$$M_x = Wx \qquad (11–6)$$

If the beam is such that the load *W* is acting at a distance *L* from the root, then there must be an equal and opposite fixing moment at the root:

$$-M = -(WL) \qquad (11–6a)$$

The bending and fixing moments are not the total values in the example, they only represent the incremental increases due to the addition of some load *W*. The weight of the beam must also be taken into account, as well as any other distributed or point loadings, and it is in this way that the principle of superposition comes to our aid.

If, in the example given, the load *W* was offset some distance *y* from the flexural axis, then the load would also apply a torque along the length of the beam equivalent to:

$$T = Wy$$

It follows that to fix the beam under these conditions the root must exert an equal and opposite torque $-T$.

These ideas can be applied to the airframe, where they can be visualized in the case of a swept aerofoil surface, Fig. 11.7. The lift of the surface, for example a wing, is equal to half the weight of the aeroplane, which acts at the aerodynamic centre for the purposes of calculation (but which really acts at a point downwind of the aerodynamic centre, called the centre of pressure—the difference is irrelevant here). The torque of $+W/2$ about the *O–Y* axis is reacted at the root by the torque $-T_w$. The bending is reacted at the root by a fixing moment $-M_w$. To complete the picture a shear reaction $-W/2$ must be added at the wing root.

The picture in Fig. 11.7 is essentially simplified and in practice there are complications which affect the reduction of reacting forces and moments. For example, the figure lacks the drag resultant which introduces a further reacting moment and shear force, preventing the wing from sliding and folding rearwards. And the pitching

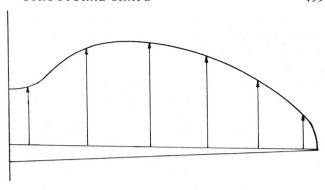

a. Lift distribution giving rise to W/2.

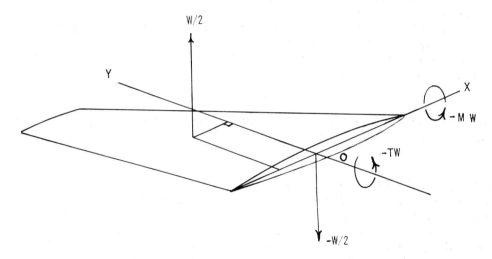

b. Half lift resultant reacted by fixing moment and torque at root.

Fig. 11.7   Bending moment and torque reactions at a wing root due to lift alone

moment about the aerodynamic centre must be added, which increases the required torque reaction at the root to prevent the wing being twisted off the fuselage in a nose-down sense. Further pitching moments, bending moments, torques and shears are introduced by wing-mounted stores (external fuel-tanks and bombs), engines, flaps and undercarriage units.

11.2   Stress-Strain Reversal and Fatigue

In flight the aerodynamic loading on the airframe is constantly changing and the inertia loading with it. Variations are caused atmospherically and by the pilot through his flying controls, while further variations are caused by pressurization and de-pressurization of the cabins, acoustically by jet effluxes and when taxying on the ground. Fatigue failure, *i.e.*, cracking of members under repeated stresses much lower than the ultimate static tensile stress is exhibited by most metals and their alloys, by some plastics, woods, and other materials that possess some ductility.

It is only recently that a study of the mechanism of fatigue has become possible, with such instruments as the electron microscope. The fatigue characteristics of a material are related to its atomic structure: the atomic lattice. It is impossible to make homogenous materials with perfect lattices and dislocations appear—in effect

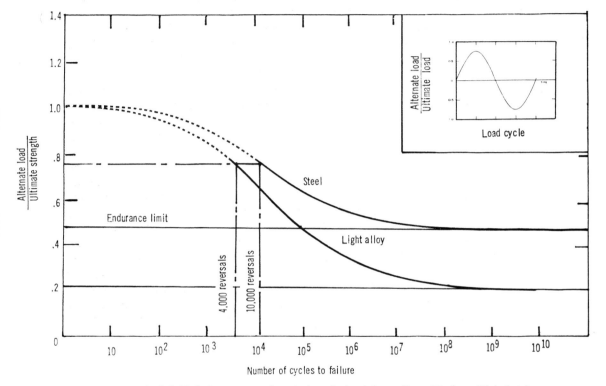

Fig. 11.9 Typical S–N fatigue curves for steel and aluminium alloy. Modern 'high-duty' aluminium alloys do not exhibit such a marked resistance to fatigue failure as the older, softer, aluminium alloys although they have much higher ultimate strengths

irregularities in the pattern of the atoms—that allow certain lines of atoms to move unevenly under the influence of shear stresses. The lines of atoms move in planes, one plane slipping over another. A dislocation causes some planes to slip individually. Eventually a minute portion of material is extruded, squeezed out, along a slip-plane. It is thought that the extrusion leaves behind it the embryo crack. When the crack appears the cross-sectional area of the remaining material is reduced and the stress intensity rises. A fatigue crack is shown in Fig. 11.8(*a*) with crack growth due to fatigue appearing as light marks, and that due to tension as dark. Typical fatigue curves for steel and aluminium alloy are shown in Fig. 11.9. Apparently modern 'high-duty' alloys do not exhibit such a marked resistance to fatigue failure as the older, softer, aluminium alloys—although they have much higher ultimate strengths.

11.3 Structural Principles

A structure is a system of individual members arranged in frames. The simplest kinds of structures are readily recognizable as frames, but more advanced structures lose any obvious indication of framework as members are made to do more than one job. For example, a fuselage must be composed of a structure supporting a load-bearing floor and an external skin, fairing and protecting the internal load. Early aeroplanes had an internal load-bearing structure separate from the skin (in effect a fabric envelope stretched to shape over a light fairing structure). Later machines featured load-bearing skins, in which the envelope served the dual purpose of supporting the internal payload as well as resisting air-loads. The latter kind of structure, known as monocoque, was no less a structure than the first. One may draw analogies between the human anatomy, with a soft external skin fairing and protecting a load-bearing skeleton, and the anatomy of a lobster or a crab, with a hard load-bearing skin on the outside. Both are different, yet both display structural arrangements that obey the same principles.

Almost classical examples of both kinds of structure were the Hawker Hurricane and Supermarine Spitfire which formed the bulk of the R.A.F. fighter force in the Battle of Britain. The Hurricane, with its tough internal tubular structure and soft skin of fabric and metal was easily repairable at station level, and its serviceability was remarkably high, at 63 per cent. The Spitfire, on the other hand, had a load-bearing skin which suffered badly and repairs had to be made at maintenance units and factories. Although the Spitfire was superior in performance it had a lower serviceability of 37 per cent. No doubt the better serviceability rate of the Hurricane, together with its superior numbers, enabled it to shoot down three aircraft to every two of the Spitfire—even though the Spitfire was the better gun-platform. But no philosophy of structural design should be based upon an observation on the state-of-the-art at that time.

11.3.1 Simple Frames

A simple frame is a structure consisting of a number of bar-like members fastened together, ideally, by hinged joints. The hinged joints ensure that loads carried by the members are pure tension and compression, unadulterated by bending and torsional effects. A perfect frame has just enough members to keep it stable in equilibrium under any system of forces acting at its joints. If it has too few members it is called deficient, if too many, redundant. Paradoxically, aero-structures feature a great number of redundancies in the never ending search for economy: this introduces difficulties in the way of calculating stresses.

In Fig. 11.10 are shown a number of simple frames with pin-joints. A space-frame, shown in (c) is a development of the two-dimensional plane-frame into three dimensions. Resolution of forces is the same in both examples, by the use of force-diagrams, the treatment of which can be found in any good book on statics.

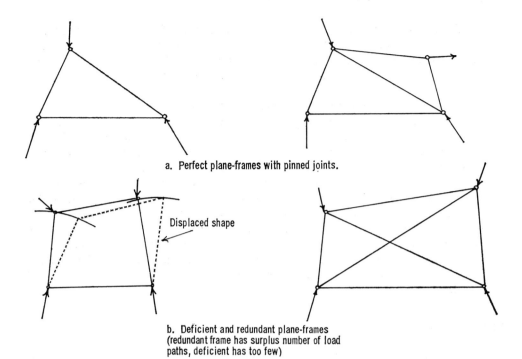

a. Perfect plane-frames with pinned joints.

Displaced shape

b. Deficient and redundant plane-frames (redundant frame has surplus number of load paths, deficient has too few)

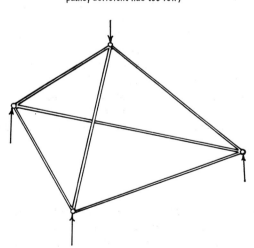

c. Space frame made from four triangular plane frames, with surplus members removed.

Fig. 11.10   Simple pin-jointed frames

11.3.2 Complex Frames with Fixing Moments

Imagine a simple frame to have its joints welded instead. If the frame was initially deficient, as shown in Fig. 11.10(*b*), then it would be improved by welding and would become, for many purposes, a good approximation to a perfect frame. Furthermore it could possibly be lighter than the pinned version, because of the omission of the diagonal member.

In the pinned case the forces in the members can be resolved as pure end-loads, with no bending. In the welded frame, compared with the pinned in Fig. 11.11, bending is transmitted to the members by means of the frame distorting while the angles at the corners remain unchanged. Instead of pure end loads each member is subjected to a system of forces such as that shown in Fig. 11.11(*d*).

This kind of arrangement of forces and moments happens constantly in aircraft work as structural members, which have torsional and bending strength, must be arranged to take torsion and bending, and thus pay a little more fully for the carriage of their bulk. Such arrangements of members to satisfy a vast number of different stressing cases give rise to the apparent paradox of redundancy in aircraft structures. Some examples of complex frames with fixing moments are shown in Fig. 11.12. To analyse them rather elegant strain-energy methods must be employed in place of the simpler force-diagram.

Strain Energy

If a force applied to a body causes the point of application to be displaced, then work is done in causing the displacement. The magnitude of the work is given by the product of the force and the distance through which it moves. In a similar way, when a force or a stress is applied to a body, strain occurs and the force is said to do work. In each of the frames shown so far each force causes a component strain in each member. Equations can be stated for each structure which, when resolved, describe the distribution of strain-energy (work causing strain) between the members caused by the individual forces. Solution of the equations depends upon the principle that a load 'chooses' the path of least work, for structures too obey the law of conservation of energy.

11.4 Structural Design

Historically the main parts of an aircraft structure are the fuselage, wings and tail Most bodies are built in the same way as a fuselage, most aerofoil surfaces in the same way as wings. The sketch in Fig. 11.13 suggests the salient features of an aircraft structure.

Taking the fuselage first, the skin is usually formed of metal sheets riveted, or spot-welded, to metal frames, formers and bulkheads. Generally speaking a frame has the outline of a cross-section of a body and is built up from a number of smaller members. A former has the same outline, but is much lighter and is usually pressed from sheet metal. The centre is cut away, so that a former is really a stiffening outline for maintaining the form of the skin. In section it may be of 'Z' (⌐L) or 'top-hat' (_⌐L_) section: the latter being in effect two 'Z' sections facing each other and joined together

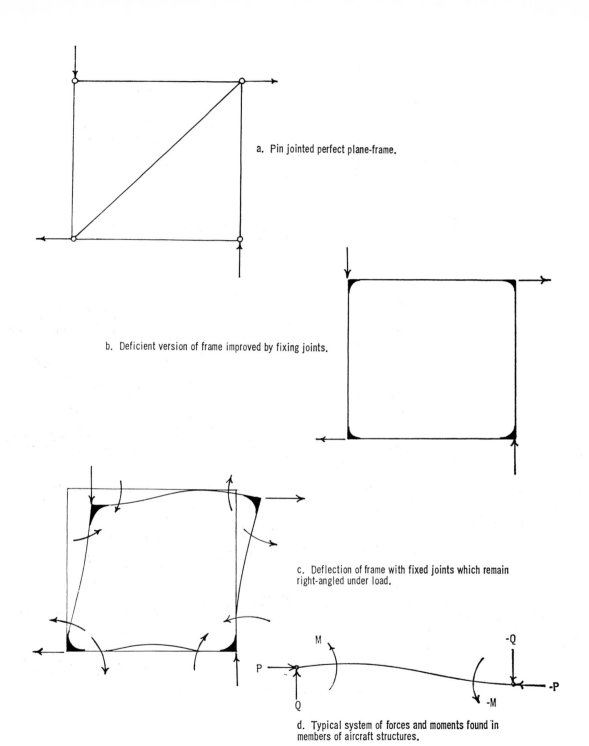

a. Pin jointed perfect plane-frame.

b. Deficient version of frame improved by fixing joints.

c. Deflection of frame with fixed joints which remain right-angled under load.

d. Typical system of forces and moments found in members of aircraft structures.

Fig. 11.11   Plane frame with fixing moments at joints

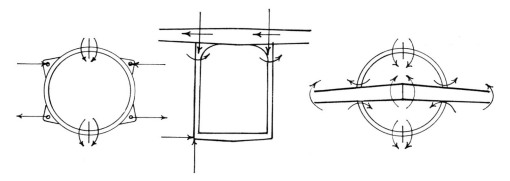

Fig. 11.12 Three examples of redundant frames with applied loads and moments from wing and undercarriage

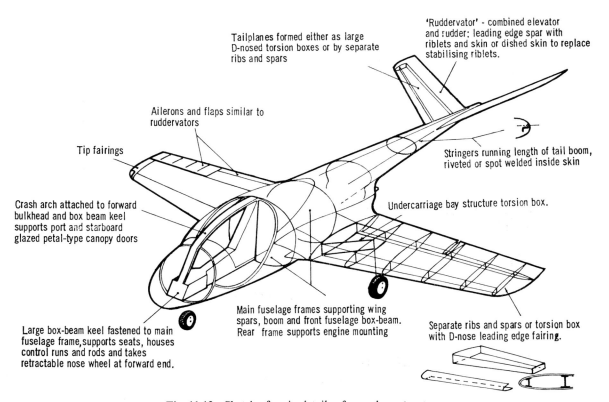

Tailplanes formed either as large D-nosed torsion boxes or by separate ribs and spars

'Ruddervator' - combined elevator and rudder: leading edge spar with riblets and skin or dished skin to replace stabilising riblets.

Ailerons and flaps similar to ruddervators

Tip fairings

Stringers running length of tail boom, riveted or spot welded inside skin

Crash arch attached to forward bulkhead and box beam keel supports port and starboard glazed petal-type canopy doors

Undercarriage bay structure torsion box.

Large box-beam keel fastened to main fuselage frame, supports seats, houses control runs and rods and takes retractable nose wheel at forward end.

Main fuselage frames supporting wing spars, boom and front fuselage box-beam. Rear frame supports engine mounting

Separate ribs and spars or torsion box with D-nose leading edge fairing.

Fig. 11.13 Sketch of main details of aeroplane structure

along the upper edge. A bulkhead is a complete section cutting like a diaphragm across a body. As such it may be built up like a frame, or pressed from sheet. A bulkhead may be pierced by holes and doorways, but these are usually covered by plates and doors that form part of the load-bearing bulkhead structure.

Running lengthwise along the fuselage, supported by the bulkheads, frames and formers and, in turn, supporting the skin are the stringers. Stringers are light members that may be of 'Z' or 'top-hat' section. Related to the stringers in that they run fore and aft, but serving a major structural purpose in that they are designed to take end-loads, are the longerons. If the fuselage is viewed in elevation it is seen to be a long beam, supported by the wings somewhere between 40 and 50 per cent of the length from the nose. There are local loads applied to the beam from tail and nosewheel, and perhaps from engine-mountings, with local distributions of loading from payload and equipment. Tension and compression in the structure above and below the neutral axis of the fuselage must be met by end-loads in the longerons aided by the skin. In a similar way side-loads on the fuselage are met by longerons and skin. If the skin is thick enough there may be no longerons as such, the end loads being met by an arrangement of stringers, slightly heavier in section than usual.

Across large cutouts a structure may contain internal bracing members made up of struts and ties. Depending upon the load directions in Fig. 11.10 the individual members may be either struts or ties: struts being members end-loaded in compression, ties being loaded in tension. Struts and ties are rarely intended to take torsion and bending.

Aerofoil surfaces consist of spanwise beams, called spars, and chordwise formers called ribs. The shape of the skin may also be maintained by spanwise stringers that serve a major purpose in effecting a reduction in spar sections and weights, by distributing end-loads into the skin. Ribs may be built up like frames, be light as formers, or be made like bulkheads. The latter are found in wing structures used to contain fuel, without recourse to internal, separate, fuel tanks. Spars, ribs and skin form the tank surfaces.

The remaining shape of an aeroplane is largely non-structural, in that it consists of fairings, cowlings and fillets. These items are made of shaped skin, stabilized by stringers and formers.

11.4.1   Thin-Walled Tubes, Cutouts and Panels

The modern aeroplane can be looked upon more conveniently as a system of thin-walled tubes designed to take torsion and bending. In a way we must change our present point of view to look from the outside in, by way of the thin-walled tube, instead of from the inside outwards (as we have just done) from structure to skin. A thin-walled tube is an interesting phenomenon because it amounts to a piece of thin sheet, wrapped around into a tubular shape that may be cylindrical, conical or ogival. It is called thin-walled because of the relatively small ratio of wall thickness to tube diameter.

The modern metal aeroplane may be approximated to a family of thin-walled tubes for the purposes of some stress analyses. The fuselage is, in effect, two tapering tubes joined at their bases to a cylinder. The wings and tail surfaces are approximately flattened tubes, tapering from roots to tips. Ribs, spars, frames, longerons and stringers are methods of internal stiffening. In many respects the tubes are also torsion boxes, which are developments of the pure thin-walled tube, in that the strength of such members is vested in the ability of the skin to resist shear forces. The skin takes a moderate range of end loading, but its great virtue lies in the way it is made to work in shear.

In Fig. 11.14 an aeroplane is shown as a family of thin-walled tubes. The weights of the fuselage ahead of and behind the wings are reacted at the centre-section shown, for simplicity, as a single frame—part of which is an arc CD. Clearly, the fuselage is in bending and shear, as shown in (b), where the split arrows show that the side AB of one panel, $ABCD$, is being displaced downwards relative to CD. Similarly, the side EF of the rear fuselage panel is being displaced downwards relative to side CD. If the fuselage is in torsion due, for example, to fin sideload or to a sideload from the nose-wheel undercarriage, then torsion is transmitted as shear around each section. Depending upon the direction of normal bending loads (such as those shown), the shear caused by a system of bending loads is increased on one side of the fuselage, and decreased on the other by the additional torsion.

Now, panels $ABCD$ and $CDEF$ are in equilibrium in that they cannot change their positions relative to the aircraft datum. To be in equilibrium the torque of the shear along AB and CD (which tends to rotate the first panel in an anti-clockwise direction) must be opposed by an equal and opposite torque due to opposing shear along sides AD and BC as shown. The same argument applied to panel $CDEF$ enables us to postulate the existence of counter-shear along sides DE and CF. Here then is the interesting property of the thin-walled tube/torsion-box: loads normal to the length are reacted by complementary shear stresses along the length.

Each panel, $ABCD$, $CDEF$, is formed by a boundary-frame consisting of portions of fuselage frames or formers and longitudinal stringers, and skin. Ignoring the skin for a moment we see that each panel boundary is tending to distort in a similar way to the deficient frames in Fig. 11.10(b) and Fig. 11.11(c). The skin reacts against the distortion by providing tensile strength parallel with diagonals BD and DF. The tension-fields are accompanied by compression parallel with diagonals AC and CE. The existence of tension-fields and wrinkling, as shown in Fig. 11.14(b) and (c), can often be seen in flight. Looking along the upper surface of the wing of an airliner which, for economy, has a light thin skin one can often see diagonal wrinkling during turns. The wrinkles are caused by compression in the upper skin, aerodynamic pitching moments and by torques from the engine-mountings.

The fuselage shown in Fig. 11.14 is in bending as a beam, so that the structure above the neutral axis (lying along the fuselage length) is in tension, while that below is in compression. The total loading applied to the structure is, therefore, a combination of tension, compression and shear. Stressing cases are examined to see what combinations of manoeuvres and atmospheric accelerations result in the highest resultant sums of tension, compression and shear. Of course, wings and tail surfaces behave, and are treated, in a similar way to the fuselage. The only difference is that some of the applied loads have different origins, but all come together to be met by the structure as a complete whole.

Cutouts

Cutouts: *i.e.*, windows, doors, servicing panels, hatches, bomb-bays etc. cause a recurring headache for the structural engineer. As soon as one makes a hole in a

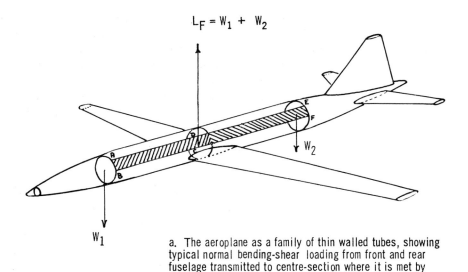

$$L_F = W_1 + W_2$$

W_2

W_1

a. The aeroplane as a family of thin walled tubes, showing typical normal bending-shear loading from front and rear fuselage transmitted to centre-section where it is met by lift component L_F

Complementary shear

Complementary shear

A

D

E

Applied shear

Tension field

Tension field

Applied shear

B

C

F

Complementary shear

Complementary shear

b. Applied shear on side panels ABCD and CDEF, showing complementary shears and panel reactions as tension fields to applied and complementary shears.

A

C

c.   Compression across tension fields appearing as skin wrinkling (example shows appearance of diagonal AC)

Fig. 11.14   The aeroplane as a family of thin-walled tubes. In addition to shear in the fuselage sidewalls, the top skin is in tension and the bottom in compression

load-bearing skin a stronger surrounding structure must be introduced to provide adequate paths for the detour of the stresses. Perhaps the most noticeable feature of cutouts is the rounding of the corners: sharp corners cause excessively high stress concentrations. Fig. 11.15 shows the cylindrical form of an ideal pressure-cabin. It may be shown that a cutout of elliptical form with the proportions $2:\sqrt{2}$ is neutral in its effect upon the overall tensile stress concentration, in that the maximum principal tensile stress in the vicinity of the hole is no greater than the hoop stress. The principal tensile stress factor for each cutout, K, is given by:

$$K = \frac{\text{Maximum Principal Tensile Stress}}{\text{Hoop Stress, } 2p_t} \qquad (11\text{–}7)$$

Many airliner windows are variants of the 'neutral-hole'. The variants lie between the pure neutral-hole form and the rectangular, 'corners' being introduced to improve the view. The stresses caused by pressurization must be added to those already mentioned. Pressurization is increased with height and hence the pressure differential varies from zero to some required value each time an aeroplane flies. As such it must be taken into account in the calculation of fatigue and airframe life. As airframes grow older the pressure differentials, and consequently operating heights, are usually reduced as a means of reducing the tensile stress levels.

11.4.2 Beams, Booms and Grids

We have seen how the skin and internal structure of an aeroplane is made to work in shear and tension, the final view is of the behaviour of the structure as a family of beams, *i.e.*, in compression as well as tension and shear. If the aerofoil surfaces can be approximated to thin-walled tubes, flattened about one axis, then such flattening works against the general value of the tube as a member able to resist bending.

Wing spars are a development of the simple beam designed to take bending and shear loads. The type of beam we are most concerned with in aircraft work is the cantilever variety, which is supported at one end only. However, other types of beams, usually having encastre or 'built-in' fixing at both ends are met with in component design. Examples are bomb-bay structures and floor-beams running across a number of frames.

The weight of material making up a spar depends upon the length and cross-sectional area. For greatest efficiency spars must have the greatest area of cross-section furthest away from the neutral-axis: the moment of inertia of the cross-section about the neutral axis must be a maximum. In Fig. 11.16(*a*) a spar is loaded with a shear-load, W, which is reacted at a distance x further away along the spar. The moment of the shear-force is Wx and this is reacted by end-loads in the top and bottom booms. If the moment is 100,000 lb in and the depth of the spar, z, is 20 in then the tension in the top boom is around 100,000/20, *i.e.*, 5,000 lb, and the compression in the bottom boom also 5,000 lb. If the same bending moment must be met by a spar of half the depth, then the end-loads in tension and compression are 10,000 lb respectively. In fact we have erred on the dangerous side by using the spar depth overall, the depth we should have used is the distance between the centroids of the booms—a smaller distance. Even then the calculation is approximate, serving to make the point that the deeper a spar the smaller are the end loads in the booms and, therefore, the lighter is the required structure. The minimum amount of material

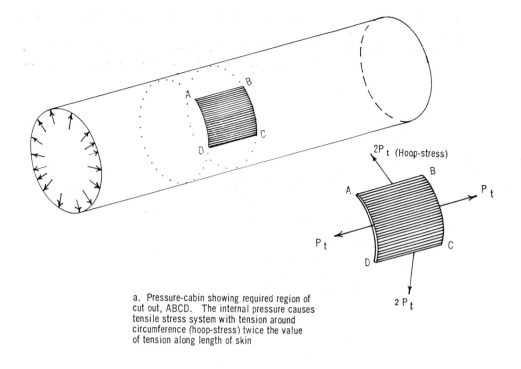

a. Pressure-cabin showing required region of cut out, ABCD. The internal pressure causes tensile stress system with tension around circumference (hoop-stress) twice the value of tension along length of skin

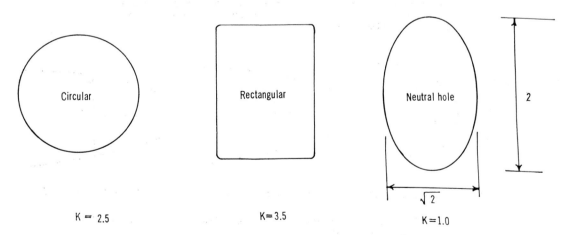

Circular

K = 2.5

Rectangular

K = 3.5

Neutral hole

2

√2

K = 1.0

b. Cutouts of various shapes, the "neutral hole" with proportions $2:\sqrt{2}$ causes no stress higher than the hoop - stress, $2P_t$.

$$K = \frac{\text{Maximum principal tensile stress}}{2P_t}$$

Fig. 11.15   Shapes of cutouts in skin

needed in a cross-section depends also, of course, upon the required levels of shear and bearing strength needed.

From the foregoing we deduce that the thicker a wing in absolute measure the lighter it will be. A delta wing is lighter than a straight or swept wing with sections

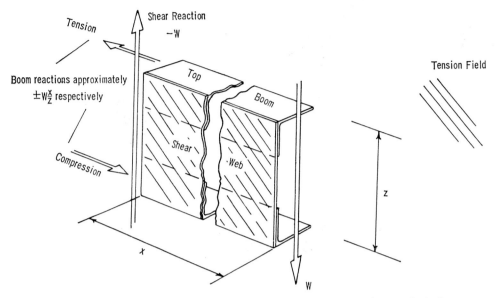

a. Spar formed by two L-booms and shear web carrying shear W. Taking moments about any corner, the shear and its reaction is met by tension in top boom and compression in bottom boom. For a given spar length, x, and shear force W, the boom end-loads depend only upon the spar depth, z.

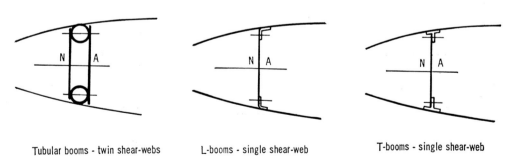

Tubular booms - twin shear-webs L-booms - single shear-web T-booms - single shear-web

b. Types of spars, showing how members with heaviest cross sections are placed furthest away from neutral-axis of spar.

Fig. 11.16 Wing spars

having the same thickness distribution or, weight for weight, a delta wing can be designed with a finer section. This means that there is a 'trade-off' as it is called between structural and aerodynamic design. One may have a thin very low drag delta wing with more surface area than straight or swept versions, and relatively simple high-lift devices, or one may have smaller straight or swept wings with more compli- cated high-lift devices. The choice is not as simple as it might seem, however, for it

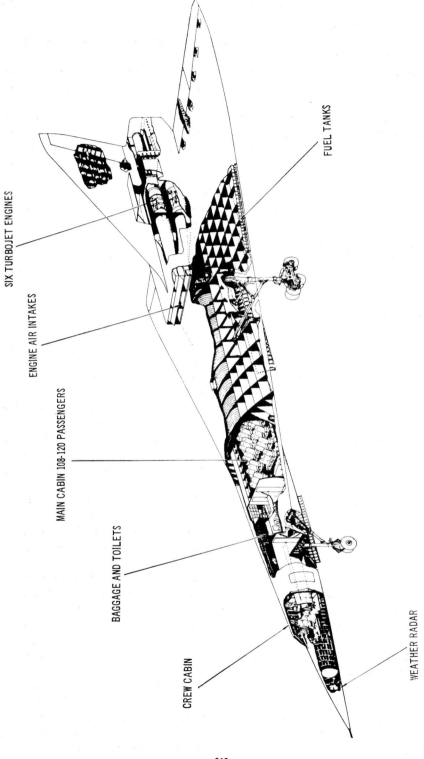

SIX TURBOJET ENGINES

ENGINE AIR INTAKES

MAIN CABIN 108-120 PASSENGERS

BAGGAGE AND TOILETS

CREW CABIN

FUEL TANKS

WEATHER RADAR

Fig. 11.17 Advanced structure of a M=2·2 supersonic transport, College of Aeronautics, Cranfield, 1960

depends upon stability, control and a number of other factors. The uncertainty accounts for the large number of straight, swept and delta planforms one sees around the world on aircraft designed for similar (usually interceptor) roles.

The relatively simple structure shown in Fig. 11.13 cannot be used in more advanced layouts. The arrangement of spars and, supporting ribs which serve to maintain profiles and to transmit diffuse aerodynamic loads into concentrations of members give way to more complex arrangements of many spars and many ribs, all of which behave rather like a flexible network of intersecting beams. An arrangement of this kind is shown in Fig. 11.17, for a $M = 2 \cdot 2$ SST designed in 1960 by the College of Aeronautics. The spars and ribs form a structural grid, which is again reproduced in the fin. The box-like cells formed within the wing structure contain fuel.

The analysis of stress and strain in advanced aircraft structures has forced the development of very elegant and complicated mathematical techniques. The structural engineer must relate the effects of weights, aerodynamic inputs, elastic responses and stress distributions throughout the structure as one whole, for a wide variety of different shapes. Fortunately, the grid-like construction allows accurate analyses to be made and translated into mathematical statements that can be handled by computers.

11.5 Fabrication

Early aeroplanes were made of spruce, fabric and piano-wire, and this form of construction is still to be found in some light aeroplanes. Later the welded steel tube framework, fabric covered, became the standard for light aircraft engineering, with plywood sandwiched balsa wood as a good material for light monocoque structures.

Airframes made from strip and sheet metal are riveted, welded, or stuck together with special glues. Sheet metal is provided in a number of standard thicknesses, called gauges, and one uses the next thickness of gauge above the required thickness of material as determined by stress analysis. In the pursuit of efficiency and low weight in large aircraft one must turn to more expensive methods of manufacture. Using gauged sheet, that is manufactured in stock sizes within certain tolerances, it would be possible for an aircraft with a wing area of 2,000 ft^2 to show an increase in weight of 3,000 lb if the skin was on the high side of the tolerance. American aircraft built in the U.K., using British standard gauge materials, tend to be heavier than their American counterparts, because the Americans have a more finely graded range of gauges from which to choose.

Modern manufacturing techniques involve machine milling of skins and stabilizing members as complete units from solid billets of material. Machining is expensive, but for large, costly, aircraft the expense is worth the dividends. Chemicals are used to etch and dissolve away unwanted metal, and the use of chemicals and machining in this way enables structures to be made with fewer joints. Weaknesses usually originate in the joints and their elimination enables the behaviour and life of the structure to be predicted with far greater accuracy.

New techniques are being introduced in the manufacture of light aeroplanes, and other low subsonic aircraft that have become so long established as to be rated 'traditional' designs. Skins can be made of fibreglass, or plastic sheet sandwiching foam plastic or honeycomb filling. Honeycomb structures—in effect corrugated walls forming hexagonal cells, in which the walls run more or less at right angles to the confining skin—can be made in both plastic and metallic materials, welded or bonded together. Thin metal skins have been successfully stabilized by bonding foam plastic sheeting on the inside. A test example, for a light aircraft, featured 0·25 in. poly-vinylchloride (PVC) foam sheet bonded to 30 swG (0·0124 in.) sheet aluminium. The aluminium, which is normally structurally useless in the pure state, became as stiff as 18 swG material (0·048 in.), with a weight equivalent to 22 swG, (0·028 in.).

We have seen how structures are built up and the part that they play. It is useful to see how the weight of the structure is affected by the shape of the aeroplane, and the effect this can have upon the final design.

CHAPTER 12

The Final Aeroplane

Low wing loading is the most important parameter of all affecting the operation of an aeroplane. In the early days wing loadings were low to enable aeroplanes to operate from small fields. With the coming of the flap designers tended to forget that the slower one landed the safer the landing. The tendency was to look towards the combination of high wing loading and high performance. In the twenty years from 1930 wing-loadings increased from 12 lb/ft² to 60 lb/ft², while modern wing loadings approach 120 lb/ft². Unfortunately high wing loadings are essential if aeroplanes are to remain competitive. As we have seen, variable geometry is helping to reduce the trend, while the by-pass engine provides high thrust/weight on take-off (thus keeping take-off time as short as possible) and good cruising economy. The large percentage weight of fuel burnt by the jet aeroplane helps to ensure a comparatively low wing-loading for landing.

The structure weight has the largest potential effect upon the eventual wing-loading, while the weight of the structure depends in turn upon the shape of the aerodynamic surfaces and the materials used in construction. Let us look at the effect of aerodynamic shape upon weight.

12.1   Physical Factors Affecting Weight

The structure consists of wing, fuselage, engine nacelles, tail-unit and landing-gear, and the weight of these items is influenced by many factors. The calculation of structure weight, all-up weight and the resulting centre of gravity involves many estimates and approximations, and we shall only look at the subject in the broadest of terms.

12.1.1   Wing Weight

The general principles applying to the weight of wings applies to aerofoil surfaces of all kinds, so that in saying, for example, that a swept wing is heavier than a straight wing, we are also saying that a swept tail is heavier than a straight tail. Two factors are important in their effect upon wing weight: the structural aspect ratio and the thickness ratio of the aerofoil sections used. The aerodynamic aspect ratio, A, is shown in Eq. (5–11) to be a function of span², the span being measured from tip to tip along a line normal to the axis of symmetry of the aircraft. Bending takes place

215

along the flexural axis of a wing, however, which is usually inclined at some other angle to the axis of symmetry. Very roughly the structural aspect ratio A_S is given by:

$$A_S = \frac{A}{\cos^2 \wedge} \qquad (12\text{--}1)$$

where $\wedge$ is the angle of sweep of the $\frac{1}{4}$ chord-line.

The greater the aspect ratio of a wing the greater the bending-moment of the lift at the root. As the actual thickness of a high aspect ratio wing (*i.e.*, not the thickness-ratio of the section) is usually less than that of a wing of lower aspect ratio with the

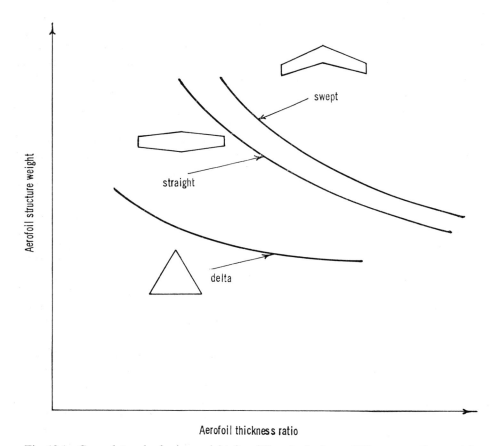

Fig. 12.1   General trend of wing weight for different planforms lifting same all-up weight

same area, then the heavier is the structure—because of the smaller depth of spar and higher end-loads in the booms. A swept wing requires additional structural strength to resist torsion caused by sweep, and this results in a heavier structure.

Wing structure weight is relieved by inertia-loads distributed across the span. Wing tip mounted fuel tanks and integral tanks distributed far outboard, engines and stores of various kinds all provide bending-relief and enable lighter structures to be designed. The swept and delta aircraft shown in Fig. 8.11 have low structure weights because their sections are very deep to provide accommodation.

Planform affects the weight in the way of stiffness that must be built into the structure to resist control-reversal and flutter. Flutter is a cyclic, high-frequency oscillation of the aerofoil surfaces caused by a struggle between the aerodynamic forces and the stiffness of the surfaces. Flutter is dynamic, arising from a wing, tail-plane or fin being relatively free in bending, so that an aerodynamic load caused by a gust or control movement causes distortion. As the structure deflects the reacting moment increases, until action and reaction balance. When the gust or control movement ceases the structure springs back, overshooting its original position. The inertia and 'trail characteristics' of the control surfaces can modify the overall aero-dynamic state, so that the initial disturbance is increased or the tendency to overshoot the original condition is increased. This can lead to a cyclic 'fluttering' of the structure which, if it does not subside, can be catastrophic, or may severely reduce airframe life. High aspect ratio surfaces are more flutter-prone than those with low aspect ratio. Podded engine-installations are usually combined with high aspect ratio swept wings to provide anti-flutter mass-balancing and, hence, a lighter wing structure. A podded engine slung forward of the flexural axis of the wing causes a nose-down torque, reducing the angle of attack and lift, thus countering the initial disturbance that increased the lift and caused displacement in bending.

The effect of aspect ratio on the weight of the wing is very marked. A wing with a high aspect ratio carries the lift further out from the root and the bending-moments, boom sections and weights are larger than those of a wing of smaller aspect ratio. One must be careful not to generalize too readily, however, because once the aspect ratio is calculated for a given aircraft a decrease in the value (signifying a smaller span) results in an increase in structure weight. We may deduce that there is an optimum aspect ratio wing, and this is shown in Fig. 12.2. The increase in structure weight at smaller aspect ratios is caused by the additional wing area needed to compensate for the decreased efficiency of the wing as a lifting member. The increased weight at higher aspect ratios is caused by the need to meet increased bending-moments.

Modern aeroplanes have aspect ratios of 11 or 12:1, although 14:1 is generally thought to be the economical limit. Sailplanes are exceptional and may have ratios of 30:1 or more. High aspect ratio wings invariably have thick skins and heavy spar booms, or many stringers.

At subsonic speeds the low aspect ratio wing is inefficient aerodynamically, but may be of great use structurally. An example is the use of low aspect-ratio on a low altitude strike aeroplane designed to operate in dense air at high EAS. The shallow slope of the lift curve of such a wing prevents the structure suffering large changes of stress from atmospheric turbulence. Because the lift increments are smaller for a given gust, bending, torsion and normal accelerations are reduced. The whole structure can therefore be made lighter than would have been the case with a wing of longer span and greater aerodynamic efficiency.

Taper is used to reduce wing structure weight, the inboard shift of the lift reducing the bending moment, but it can be a nuisance and may lead to complications. The Supermarine Spitfire and Hawker Tempest of the Second World War might have had straight taper but featured elliptical planforms instead, that were harder to produce. It was commonly thought that the elliptical wing was used to reduce lift-dependent drag to make the fighters faster. In fact the elliptical planform gave greater spar depth and gun stowage volume outboard of the undercarriage units, while allowing sections of reduced thickness ratio to be used that had lower zero-lift drag.

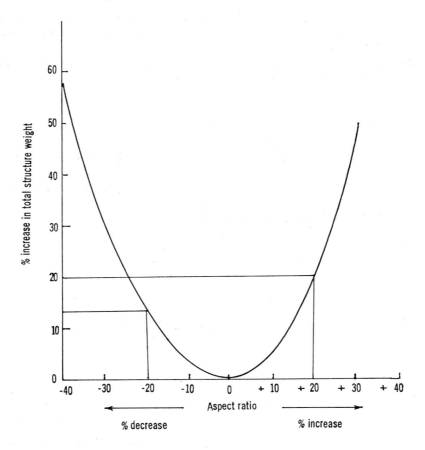

Change of aspect ratio from aerodynamic 'ideal' for a given aircraft

Fig. 12.2   Effect of a change of aspect ratio from the calculated 'ideal' for a given aircraft
upon the total structure weight. Section thickness/chord ratio constant

12.1.2   Fuselage Weight

Every fuselage has a limiting minimum cross-section and forms two cantilever
beams, one forward and the other aft of the centre-section structure. The deeper the
fuselage section for a given cantilever length, the lighter the structure. As the minimum
volume of the fuselage is determined by what it must carry, structure weight can be
saved in large aircraft by building 'double-bubble' fuselages which effectively increase
the depth without destroying a reasonable fineness-ratio. Although fuselages for
supersonic aeroplanes are nearly twice as long as their subsonic counterparts, the
structure weights do not increase in the same ratio. The lower aspect ratio of the
supersonic machine results in a much longer centre-section structure which provides
support, shortening the cantilever lengths of the overhanging nose and tail.

Fig. 12.3 shows in a general way the effect of wing planform upon the length of
cantilever for three geometrically similar fuselages. The swept wing of high aspect-
ratio has the heaviest fuselage structure weight, because of the dominance of the rear
fuselage in the effect upon the whole. It must be remembered too that the rear fuselage

must be strong enough to support the stabilizers. The landing case is the most critical for a large aircraft, the weight of the fuselage depending upon strength needed to meet the pitching inertia loads.

Fuselage weight increases with cabin pressure-differential, because of the tendency of the skin to split like a sausage. If the fuselage diameter is increased with a given

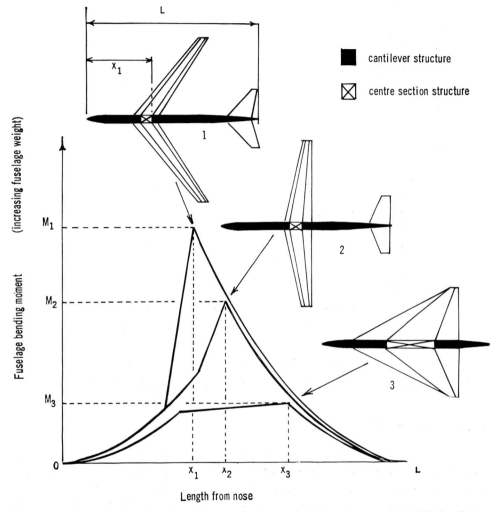

Fig. 12.3 Generalized effect of planform on fuselage weight for a given payload. The landing case determines the critical bending moment governing rear fuselage weight, which in turn dominates the fuselage weight equation. Fuselage 1 is the heaviest and fuselage 3 the lightest

pressure differential then the fuselage structure must grow heavier—the reverse of what was said for a simple beam (the weight of which decreases with increasing depth)—because the hoop stresses, set up in the skin by the pressure acting over a greater projected area, increase with fuselage diameter.

The shape of fuselage cross-section affects the structure weight, in that the amount of structural material is a function of the surface area. A rectangular section has a longer circumference than a circular or elliptical section having the same overall dimensions. One might expect a fuselage with a square cross-section to be some thirty per cent heavier than one having the same overall dimensions and a circular section.

Most aeroplanes have nosewheel undercarriages and the cantilever forward fuselage must be strong enough to take loads from the nosewheel unit. The greater the all-up weight the stronger must be the forward fuselage.

12.1.3 Powerplant and Fuel Weight (Turbojet Engines)

For a given thrust and EAS the higher an aeroplane is to fly the heavier will be the required engine. The reason for this is that high altitude engines must have bigger cross-sections—greater swallowing capacity—than engines designed for efficient operation in the denser air low down. Area is a function of the square of the linear dimension, while weight is a function of its cube. Therefore for a given standard of design merit, the specific weight of the engine:

$$\bar{p} = \frac{\text{engine weight}}{\text{net thrust}} \qquad (12\text{--}2)$$

increases with altitude. The specific weight must be related to a representative height and speed, i.e., to the design point. The aerodynamic efficiency of the aeroplane changes with design point, and Eq. (12–2) can be usefully developed in the form:

$$\bar{p} \text{ varies as } \frac{\text{engine percentage weight}}{\text{net thrust/weight}}$$

$$= \left(\frac{L}{D}\right) \text{ (engine percentage weight)} \qquad (12\text{--}2a)$$

Specific weight increases roughly as the 3/2 power of the thrust, which is a function of the pressure within the engine: the higher the pressure the greater the weight of material to provide the required strength. On the other hand specific weight falls with increasing design EAS, because of the increasing overall efficiency of the jet engine as a prime mover. But once the speed is high enough for kinetic heating to be a problem the specific weight begins to increase, because more material must be added to the engine structure to offset the effect of 'creep': lengthening of, for example, the compressor blades with elevated temperature caused by diffusion of the air in the intake ducting.

The practical determination of specific weight is not as easy as it might at first appear, because the definition is not embracing enough to be universal. It is hard to agree what exactly constitutes 'engine weight'. In the case of a turbojet the weight of intake and tailpipe, and all of the associated variable geometry mechanisms, may equal the weight of the bare engine. If a unit is suspended in a pod more or less outside the main structure of the aeroplane, then one might reasonably count the weight of wiring, controls, mountings and cowlings under the heading engine weight. When this is done it is usually better to refer to powerplant weight instead.

On the side of bare engine weight alone a modern turbojet with a reasonable working-life expectancy has a specific weight around 1/5. A special short-life, or lightweight engine may have a specific weight around 1/7, while a lifting engine must achieve 1/10 to 1/15 lb weight per lb thrust. The values given refer to net thrust at sea level. At the tropopause the values would be about three times higher, because the thrust is less.

Because of the 'square-cube law' that causes big engines to become heavy one must resort to some complexity in order to reduce specific weight. Assuming engine thrust to be proportional to intake area, all else remaining equal, the total engine weight can be shown to vary theoretically as $1/\sqrt{n}$, where n is the number of engines used to generate the required thrust. Thus, two smaller engines weigh something like 75 per cent of the weight of a single engine giving the same thrust. Three engines are around 60 per cent, and four engines around 50 per cent of the single engine weight. But as the number of engines is increased, however, the weight of control and fuel systems increases too, and the overall specific weight does not show the same theoretical trend as the bare weight. The square-cube law is also affected by the unavoidable fact that small engines suffer from (relatively) large nuts, bolts and other standard items. And their smaller scale results in lower component efficiencies.

One cannot aim to increase the number of engines in a design without due regard to economics. A large number of small engines cost more to manufacture and maintain than a smaller number of larger engines. Taking one typical manufacturer's quotation: one engine of 15,000 lb static thrust would cost £76,500, but two engines of 7,500 lb thrust apiece together cost £109,000. Increasing the number of engines increases the probability of sympathetic failure, as well as the number of actual failures for the same engine mean time between failures, and this will be reflected in the maintenance costs. The principal advantage of a multi-engined installation is the overall increase of safety factor and a possible reduction in the installed thrust if the engine-failed climb-out is a design requirement.

Fuel consumption is proportional to thrust and specific fuel consumption, Eq. (4–9). Therefore, the weight of fuel carried for a given job and standard of design merit will vary as the engine weight. For simple analyses powerplant-plus-fuel weight is often considered as one whole. The more efficient an airframe structure the more the fuel that can be carried and the further an aeroplane will fly.

12.1.4   Equipment Weight

The weight of equipment carried by an aeroplane to make it efficient in its operational role depends both upon the role and duration of a sortie. In the case of a passenger transport, there must be provision for seating, furnishings, galley, toilet, air-conditioning and sound-proofing, all of which affect the total weight. The volume per passenger more or less establishes the size of the fuselage. It happens that the surface area of a fuselage is linearly related to the two-thirds root of its volume, and the volume occupied by passengers is roughly three-quarters of the fuselage volume. For a given standard of comfort (the greater the comfort the greater the weight of furnishings and equipment) the equipment and fuselage weights are related almost linearly, the fuselage weight per passenger varying with the number of passengers.

The net result of the connection between equipment weight and fuselage weight for a passenger aircraft is that the equipment weight is almost a constant percentage of the all-up weight. Navigational and other equipment is heavy, so that one cannot generalize too much: the standard of navigational equipment of course varies with the size of aircraft and the route facilities available. The more advanced the aeroplane the more flight-equipment that must be carried to enable it to operate efficiently.

12.2   Design Requirements Affecting Weight

We saw in Chapter 4 that the flight envelope of an aircraft is rationalized for the purposes of safe and efficient design, by the introduction of a basic manoeuvring envelope and a basic gust envelope, shown as *V–n* diagrams in Fig. 4.4. An aircraft is designed in such a way that it should not fail structurally anywhere within the flight envelope, when handled properly. To cater for a certain amount of mishandling and rough treatment the manoeuvring and gust load factors are increased (*i.e.*, factored again) and the structure is designed to meet the increased values.

12.2.1   Load Factors

From an investigation of the flight regime covered by a given design case an estimate is made of the largest load that is likely to occur under operational conditions. This is called the limit-load, or unfactored load and corresponds with the *V–n* diagrams of Fig. 4.4. By multiplying the limit load by the ultimate factor of safety, varying from 1·5 to 2·0, the ultimate load is obtained. The ultimate load is the load that the structure must withstand without collapsing, and the structure weight is a function, therefore, of both the limit loads and the ultimate factors of safety involved.

It is very difficult to design a structure that will have exactly the required ulltimate factor of safety at every point, and one usually finds that the safety factor is exceeded by a safe margin. It is useful to know how much reserve strength lies in a structure, especially when designs will probably have to be stretched to meet future requirements. The reserve factor is the ratio of the actual strength to the specified strength. In British practice it is never less than 1·0, whereas the Americans quote the ratio minus unity, and in their system the result must never be less than 0.

The ultimate load is achieved beyond the yield point of a material, and a structure shows signs of permanent deformation long before actual failure occurs. To ensure safe design structures must be proof-loaded to a certain limit without showing signs of detrimental distortion. The proof load is obtained by multiplying the limit load by a factor sometimes as little as 1·0, sometimes as much as 1·33. If, for example, an ultimate load is 1·5 × limit load and the proof load is 0·75 × ultimate load, then the proof load will be 1·125 × limit load.

12.2.2   Design for Reliability and Maintainability

One cannot think of design and weight without also taking some account of fatigue-life and the requirements of reliability and maintainability. The life of any part of the aeroplane depends upon many things: cyclic variations of loading heat, cold, moisture, wear and corrosion. The life of the aeroplane depends upon the individual life of the parts. The designed life of a part has a direct effect upon its strength and therefore weight, and *vice versa*. It goes almost without saying that the life of the whole aeroplane must be matched to its role. An example is the design of the transatlantic transport aeroplane. On such a competitive route, with fashion playing an important part in passenger-appeal, it would be unwise to build an aeroplane to last for as many years as, say, a utility transport for the Australian outback.

Life and Failure Hazard

A number of similar components all have different lengths of life under the same operating conditions, and 'life' becomes instead the more meaningful and convenient *mean time between failure*, or MTBF, expressed in hours. In this way the failure hazard can be expressed as the probability of a single failure in a particular period of time. If a piece of equipment has a probability of failure of 1 in 10,000, then the probability of failure is expressed as:

$$Q = \frac{1}{10,000} \quad \text{or} \quad 0.0001$$

and the probability of reliability:

$$R = (1 - Q) \quad \text{or} \quad 0.9999 \qquad (12\text{--}3)$$

The overall reliability of a system is a product of the individual reliabilities of the components:

$$R = R_1 \times R_2 \times R_3 \times \ldots R_n \qquad (12\text{--}4)$$

A system with 100 components each with a reliability of 99 per cent has an overall reliability of something like 37 per cent. If the reliability of each is only 98 per cent, then the overall value drops to about 14 per cent. This is shown in Fig. 12.4(*a*).

The total cost of an aeroplane depends upon the first cost—a function of the structure weight and upon the maintenance costs. The first cost rises with MTBF while the maintenance costs decrease inversely with MTBF. The cost of optimum reliability—of optimum 'life'—is therefore the minimum total cost shown in Fig. 12.4(*b*). It is worth remembering at this point that an aeroplane represents a set of compromises determined by economic necessity.

Maintainability

An aeroplane is maintainable if defects can be simply and quickly serviced, *i.e.*, parts can be adjusted, repaired and replaced after failure. There is a connection between MTBF and the degree of accessibility that must be provided for a component. Accessibility and long MTBFs both affect the ultimate weight of an aircraft: accessibility the number of cutouts and compensatory weight in a structure, design MTBF the weight of all lifed components.

Fail-Safe, Inspect-Safe and Safe Life

The breakdown of weight is affected by design for fail-safety or inspect-safety. A fail-safe structure is one in which the limit load can still be met even though one of its elements has failed. Such a structure tends to be heavier than an inspect-safe structure, because in the first alternative load-paths are provided, while in the second accessibility enables inspectors to detect potential failures before they become catastrophic.

It is becoming standard practice to estimate the safe life of a structure from fatigue

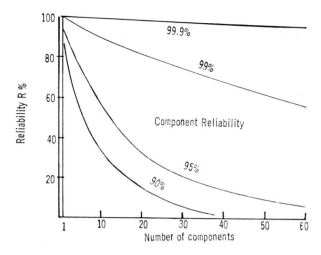

a. Overall reliability as a function of the number of components and the individual reliability of each.

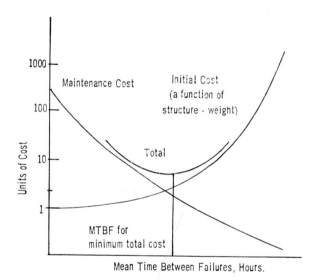

b. Typical variations of initial, maintenance and total costs with M mean time between failure.

Fig. 12.4   Reliability and life of equipment

tests, carried out on specimens of the more highly stressed tensile members of the structure, such as spar booms. Such tests are designed to produce a tensile load in the member equal to that in steady flight, and on top of this is imposed a small fluctuating load corresponding with an upgust immediately followed by a downgust. By means of the *S–N* curve, similar to that shown in Fig. 11.9, and assuming that damage is cumulative, it is possible to relate the tests to particular critical flight conditions. In this way, by factoring the laboratory life of a specimen, one may calculate a statistical safe life in flying hours. The accuracy of the method depends upon the accuracy of estimation of the conversion factor, which depends in turn upon the way the tests are carried out and, less predictably, a knowledge of the expected flight conditions. Much work is being done throughout the world in the measurement of gusts at different altitudes on different routes, so that unnecessary weight might be pared away from the structures of advanced aircraft. The method is applied in retrospect for the assessment of expected life of aircraft already in service.

12.3 Weight Breakdown

The proportional weight of each component to the all-up weight is not constant, but varies with role and design point within a flight regime. Tables 12.1 and 12.2 show, very approximately, the variation in percentage weight of the more important items, with respect to both role and flight regime. The first three aircraft: the sailplane, the light/executive and the transport are all subsonic. The last three: the SST, the fighter and the bomber are all supersonic. The figures are very general, the first four being digested from published figures, the last two being estimated for the purpose of the tables. Table 12.3 has been added to give substance to Tables 12.1 and 12.2.

Neglecting the sailplane it should be noted that the light/executive and subsonic transport aeroplanes, being mainly piston-propeller driven, have much heavier percentage weights for the powerplants than do the supersonic jet aeroplanes. If the subsonic transport had been turboprop driven, then the powerplant weight would have been around 12 per cent, and 9 to 10 per cent for a jet aeroplane. The saving in percentage weight would have appeared as an increase in the fuel and systems weights, because of the increased specific fuel consumptions.

Although the military aircraft estimates cannot be confirmed they show interesting trends. The supersonic fighter must carry a mass of heavy electronic equipment, and requires power services to fulfil its role with a relatively small payload—perhaps 2 or 4 guided weapons. The fuel percentage weight cannot be accurately assessed because most fighter aircraft are fitted with overload tanks that grossly alter the original all-up weight. The structure weight of a fighter is high because much larger normal accelerations must be catered for. Large fins cause the structural weight of the stabilizers to be heavier than for any other aircraft. The engine weight is large because a high thrust/weight ratio is required for fast climb, and acceleration at height.

The structure weight of the light aeroplane appears to be large because of aerobatic, or semi-aerobatic design requirements. Stabilizer weights tend to be small because of the large number of single-engine aircraft taken into account, and because of propeller slipstream effects that allow smaller tail areas to be used.

Two supersonic bomber variants are shown, one with a relatively large wing for operations at high altitude, the other with a small wing for low-level strike. The structure weight of the high altitude machine is increased by the larger wing. A low-level strike aircraft would need to carry a lot of fuel to meet the increased fuel consumption, and this would tend to spoil any benefit from reduced weight of wing structure. Bomber payloads are assumed to be low because of the low weight and high yield of nuclear weapons.

The supersonic bomber and transport may be compared very broadly (as may be their subsonic counterparts). Both must fly long distances with great economy. The requirement is reflected in the low structure weight and powerplant weight—the choice of powerplant being largely determined by cruise requirements. The low weight of the stabilizers may be favoured by the slenderness of such aircraft, for the close-set engines and relatively long tail moment arms reduce the size of fin for engine failure. The subsonic transport, on the other hand, is not slender but has long wings, engines further outboard, a relatively short fuselage, and a correspondingly heavier tail.

The extreme simplicity of the weight breakdown for the sailplane belies the skill and care inherent in its design and construction. The wing is the largest and heaviest component, while the undercarriage is almost vestigial. Advanced structural techniques will probably reduce the structure weight and all-up weight still further in future. The large percentages of structure weight and payload are due to there being little else to such aircraft.

TABLE 12.1

Breakdown of All-up weight

Item	Approximate Percentage All-up weight					
	Sailpane	Light and Executive Aircraft	Subsonic Transport	Supersonic Transport	Supersonic Fighter*	Supersonic Bomber*
Powerplant	—	23	18	15	20	13
Fuel ⎱ Disposable	—	(10–15)	(22–31)	(45–50)	(25–30)	(50–55)†
⎰ load		35	40	55	35	58†
Payload	36	(20–25)	(9–18)	(5–10)	(5–10)	(3–8)
Structure	60	30	28	21	32	20
						(17 low level)
Equipment and Services	4	12	14	9	13	9
Total %	100	100	100	100	100	100

* Unconfirmed estimates.
† Add 3 per cent of AUW for low-level aircraft.

TABLE 12.2

Breakdown of Structure Weight

Structural Component	Approximate Percentage All-up weight					
	Sailplane	Light and Executive Aircraft	Subsonic Transport	Supersonic Transport	Supersonic Fighter*	Supersonic Bomber*
Wing	30	13·5	11	8	12	7
						(4 low level)
Fuselage	25	10·5	9	7	12	7
Stabilizers	3	2	3	2	4	2
Undercarriage	2 (+ballast)	4	5	4	4	4
Total %	60	30	28	21	32	20 (17 low level)

* Unconfirmed estimates: for variable sweep add 20 per cent of wing weight, *i.e.*, 2 to 3 per cent of AUW and a further 1 to 2 per cent AUW for additional services, in Table 12.1. Fuel weight may be correspondingly reduced.

TABLE 12.3

Typical Aircraft Parameters

Design Parameter	Aircraft					
	Sailplane	Light and Executive Aircraft	Subsonic Transport	Supersonic Transport	Supersonic Fighter	Supersonic Bomber
Take-off thrust loading (Wo/F) lb/lb or Take-off power loading (Wo/P) lb/hp	—	13	3·9 (jet) 7·7 (turbo-prop)	2·3	1·8 (dry) 1·3 (wet)	2·5
Take-off wing loading (Wo/S) lb/ft^2	5·2	17	93 (jet) 90 (turbo-prop)	85	70	95
Take-off span loading (Wo/b) lb/ft	14·75	82	1500 (jet) 1200 (turboprop)	3900	1000	3500
'Slenderness ratio' (l/b)	0·45	0·75	1·1 (jet) 0·9 (turbo-prop)	2·2	1·7	2·5
Aspect ratio (b^2/S)	18·75	6·9	7·2 (jet) 10·6 (tur-boprop)	1·8	2·25	2
Cruising ($L/D)_R$	30	14	18	7	6	7·

Variable geometry in the way of variable wing-sweep imposes a weight penalty that shows up in the wing structure weight and the weight of operating mechanism. Less fuel is needed, however, so that the apparent structural penalty becomes hidden by the beneficial effect reflected in the disposable load. The wing may be heavier, but the fuel carried may well allow the aeroplane to fly further, or carry more payload. If more payload is to be carried then there will be a corresponding increase in fuselage and equipment weights.

The figures given in the tables are general in the extreme, in most cases differences of 0·5 per cent have been ignored, yet 0·5 per cent could mean a difference of anything from 15 to 1,500 lb, depending upon the aeroplane concerned. In this respect they do not give a fair impression of the effort put into saving weight. A modern aeroplane starts as a mass of raw materials costing a few shillings per lb and ends up as a complicated machine costing perhaps £20 per lb of equipped airframe weight, *i.e.*, the all-up weight less disposable load and powerplant weight, Eq. (3–2). When weight breakdowns are seen in the light of economics the importance of fine differences in percentage AUW fall into better perspective

12.4   Centre of Gravity and Wing Position

Throughout the book we have talked as though the centre of gravity and wing position had already been fixed, so that it would then be possible to show how the resulting shape of the aeroplane depended upon a number of other factors. In fact one must make an enlightened guess as to the CG/wing relationship at an early stage in design, work out the sizes of surfaces, probable performance, strength and weight of the parts of the aeroplane, and then return to the CG/wing calculations, perhaps several times.

12.4.1   Calculation of CG

The CG of a body is the point about which the sum of the moments of the masses of all of the parts is zero. The point lies, therefore, on the line of action of the total weight. To calculate the CG a datum is fixed, the sum of the moments about the datum taken in the required plane, the sum is then equated to the moment of the total mass about the same datum, from which can be calculated the moment arm of the total mass from the datum. The moment arm is the distance of the CG from the datum. In practice one uses the weights of the masses under the influence of gravity. For the purpose of calculation the same acceleration can be assumed to act in any required direction, so that the CG position can be calculated in any required plane.

Fig. 12.5(a) shows an arbitrary arrangement of masses with weights W_1, W_2, etc. The moments are taken about the datum O with reference to the O–Z and O–X axes to find the CG coordinates, $\bar{x}$ and $\bar{z}$ respectively. The same principle is applied to an aeroplane in Fig. 12.5(b). In practice the vertical position of the CG can often be guessed, being about level with the passenger seats in a low winged aeroplane, and level with the shoulders when high winged. No calculations are involved in the figure, the CG of the aeroplane is assumed to lie slightly below the O–X and slightly aft of the O–Z axis, and the lengths of the arrows are unconnected with the magnitudes of the weights.

The centre of gravity can be calculated for Fig. 12.5(a) as follows:

$$W\bar{x} = (W_1\,x_1) + (W_2\,x_2) + (W_3\,x_3) + (W_4\,x_4)$$

so that,

$$\bar{x} = \left(\frac{W_1}{W}\right)x_1 + \left(\frac{W_2}{W}\right)x_2 + \left(\frac{W_3}{W}\right)x_3 + \left(\frac{W_4}{W}\right)x_4 \tag{12-5}$$

If there had been n parts to the whole, then the terms to include $(W_n/W)x_n$ would have appeared as well. The ratio (W_n/W) is a measure of the percentage weight of part n, so that in the calculation of the CG position of the aircraft one may conveniently use percentage weights of the units shown in Tables 12.1 and 12.2.

In a similar way the coordinate of the CG about the O–X axis, i.e., $\bar{z}$, can be found from:

$$\bar{z} = \left(\frac{W_1}{W}\right)z_1 + \left(\frac{W_2}{W}\right)z_2 + \left(\frac{W_3}{W}\right)z_3 + \left(\frac{W_4}{W}\right)z_4 \tag{12-6}$$

If a weight W_n is moved or is altered in some way, the effect upon the CG can be shown to be:

$$\frac{d\bar{x}}{dx_n} = \pm\left(\frac{W_n}{W}\right)$$

i.e.,

$$\Delta\,\bar{x} = \pm\left(\frac{W_n}{W}\right)\Delta\,x_n \tag{12-7}$$

and,

$$\Delta\,\bar{z} = \pm\left(\frac{W_n}{W}\right)\Delta\,z_n \tag{12-8}$$

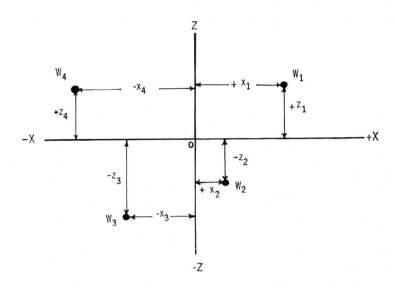

a. System of co-ordinates for calculating CG position
   with reference to two mutually perpendicular axes

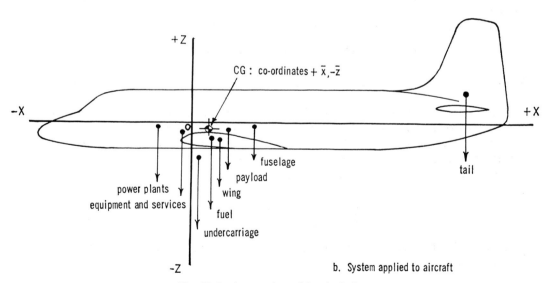

b. System applied to aircraft

Fig. 12.5   Approach to CG calculations

This is useful, because if, for example, a wing is 10 per cent of the all-up weight, and if, through redesign, the CG of the wing moves forward 1 in, then the CG of the whole aeroplane will move forward about 1/10 in.

12.4.2   CG Position

For trimmed flight the total lift ahead of the CG must equal the total lift behind, and the resultant pitching moment must be zero. For minimum trim drag the CG of the complete aeroplane must be so placed relative to the aerodynamic centre of the whole that the moment of the CG about the aerodynamic centre just balances the aerodynamic pitching moment. The combination of wing-fuselage-stabilizer alters the aerodynamic centre of the complete aeroplane from the quarter-chord point of the wing alone to a position about 2 or 3 per cent of the mean chord further forward.

The CG moves in flight and with different loading conditions. It is arranged to lie between closely controlled limits: the most forward position being around $0.15\bar{c}$ and the most aft about $0.35\bar{c}$. The limits bracket the aerodynamic centre of the wing, which lies around $0.25\bar{c}$. The forward limit is fixed by the elevator power, required to prevent the nose from sinking below a certain speed. If the CG is too far forward then the approach and take-off speed must be increased to obtain an adequate airflow over the elevators. The aft limit is set by the most critical neutral point, which depends upon configuration and the stability margins.

For the purpose of calculation early in a design, the wing and undercarriage are considered as one unit. The CG lies close to the aerodynamic centre of the wing and it is convenient, therefore, to relate the undercarriage to the wing as one complete unit in the first place. In the trimmed condition in which there is no contribution from the stabilizer, the arrangement of lift, drag, thrust and weight might be as shown in Fig. 12.6. Although thrust equals drag, the thrust line is arranged to lie below the CG as far as possible, so that in the event of power failure the aircraft will tend to pitch nose down and so maintain the airspeed.

The moment about the CG is given by:

$$M_{CG} = -M_{ac} + Lx_L + Fz_F - Dz_D \qquad (12\text{–}9)$$

which must equal O in the trimmed condition. The equation can be rearranged in terms of dimensionless coefficients and transposed for the trimmed condition to give:

$$C_{M_{ac}} = C_L\frac{x_L}{\bar{c}} - C_D\frac{z_D}{\bar{c}} + C_F\frac{z_F}{\bar{c}} \qquad (12\text{–}10)$$

The vertical ordinates z_D and z_F depend upon the vertical location of the wing on the fuselage, and the position of the engines. Sometimes engines are arranged with the thrust lines well above the wing chord when an aircraft is low winged, so that the engines appear to sit higher than the wings. High winged aeroplanes often have the engines slung below. In both cases the arrangement reduces the magnitude of $z_F/\bar{c}$ and, hence, change of trim with power. Other aircraft may feature upthrust or downthrust, in which the thrustlines are inclined upwards or downwards, thus reducing the moment of the thrust about the CG.

Because C_D is usually much smaller than C_L, Eq. (12–10) is dominated by the lift term $C_L x_L/\bar{c}$. Let us imagine that the equation depends upon this term alone, but that the fore and aft location of the wing is such that the CG lies too far aft, *i.e.*,

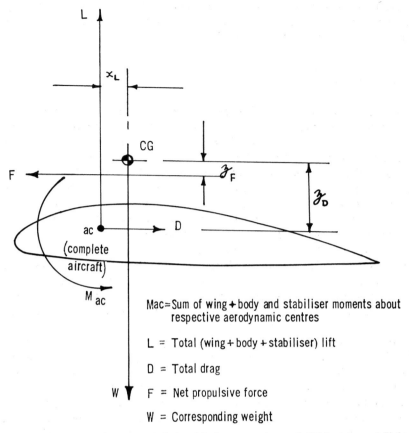

Mac = Sum of wing + body and stabiliser moments about
respective aerodynamic centres

L = Total (wing + body + stabiliser) lift

D = Total drag

F = Net propulsive force

W = Corresponding weight

Fig. 12.6   Force and moment relationship between wing and CG in trimmed flight

$x_L/\bar{c}$ is too large. Knowing the required CG position one may calculate the difference between the two by simple subtraction. Then, using Eq. (12–7), and letting $W_{(w+u)}/W$ represent the combined weight of wing plus undercarriage as a fraction of the all-up-weight, the required movement of the wing-undercarriage combination, $\Delta x_{(w+u)}$ can be calculated from:

$$\Delta x_{(w+u)} = \Delta \bar{x}\left(\frac{W}{W_{(w+u)}}\right) \qquad (12\text{–}7a)$$

where, Δx is the difference between the estimated and required CG positions.

If a design has reached an advanced stage and the location of wing root attachments cannot be altered, then the sweep of the wing can sometimes be adjusted instead, to produce the required CG/ac relationship. The measure is usually confined to low subsonic aeroplanes, because of the more involved sweep/Mach number relationship at higher speeds. Whenever a planform shows signs of unusual crank one can be certain that the CG is involved. An example of such an alteration is shown in Fig. 12.7. The projected Blackburn YA7, a naval aeroplane of the late 1940s, was re-engined and the equipment changed to make it into the later experimental YB1. Although the basic aeroplane remained largely the same (because of

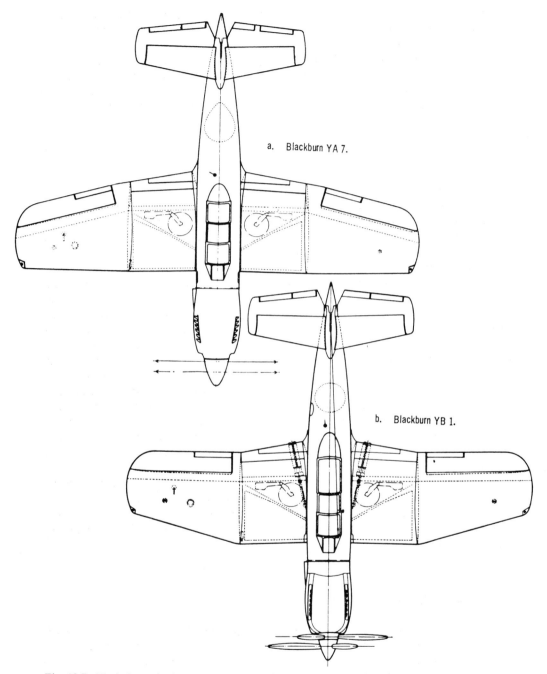

Fig. 12.7 Variation of wing sweep to achieve required centre of gravity and aerodynamic centre relationship, (*a*) Blackburn YA7, (*b*) Blackburn YB1 (that had a CG further aft than the YA7)

length and span limitations on aircraft carriers) the outer panels of the wings were swept rearwards to achieve the right couple between lift and weight. The inclination of the engine thrust line was also altered.

If the wing cannot be altered, then the engines, fuel, payload and equipment may possibly be moved to achieve the required combination. It must be realized that much of the early work in aircraft layout depends upon the inspired guess, calculations then being made for performance and balance to determine the best arrangement.

12.5   Design Method

We have now reached a point in the development of the book where from considerations of the environment to the final shape of the aeroplane, a summary should be made of aircraft characteristics and the requirements that each helps to fulfil.

In the design of an aeroplane it is impossible to calculate an exact solution at the first attempt, and by now the reason should be obvious. The design of every component is so inextricably related to the design of every other, and to the aeroplane as a whole, that no single element can be fixed with enough finality at such an early stage. All is compromise, followed by further compromises, and so on *ad infinitum*. Much of the art of aircraft design depends upon judging when to stop. The ability to make such a judgement comes only with long years of practice. The most successful designer is the one with the greatest feeling for real problems, and the wit to know when to stop the paper studies running too far into the realms of fantasy. By fantasy we do not mean only fantastic shapes and their impracticable combinations: one of the most common fantasies is that of being too accurate. Ultimately, one must be impeccably accurate in aircraft design, for in designs of the near future an error of relatively small order may lead to, for example, the untimely end of two hundred and fifty people in a 250 seat transport aeroplane. But one should only be as accurate as necessary, and no more, at each design stage. An excess of accuracy in an estimate wastes time and leads to poor design.

The design of an aeroplane is dictated by the specification. Table 12.4 shows the simplest relationships between aspects of the specification and the physical characteristics of the resulting aircraft. The items are arranged in the typical order in which they are determined. Each characteristic is shown to depend in turn upon a number of other factors.

12.6   Technology and Timescales

The time taken to design, build and fly an aeroplane of major importance increases year by year. Whereas a light aeroplane might take one or two years, a large bomber or transport can take ten or more. Aeroplanes that take a long time usually involve a number of important preliminary steps forward into regions of little knowledge.

Every advance in aeronautics is the result of long and painstaking research. More often than not the development of a particular kind of aeroplane cannot take place because the time is not yet ripe, and revolutionary ideas must be laid aside until the materials and techniques, *i.e.*, the technology, have caught up. Jet propulsion and rocketry are cases in point. The invention of the practical aeroplane itself had to

TABLE 12.4

Specification	Main Design Characteristics
Speed (compressibility drag rise)	Low drag (D): Wing sweep ($\wedge$) and thickness ratio (t/c); body fineness; area distribution High thrust (F): Choice of powerplant
Altitude and rate of climb	Low wing loading (W/S): Wing area (S) and weight (W) at altitude; Low thrust or power loading (W/F), (W/P): Choice of powerplant
Airfield take-off run Landing run	Thrust loading (W/F): Number of chosen powerplants; Lift: All-up weight (Wo) and wing area (S); wing section characteristics (C_{Lmax}); high lift devices (ΔC_{Lmax}); lifting engines and vectored thrust Lift/drag (L/D): Wing loading (W/S) high lift and drag devices ($\Delta C_L/\Delta C_D$); lifting engines, vectored and reverse thrust Landing gear: Undercarriage layout and brake system (mechanical and aerodynamic)
Range	High propulsive aerodynamic and structural efficiency: Fuel weight (W_F), cruising speed and altitude, take-off weight (Wo), wing area (S) and thrust (F) optimum lift/drag ($L/D)_R$, aspect ratio (A), weight of fuel (W_F)
Direct operating cost	Take-off weight (Wo), wing area (S), thrust (F), payload weight (W_P), range (R), cruising speed (M) or (V), weight of fuel (W_F)
Optimum aeroplane	Balance of: Direct operating cost, aspect ratio, combination of sweepback and wing thickness ratio

wait for centuries as little more than a dream until the technology was advanced enough for the light petrol engine to be made.

Basically there are three prerequisites to be met before an aeroplane can be built with much hope of success:

(a) The principles must be right.
(b) The materials must be available, and for this it may be necessary to develop new ones.
(c) It must be possible to build the aeroplane within the required tolerances.

For the first, research and development is usually necessary to prove the practicability of notions and to provide a basis of experience. It is always wise to pay heed to the ideas of other people in the field and there is no shame in judicious copying. Most successful aircraft built by all nations are copied to a certain extent, or derived from the ideas of others.

Of the new materials that have appeared since the last World War titanium is one of the best known, although it is not necessarily the most important. It has been used to replace stainless steels where heat and corrosion-resistant properties are needed. Newer materials still must constantly be invented to cope with kinetic-heating problems. At M = 4 a stagnation temperature is reached where aluminium melts (although it is already weakening around M = 2·2), at M = 6 steel melts, at M = 7 titanium melts, while at M = 10 a diamond melts. At such high temperatures special structural techniques are needed to meet the problems of softening and failure.

Manufacturing tolerances involve skills, plant and quality-control. Not only must one have machinery, one must also have properly trained personnel and thorough inspectors. Technology, which is the science of the industrial arts, must be well developed in any country aspiring to build and operate high performance aeroplanes.

12.6.1 The Time Scale—how long it takes

The time taken to design, build and fly an aeroplane is shown as a number of separate stages in Fig. 12.8 as a typical development programme. Very often it will be necessary to develop an engine simultaneously, along with the installation in the airframe, and a close liaison is maintained between the engine and the airframe manufacturer at all times. It is true to say that where such liaison is poor an aeroplane will probably be a failure.

The time taken to bring a large turbojet (around 15,000 lb thrust) into production may be anything from five to seven years, with costs around £8m to £10m. The time scale can be expected to lengthen. In the past, with few exceptions, civil engines have been developed from military engines. Many large military aircraft programmes in the developed world were cut back with the advent of the ballistic missile and the space-race, with the result that the aircraft research and development burden is being thrust more heavily onto civil affairs. Because civil programmes cannot obtain as much financial backing as military, we may expect the aircraft and engine timescales to lengthen still more, with much smaller steps. It is always dangerous to forecast though, and one can never be sure of the magnitude of benefits from 'spin-off', as the Americans call the generation of useful ideas and material that can be used beyond the limits of a particular narrow programme.

Proving Airworthiness

Before a Certificate of Airworthiness is given to an aeroplane a detailed assessment is carried out on paper. For the purpose of the assessment the constructor must prove the suitability of the aircraft by mathematical calculations, physical tests both on the ground and in the air, and by prolonged tests of endurance. The validity of the calculations depends upon the accuracy of the assumptions made in the early stages of the design, which depend in turn upon the care and intelligence with which the operational requirements were stated.

Ground testing is of great value and can be looked upon as the foundation of the work covered by the flight tests. The flight tests have as their main objectives:

(i) Demonstrating that the specification has been met.
(ii) Proving that the design-safety and airworthiness requirements have been complied with.
(iii) Providing operating data.
(iv) Establishing the reliability of the aeroplane and its equipment.
(v) Checking maintainability.

The endurance testing proves (iv) and (v), by forcing the machine to work hard over the widest range of operating conditions that it is possible to achieve.

Proving airworthiness is the final step in a development programme, all that

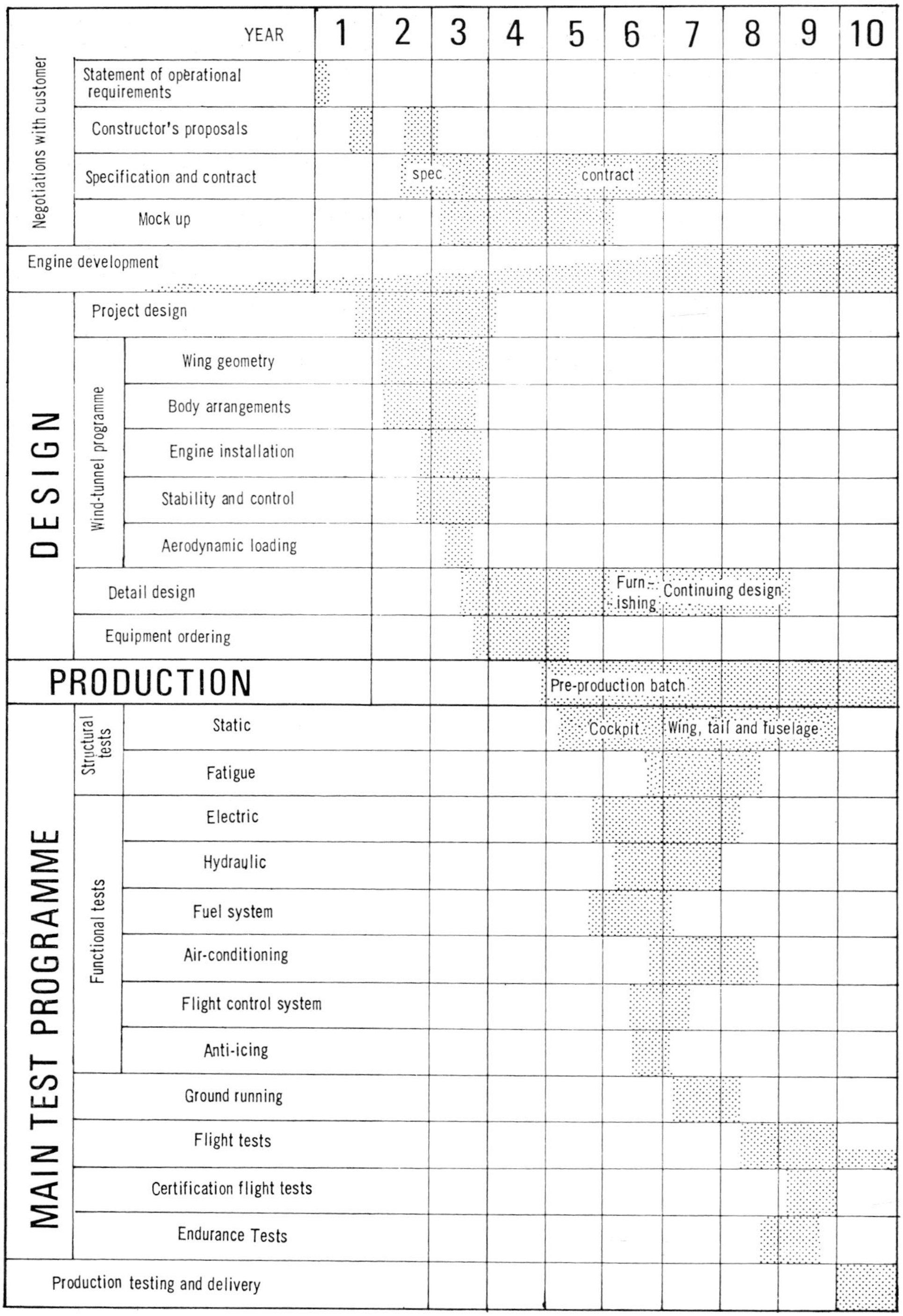

Fig. 12.8 Typical development programme

			YEAR	1	2	3	4	5	6	7	8	9	10
Negotiations with customer		Statement of operational requirements		▓									
		Constructor's proposals			▓	▓							
		Specification and contract				spec		contract					
		Mock up				▓	▓						
Engine development					░	░	░	░	░	░	░	░	░
DESIGN		Project design				▓	▓						
	Wind-tunnel programme	Wing geometry				▓							
		Body arrangements				▓							
		Engine installation				▓	▓						
		Stability and control					▓						
		Aerodynamic loading					▓						
		Detail design					▓	▓	Furnishing	Continuing design			
		Equipment ordering					▓	▓					
PRODUCTION		Pre-production batch						▓	▓	▓	▓	▓	▓
MAIN TEST PROGRAMME	Structural tests	Static						Cockpit	Wing, tail and fuselage				
		Fatigue							▓	▓			
	Functional tests	Electric							▓				
		Hydraulic							▓	▓			
		Fuel system							▓				
		Air-conditioning								▓			
		Flight control system							▓	▓			
		Anti-icing							▓	▓			
		Ground running								▓			
		Flight tests									▓		
		Certification flight tests									▓	▓	
		Endurance Tests										▓	
		Production testing and delivery											▓

remains is the formal production flight-testing of an aeroplane before it is handed over to the operator. The whole programme—from the first tentative notions of the man who wants an aeroplane to the final delivery by the manufacturer—is a long, hard, painstaking process. There are no short cuts and, very often, there is no prepared highway. There is a lot of backbreaking work, sometimes great bitterness in the learning from inevitable mistakes, but there are also moments of great joy—and that is why most people who stay in aeronautics do so for love of it.

In learning to use the air, man has made one of the greatest of all leaps forward. The aeroplane, in every form, has many possibilities for benefitting mankind for as far ahead as we can see into the future. But these possibilities cannot be realized without true understanding of both the potentialities and the limitations of such machines, for in aeronautics there can never be one without the other. It is in the discovery of both that the greatest aesthetic satisfaction is realized.

APPENDICES

APPENDIX A

Light Aeroplanes

Light aeroplanes are growing in numbers in almost every part of the world, especially in the U.S.A. and now in Western Europe. It is often hard to differentiate between those aircraft used for pleasure and those used for business, except that aeroplanes weighing less than about 6,000 lb loaded tend to be used more often for pleasure than for business. Aircraft heavier than 6,000 lb include utility transports and business aircraft carrying the navigational equipment needed to ensure regularity and reliability of service in all weathers.

The light aeroplane is the nearest that the man-in-the-street can come to realizing his dreams of flying as freely as a bird to any place he chooses. Because of their accessibility to people who, from reasons of cost and occupation, are limited to irregular flying practice, light aeroplanes must be simple and easy to fly. Flying is expensive at any time, and it is of the utmost importance that costs are cut to the minimum. Light aircraft tend to be designed with the intention of combining reasonable aerodynamics with low first cost. Wings are often untapered. Welded steel tube primary structures covered with fairings and fabric are still much in evidence. Engines are expensive, and most light aircraft are single engined. The size of an aeroplane is kept to a minimum, for smallness helps to keep manufacturing costs low, and the low weight reduces the number of power units needed to achieve the minimum performance.

Whereas the wing loading of transport aircraft is determined by the airfield length, the wing loading of a light aeroplane is usually determined by a landing speed requirement. Aircraft used for aerobatics are heavier than those used for touring. The higher structure weight of the aerobatic machine, that results from the higher load factors (see Table 4.2), can sometimes be reduced by designing a biplane, although the additional drag of a biplane makes it inferior to the monoplane when cruising. Biplane wings are shorter in span than those of a comparable monoplane, and the struts and bracing increase the equivalent depth of the wing structure, making it lighter overall and enabling thinner, lower drag, sections to be employed.

With one or two minor exceptions aeroplanes weighing less than 6,000 lb are propeller driven. It is possible that a useful range of jet engines will be developed for such work, but only if light aeroplanes are designed to fly high and fast for low cost. At present the poor economics of existing units does not make them as attractive as the piston engine for a light aeroplane. That is not to say that the small jet engine is not comparable in every way with the large jet engine, it is just that light aircraft owners cannot afford the high costs involved. There are some promising developments in the light turboprop field, however, and we may expect to see such units competing favourably with piston engines for aircraft upwards of, say, 3,000 lb AUW.

In this appendix we shall briefly discuss two aeroplanes. They are introduced to demonstrate a number of arguments that led to their design, together with counter arguments against the choice of each layout.

A.1   Two Seat Light Jet Aeroplane

The design study was made by the author in 1954, to the specification of a farmer who wanted a small jet aeroplane for touring and aerobatics that did not need complicated airfield facilities. The engine available at the time had a static thrust of 330 lb and ran on petrol, paraffin or diesel oil. This made it an attractive propostion for a man having stocks of all three at hand.

A.1.1   Specification

The aeroplane was to carry a pilot and passenger with at least 50 lb baggage, yet it had to be capable of being flown solo without ballast. The latter point is important, because the passenger was half the payload and a large proportion of the total weight of a small aeroplane. Examination of Eq. (12–7) shows that the passenger must sit close to the centre of gravity if one is to avoid a large change of CG position when flying solo.

It was intended that the machine should operate from small grass fields, and the range should be about 500 nml in still air. Good, safe stalling characteristics were required, and the aircraft had to be at least semi-aerobatic.

The equipment included provision for VHF radio, a dinghy and life-jackets, provision for oxygen, and fire extinguishers. An electrical system was required for engine starting without recourse to an external battery.

The aircraft had to be robust and capable of being kept in the open for long periods. Major components had to be capable of being replaced without special tools. The power unit had to be easily reached, and changed, without dismantling major structural components. Maintenance and servicing had to be within the capacity of an intelligent amateur. All systems had to be accessible, easy to inspect and to service. The structure had to be strong enough to sustain a wheels-up landing without excessive damage.

The aircraft had to be attractive to the eye and possess 'feminine-appeal' (which is the way of saying that a woman should not mind being seen with it—a point not quite as frivolous as might at first be thought). To this end it was required that a woman flying in the aircraft should be able to wear any of the clothes she might wear in a superior make of car.

A.1.2   Layout

The aircraft is shown at Fig. A.1.1.

Use of a jet engine allowed a short undercarriage to be used, and this kept the cockpit sill close to the ground—a point in favour of design for a feminine passenger, who would not want to clamber up steps or over wing roots while wearing dresses.

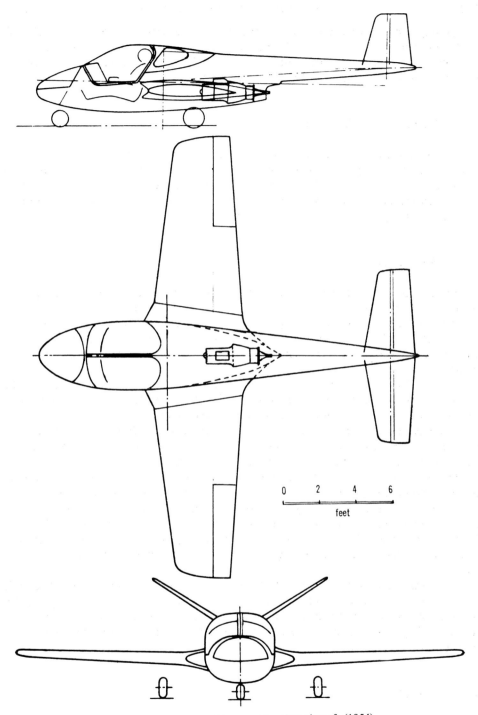

Fig. A.1.1 Layout of two-seat touring aircraft (1954)

The need for short ducting, to keep losses to a minimum, suggested a fuselage formed as a pod and boom. The engine was placed in the bottom of the pod, below the boom, so that the strong centre-section structure of the wing would provide resistance to the engine moving forwards in the event of a crash landing.

The wing was set low to provide a strong bottom structure, and to prevent the aeroplane rolling over too far if it slewed during a wheels-up landing. A low wing also kept undercarriage weight low, because shorter units could be used.

Originally a single fin and rudder was combined with tailplane and elevators. The position of the fin was an initial argument against mounting the engine above the boom, because of the hot jet efflux playing on the surfaces. When the size of the aeroplane had been determined, and a drag estimate made, it was decided to resort to a vee, or butterfly tail, because of the theoretically lower drag of such a unit. The dihedral effect of the butterfly tail affected the amount of dihedral used on the wing.

The need for robustness suggested a metal structure and skin. The need for very low weight meant that the skin would perhaps require stabilizing with PVC foam in places. Control surfaces were metal. A fully enclosed cockpit was used, formed by complete glazed panels that opened as a pair of petals. This gave plenty of access to the cockpit, but necessitated a strong and rather heavy crash arch and door frame structure. The arch was joined at front and rear to a stiff box keel housing the nose-wheel unit and control runs.

Low-speed operation demanded flaps and, possibly, drooped ailerons. A two spar wing with torsion box was chosen for the structure. Flaps, ailerons, and 'rudder-vators' were designed to incorporate the minimum number of ribs. Stiffness of the surfaces was provided by 'dished' corrugations, running chordwise in each skin. Ailerons and ruddervators were identical in planform so that a common skin could be used for all.

All panels, such as engine cowlings, had to be stiff and stand up to rough handling when removed. Fastening had to be simple—a special fastener was chosen that could be opened either with a screwdriver or a coin. Picketing points and a simple mechanical brake system were designed to allow the aeroplane to be parked outside in all weathers. Control locks could be carried in the baggage space behind the seats.

It was found that a semi-aerobatic aeroplane might be built weighing around 1,600 lb when fully loaded, whereas a fully aerobatic version would have weighed more than 1,800 lb. To achieve these weights the fuel load had to be limited and, therefore, range was restricted for an aerobatic sortie. The fully aerobatic version would have had too high a structure weight, inferior climb performance and much reduced range.

The first layout of the aeroplane was too small and, without the passenger, the CG moved too far aft. The second version had the heavy duty battery moved to the nose, so as to bring the CG further forward, reducing the distance between the CG of the passenger and the CG of the aircraft. A longer nose was needed to accommodate the battery beyond the feet of the pilot and passenger.

In order to operate from soft grass fields larger tyres and wheels were needed than for operation from hard pavements. This increased the undercarriage weight and reduced the volume available for fuel within the wings. The fuel was therefore accommodated in a large tank in the fuselage above the centre-section. This necessitated the design of a large firewall bulkhead between tank and engine bay and cockpit.

The arrangement of the fuel tank in the fuselage above the centre-section kept the fuel more or less on the centre of gravity, limiting the change of longitudinal trim

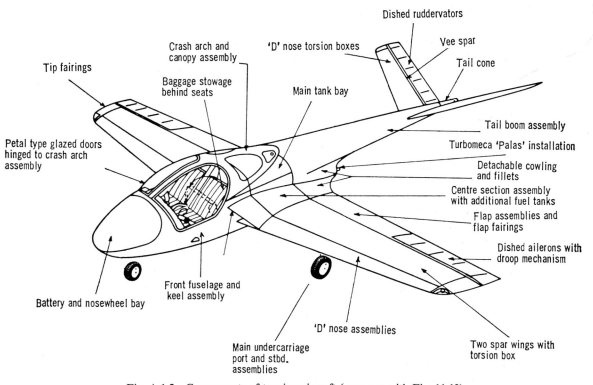

Fig. A.1.2 Components of touring aircraft (compare with Fig. 11.13)

as fuel was burnt. In order to keep the structure weight as low as possible pilot and passenger were seated side by side. This reduced the fuselage length, while the flying controls were simplified by the pilot alone having rudder pedals. The stick was Y-shaped and mounted between the occupants. Fig. A.1.2 shows the major components of the final aeroplane—it should be compared with Fig. 11.13.

A.1.3 Disadvantages of the Aircraft

The aircraft was very heavy, although weight could probably be saved now by using some of the new materials and constructional techniques. For example, the 30 SWG aluminium skin stabilized by 0·25 in. PVC foam plastic, mentioned in 11.5, could be used to advantage. The heavy weight limited the range of the aeroplane.

The short undercarriage meant that the bottom of the fuselage was only 1 ft from the ground, which might have led to damage when forced landing on a rough surface. Ground clearance was also about 1 ft with flaps fully down, and this made them susceptible to damage.

No mass production was envisaged, so that a single aeroplane would have been very expensive. The blown two-piece canopy would have suffered much wear and tear and would have been costly to replace.

On the whole the sort of light jet aeroplane that emerged appeared to be totally unsuited to the limited amenities of the operational environment. A much better piston engined aeroplane could have been designed. The moral is plain: an operational requirement must always take some account of the state-of-the-art at the time, otherwise time will be lost and money wasted. The design study was, in fact, a feasibility study and as such it would normally have been carried out before the OR was formulated.

A.2   Minimum Size Business Aircraft

The tandem-wing, or K-wing, aeroplane shown in Fig. A.2.1 was a study made by the author in 1961 to investigate the possibility of producing a minimum cost five to six-seat business aeroplane. High single-engine safety is a necessity in a multi-engined aircraft, and the arguments led to a configuration with engines at nose and tail, which eliminated asymmetric problems for the pilot. Cutting the wing in half, and then placing the halves (after suitable reshaping) fore and aft of the CG, provided working lift and longitudinal stability without the cost of a tail unit. There was little or no engine failure problem, and fin and rudder sizes could be kept to a minimum. The tail moment arm was short, although the tail volume was large, and fuselage length and structure weight were less than for an equivalent tailed aeroplane. The rear plane was mounted high on the fuselage and the foreplane low with the intention of keeping interference to a minimum.

An ultra-light experimental aeroplane was planned to investigate the layout. Powered by a rear-mounted engine, and with the pilot lying prone above the foreplane, it would have had a span and length around 18 ft, compared with the 32 ft and 29 ft of the larger machine.

Model tests indicated an interesting longitudinal instability that may have been caused by the horseshoe vortex system of the foreplane. With the CG well aft and the foreplane carrying slightly more of the weight than the rearplane, the aircraft would exhibit a very fast short-period oscillation, looking as if neither wing could make up its mind which was intended to do most of the work. Moving the CG forward increased the wing loading of the foreplane, decreased that of the rearplane, and lengthened the period of the oscillation. The forward CG increased the stalling speed considerably. Moving the CG aft lengthened the period of oscillation, but made the aeroplane directionally unstable.

Structurally the layouts looked attractive. It was intended to use common wing panels fore and aft in order to keep down production costs. The comparatively small overall dimensions of the aircraft helped to cut first cost and might have helped to reduce hangar rent. The designs were shelved as a result of the dynamic longitudinal instability.

Results of this kind should never be taken as conclusive, they merely point to the nature of a problem that is likely to be encountered with any departure from convention. Comparatively small alterations to the arrangement of the aerofoil surfaces could well produce satisfactory characteristics. Reducing the foreplane and increasing the size of the rearplane, while perhaps being forced to use different wing sections, front and rear would have produced a machine rather like the Rutan Defiant, Fig. A.2.2(a). Such an alteration would have improved the view over the foreplane for the pilot. In the form shown the pilot would be fairly blind in a turn, an undesirable quality—unless counterbalanced by a better one elsewhere.

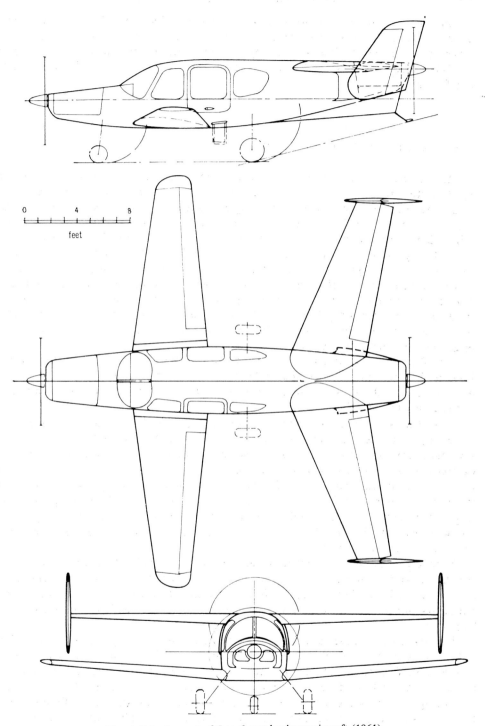

0   4   8

feet

Fig. A.2.1   Layout of 5 to 6-seat business aircraft (1961)

An equivalent twin engined monoplane could have had a span and length around 40 ft and 35 ft respectively, and a higher wing loading. Calculations indicated that the landing speed of the K-wing would have been about 15 per cent lower than the monoplane.

(*a*) Rutan Model 40, Defiant (USA, 1978)
By permission of Flight International

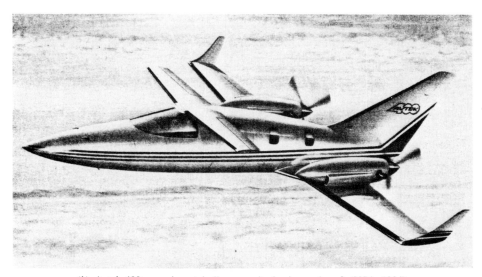

(*b*) Avtek 400, experimental all composite business aircraft (USA, 1984)

Fig. A.2.2   Examples of near tandem winged aircraft

Fig. D.4.5   Rutan Model 35 slewed-wing project, called the AD-1, which was tested successfully in 1979
By permission of Air International

Fig. E.5.4   Flying boats still excite interest; the Claudius Dornier Seastar (German Federal Republic 1984)
By permission of Claudius Dornier *and* Flight International

APPENDIX B

Utility Aeroplanes

Aircraft are extremely versatile forms of transport and can be used in a very wide range of applications over a large part of the world. Here an aeroplane is considered for work in the developing part of the world—an area inhabited by something like three quarters of the world population. The main problems to be solved by the use of aircraft are:

(*a*) The provision of a reliable transport system, as part of the industrial infra-structure of an area.
(*b*) Diversifying the economy by conservation and use of natural resources.
(*c*) Increasing and diversifying agriculture, to feed the population better and earn extra income.
(*d*) Increasing employment, which involves the mobility of labour.

It follows that two kinds of machine are needed. The first is the aerial work aircraft for agriculture, forestry, survey, pest control, and construction. In these tasks they can serve as flying platforms, cranes, vehicles of communication and for disaster relief. The second are the work-horse transports, the freighters and flying buses.

There are only two choices: either fixed or rotary-winged aircraft. Rotary-winged aircraft cost about 10 times as much as a truck and $2\frac{1}{2}$ times as much as a fixed winged machine, payload for payload, but are more useful below 100 k. It is held here, although it could be easily contested by others, that an aeroplane is the most useful large-scale answer. What is essential is that the aircraft should be utilitarian and, for eventual economy, it must also be productive.

Utility cannot be successfully measured in economic terms alone. In essence it lies in a combination of versatility and productivity, but there is no clear way of defining it. High performance costs money, safety costs money, versatility costs money. Versatility involves variable geometry in one form or another. For example, design for a good ratio of maximum to minimum speed requires anything from a variable pitch propeller and retractable undercarriage, to variable wing-sweep—by way of slots, flaps, boundary layer control and rotary wings. It does not matter whether an aircraft is financed from within or from without a country, the question that must always be asked is: 'what amount of variable geometry should be afforded?'

To achieve high utilization there are many advantages in using the minimum number of aircraft for the work. If one type can be designed for several roles, then so much the better. But a careful choice must be made between versatility and the number of aircraft to be built. This depends upon expected useful life, and upon the time in which an aircraft must pay for itself.

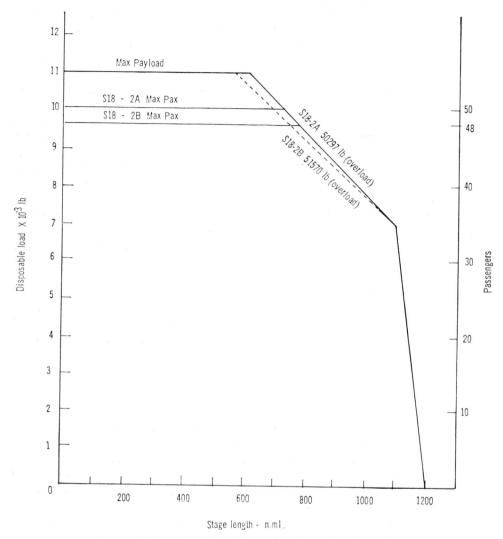

Fig. B.1.1   Disposable load and stage length

Versatility in type and distribution of payload has an important bearing upon ability to achieve high load factors. An aircraft should have an inboard profile that allows the maximum volume to be used all of the time. If there is such scope, then loading and supervision is less of a problem—although large CG margins will be needed for stability, and this must be balanced against the need for manoeuvrability. In this respect the aeroplane scores over the helicopter in terms of stability, but not in manoeuvrability.

B.1 'Flying-Mule' Aircraft

The design study of the flying-mule aeroplane was made by the author in 1964, in an attempt to provide a highly versatile and thoroughly utilitarian machine for operations in South America, Africa and South East Asia. The work to be carried out varied from crop spraying, pest control and spraying the desert with a fine oil emulsion (to hold the sand together while allowing seeds to grow) to air-freighting and the carriage of passengers. The aircraft had to be variable in configuration from one extreme of carrying tanks and spray equipment, to carrying a large panier for passengers or freight. In the latter configuration nose and tail loading was held to be essential.

The disposable load and stage length had to be fixed in order to gain some idea of the weight. Recent surveys suggested that developing countries were interested in stage lengths of anything from 50 to 1,100 n ml. Passenger needs were broadly similar everywhere, in that there seemed little occasion for more than a good busload of 48 to 50 people to travel at a time. Over the longer stages the numbers would be much smaller, around one half to two thirds, say 30 to 35 at the most. A cruising speed of 250 k was thought to be ample for most stages, and only in South America might there have been a need for a specially pressurized cabin, for flight over the Andes. The disposable load and stage length were related as in Fig. B.1.1, and the passenger payload was equated to the amount of payload, in the form of liquids or powders, to be carried in the other configurations.

With the broad requirement fixed it was thought that a turboprop aeroplane would probably satisfy most of the other requirements as well. A brief examination of the likely performance of an aeroplane carrying some 10,000 to 11,000 lb (5 short tons) of payload, and using two 3,245 ehp turboprop engines, showed that the decision was reasonable.

B.1.1   Layout

The aircraft is as shown in Fig. B.1.2. Flexibility in the carriage of payload led to the choice of detachable pods, slung from the centre section of the wing Fig. B.1.3. Twin fuselages, or booms, were needed for flight without a pod, in order to locate the tail and undercarriage units. The parent aeroplane became, therefore, a form of aerial tractor. For most regions only the freight pod (with additional seating) or the tank and spray rig would be needed.

In a passenger aircraft seating should not really be more than 4 or 5 abreast between gangways. This enables the load to be spread compactly fore and aft of the centre of gravity, while maintaining the minimum number of knees for a distressed passenger to stumble over on the way to a toilet. The cabin must be high enough, ideally, for a man to stand erect. Taken together, both requirements fix the fuselage section, length, and cabin volume. For the lowest structure weight a pressure cabin is circular: 9 ft diameter externally will encompass a standing man and four abreast seating. The fineness ratio for reasonable aerodynamic characteristics is usually around 7 or 8/1, resulting in a fuselage about 70 ft in length. Seats occupy about half the length and, with a high density seat pitch of 35 in., 48 passengers can be carried. Fortuitously this corresponded with the busload measure, and at 200 lb for a passenger and baggage, worked out a little under 5 tons.

For agricultural operations and pest control the payload requirement varied from about 500 lb for small farm fields, to 10 to 15 tons of fertilizer for areas of South East Asia. It was estimated that an aircraft carrying 5 tons of fertilizer at a block speed of 150 k could spread more than 400 acres, about 2/3 of a square mile, in 9 hours at a

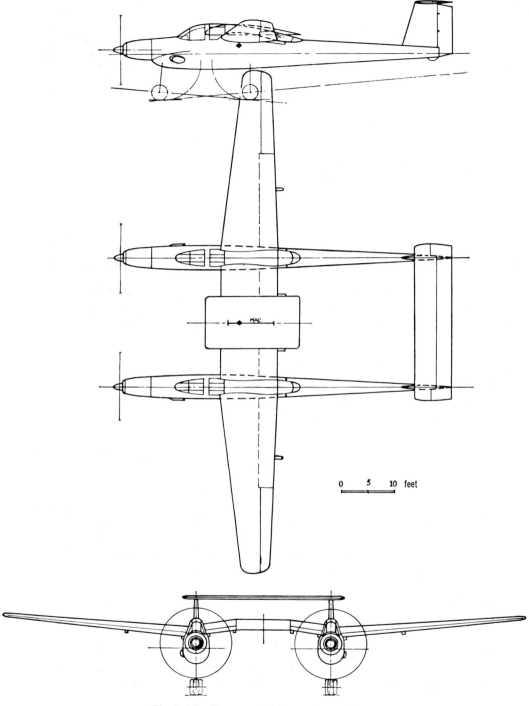

Fig. B.1.2   The parent flying-mule aeroplane

0   5   10   feet

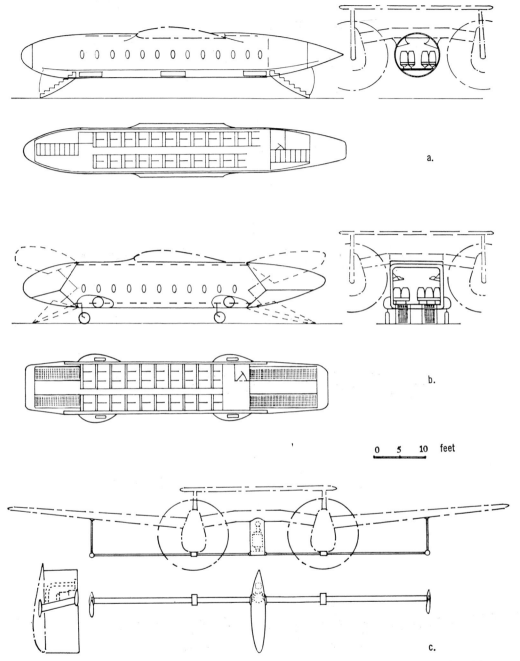

Fig. B.1.3 (a) The pressurized pod with high-density seating for 48; (b) freight pod with high density seating for 50; (c) spray boom and 1,100 gallon tank, with pressure replenishing

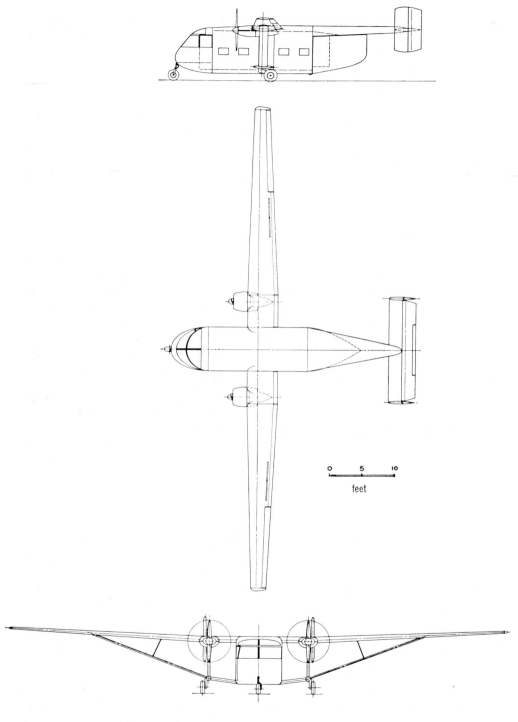

Fig. B.2.1   The Miles HDM 106 (France–U.K., 1950s)

distance of 150 nml from the airfield, but much more at shorter ranges. It was held that an aircraft lifting such a load, and powered by two engines, would strike a reasonable balance between manoeuvrability and economy of effort for the pilot.

The twin fuselage arrangement allowed an aircrew of four to be carried, with an additional 'rumble seat' at the aft end of each canopy fairing, for ground crew members.

Aiming for a field length of around 1,000 yd to 50 ft with fuel for 300 nml, resulted in a wing area of 1,000 ft^2, coupled with a power loading of 7–8 lb/hp. The resulting aeroplane had an aspect ratio of 10·5 to 11, a wing span of 105 ft and a length of 68 ft. High lift flaps were fitted. The undercarriage had four units and six wheels (one front, two rear) and a load classification number of 11 to 15, depending upon weight.

B.1.2 Disadvantages of the Aircraft

The principal disadvantage of the layout was the high structure weight. Generally speaking the penalty of carrying around an extra fuselage, no matter how slender, was a structure 1/4 as heavy again as it should have been. This increased the structure weight from 32 to 40 per cent of the 'ideal' all-up weight. Part of the penalty came from the additional undercarriage unit.

The second disadvantage was the additional drag which reduced the range by 1/3 of the range of an equivalent conventional aircraft. In order to meet the range requirement the fuel load had to be increased for the freight and passenger aircraft resulting in all-up weights between 50,000 and 52,000 lb.

Manufacturing and operating costs would have been higher than for an equivalent conventional aircraft setting the same standards in utility, but not as high as those of a luxury version. The ugliness of the aeroplane was the result of placing utility as a primary requirement. The utility depended upon variable geometry, and aircraft sales would clearly depend upon how much utility mattered to an operator—*i.e.*, upon how much variable geometry he would be willing to afford.

B.2 Miles HDM 106 Light Transport

The Miles HDM 106 was the result of collaboration between the Miles brothers of Shoreham and Commandant Hurel of Le Societé des Avions Hurel Dubois, of Villacoublay in France. The project, which belongs to the early 1950s, sought to combine the utilitarian qualities of the Aerovan aircraft of the 1940s and the very high aspect ratio wing designed by Hurel to produce a versatile and economical short-range transport.

A general arrangement drawing of the aeroplane is shown in Fig. B.2.1. The wing had an aspect ratio of 20, and the long struts were designed in such a way as to contribute to the overall lift/drag by a combination of camber and twist where they met the wing surface. The layout of the aircraft demonstrates the important properties of Eq. (4–8) and Eq. (4–8a), for the power loading was around 12–14 lb/hp while the wing loading was 28·5 lb/ft^2 (higher than a light and executive aircraft in Table 12.3). The benefit on the side of the power loading (and, therefore, thrust loading) came from the high aspect ratio.

As far as is known no HDM 106 was actually built, because of changes in the Miles Company about that time.

APPENDIX C

Subsonic Transports

The world is changing very fast at this time. Old, singular nations are joining with others in larger economic and political groupings that were unheard of when the aeroplane came on the scene at the turn of the century. Markets grow rapidly and people must move swiftly. Today it is no longer necessary to spend a night in Paris in order to do business there from an office in London, one can make the round trip by air and still find time to work in a normal-length day. Communication is the life-blood of social development, and aircraft are one of the most important links between people. The man-in-the-street is more than willing to fly, accepting what the specialist in aviation has to offer, but only if he is assured that travelling by air is cheap, safe, convenient and swift.

The word swift has been chosen with care. The block time of the whole journey is of far greater importance than the block time of flight. Most airfields are well away from the centres of the cities that they serve. The faster and noisier aircraft become, the further away they have to be moved from the cities. Cities grow too and there is an increasing hazard in aircraft, which have to make long, flat, approaches, spending much of the approach time over built-up areas.

As far as disturbance from noise is concerned, pilots already complain about the need to climb away steeply at comparatively low airspeeds, immediately after take-off in order to reduce the noise levels around London Airport and in New York. The pattern that emerges is one of airfields for the fast and noisy long-haul aircraft set well away from city boundaries, with slower and smaller feeder aircraft (including heli-copters) linking the distant airports with the cities themselves.

Transport aircraft are either passenger-carriers or freighters. Long-range freighters and passenger aircraft are broadly similar and usually related, as many freighters are modified airliners. Short-range passenger-carriers, *i.e.*, feeder aircraft and those used for internal services are similar in layout. They are slower than the long-range machines, simply because short stages do not allow any economical advantage to be gained by flying at high speeds. The departure and arrival phases at each end of the flight dominate the block-time equation and do not leave enough time in the middle for fast cruising to show any useful advantage in cost-effectiveness.

In this appendix we shall look at two concepts: the economical short-range trans-port aeroplane, the 'Aerobus', and the long-range 'strategic' transport.

C.1. Short-Range Minimum-Cost Air Transport (Aerobuses)

Short-range minimum-cost air transports may take two distinctive forms. The first, dealt with in some detail here, was the result of much work done by the Ministry of Aviation, in conjunction with the British air transport industry, on the original concept of a short-range minimum-cost aircraft. The resulting design studies were felt to merit particular mention in a book of this kind. The second form, that of the much larger transport carrying some 250 passengers, or freight, is the result of further work carried out in Europe.

C.1.1 Initial Aerobus Studies

As far as the initial MoA studies were concerned it seemed clear at an early stage that the emphasis would be more towards the accommodation of the largest number of passengers for a given wing area and, therefore, given structure weight. There was little indication of the best aircraft for the task, and three studies were made for comparison:

(a) A swept-wing design of fairly large thickness-chord ratio with passengers distributed across a fair proportion of the wing span.
(b) A delta-wing design with increased root chord, decreased thickness-chord ratio, and passengers concentrated rather more towards the centre-line.
(c) A conventional wing-plus-body aeroplane to serve as a basis against which the all-wing aircraft could be assessed.

The three aircraft are shown in Figs. C.1.1, C.1.2 and C.1.3, and it will be noted that their planforms have already been compared in Fig. 8.11. The design of the all-wing aircraft would have become very difficult below a certain size, because of head-room considerations, and it was agreed that the machines would be based upon seating for about 100 passengers.

The performance requirements included a range of 2×250 statute mile stages plus reserves, without refuelling. The cruising speed was to be $M = 0.7$, the current speeds of $M = 0.7$ to 0.85 being rejected on the grounds that they were dictated largely by fashion and the need of airlines to compete with each other. A lower speed was not selected because it can be argued that a higher speed makes an aircraft more productive in capacity-ton-miles per hour for a given amount of capital investment.

The cruising speed, which worked out around 500 miles per hour, generated the lowest cost on the 250 mile stage. This also corresponded with a block time of 50 minutes per stage (of which 13 minutes represented taxying, take-off, approach and landing), and a cruising height of 20,000 ft. Opinions on the choice of such a high speed varied, however, for it is possible to argue forcibly in favour of a slower turbo-prop aircraft for such short stages. It would seem that the key to the choice depends upon load factor. The turboprop aircraft is competitive with the jet if it can achieve the same load factors, but if passengers have a choice between a jet aeroplane and one with propellers, then all things being equal, they tend to choose the jet.

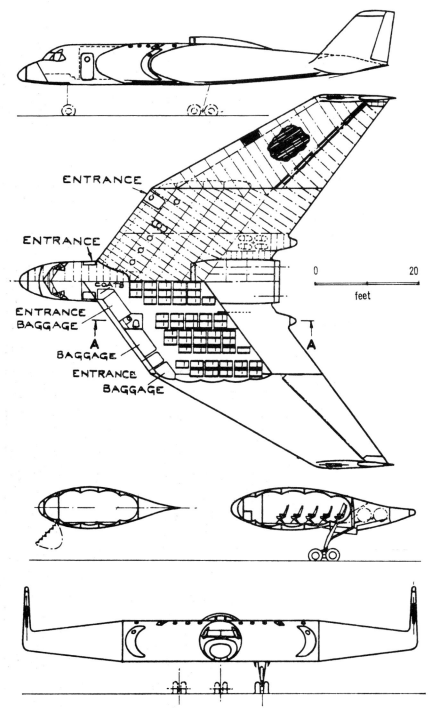

Fig. C.1.1   The 102-seat swept-wing design (Handley Page HP126)

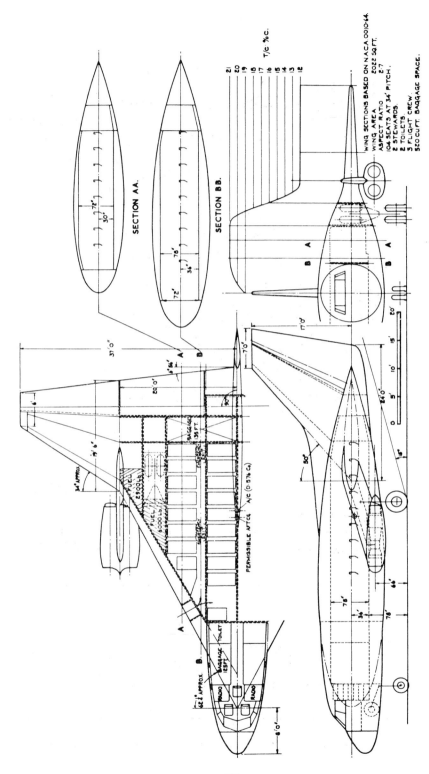

Fig. C.1.2 The 104-seat delta-wing design

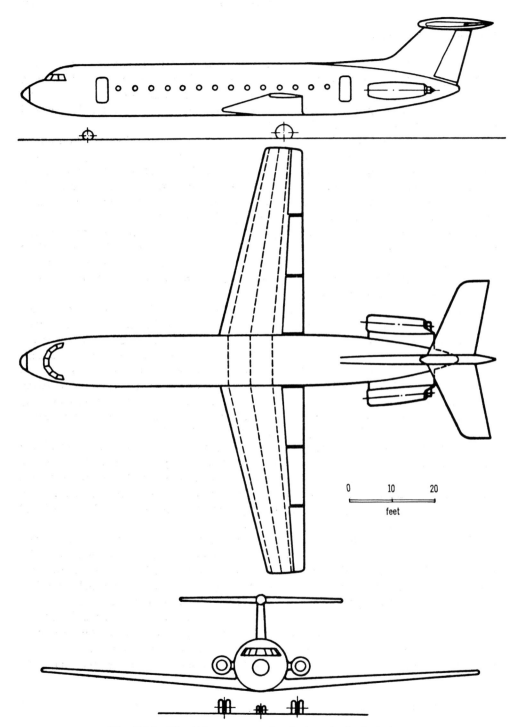

Fig. C.1.3   The 100-seat conventional wing-plus-body design

Properties of the Layouts

It was found in the design of such large short-range transport aircraft that it was more important to achieve low structure weight and large cabin space than high aerodynamic efficiency. The swept-wing and delta aircraft combine the normal functions of the fuselage with a lifting function—they represent 'integrated' layouts of the kind already mentioned in Chapter 2.

The aerodynamic disadvantages of the all-wing machines centred on the inferior lift/drag. High lift with low aspect ratio is inevitably associated with large angles of attack and high lift-dependent drag. There is the added problem of the smaller CG margin—*i.e.*, physically smaller—with the higher aspect ratio swept-wing aircraft, that makes it more difficult to balance without a more careful weighing and arrangement of payload than is theoretically necessary with the delta.

The structure weight of the all-wing designs was about 26 per cent of the all-up-weight, and 29 per cent in the case of the conventional aircraft. The powerplant weight of the all-wing aircraft tended to be higher than that of the conventional, because in the engine failure case they needed more powerful units to compensate for the lower maximum lift/drag.

Both all-wing aeroplanes had wing areas around 2,100 ft^2, giving span^2/wetted areas around 1, an aspect ratio of 2·8, a maximum lift coefficient of 1·3 and a wing loading of about 37 lb/ft^2. Thickness ratios of the wings were 25 per cent for the swept-wing and 20 reducing to 12 per cent for the delta. The conventional aeroplane had a wing area of nearly 1,500 ft^2, aspect ratio 7, maximum lift coefficient of 2·3, a wing loading of 54 lb/ft^2, and a total wetted area 25 per cent greater than the all-wing aircraft, giving a span^2/wetted area of 1·45. Using Fig. 6.23 as a guide we may estimate that the conventional aeroplane had an $(L/D)_{max}$ about 20 per cent better than the all-wing aircraft, although it may be on the low side.

The studies showed that costs were marginally in favour of the conventional design, at the 100-seat size. The formula direct operating cost was 1·84 d/seat-mile for the conventional aircraft, 1·91 for the delta and 1·97 for the swept-wing. An interesting result, however, was that as the number of passengers to be carried increased the disadvantages of the all-wing aircraft decreased, until around 150 passengers there was no difference between all three designs.

What is important, within the context of this book, is that three such widely differing layouts should be so comparable. One grows used to thin wing sections for high speed flight, and maximum thickness/chords of 12 to 15 per cent for low subsonic flight. Here instead are thick sectioned all-wing machines competing favourably, at fairly high-subsonic speed, with a classical aircraft. In so doing they lend point to the conclusion that there is no single answer to the way of meeting a requirement—there is just a range of different answers with differing merits. In drawing the conclusion one might add that the great beauty of the study of aircraft design lies in the variety of pathways that can be explored when looking for an optimum aircraft.

C.1.2 Later Aerobus Developments

Earlier aerobus studies centred around 100 to 150 passengers. Recent work carried out in Europe—in which France and Britain are cooperating—is concerned with aircraft carrying more than 250 passengers. In many ways the aeroplanes resemble

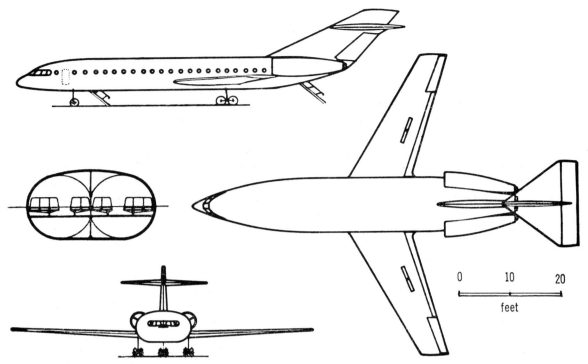

Fig. C.1.4   The Nord–600 project 'Airbus', France, published October 1965 (measurements approximate)

those to be discussed shortly, in C.2.2, except that most of the aerobuses (the trend is to call them airbuses) will carry their payloads for 800 to 1,000 n ml. We may expect transatlantic developments however.

There are a number of projects and one with particularly interesting features is the Nord–600, as published in October 1965. This aircraft is shown in Fig. C.1.4, and has a double-bubble fuselage lying on its side, four turbojets in a tail cluster, and a classical configuration. Both three and four engined versions are said to have been studied. With four Rolls-Royce RB–163–50 Spey engines of 6,400 lb static thrust, and an estimated all-up weight of 209,000 lb (payload 25 per cent of this), the wing and thrust loadings would be 95 lb/ft² and 8·2 lb/lb respectively. These values correspond with a range around 800 n ml at M = 0·8 + and a block speed of 350 k.

One may conjecture about possible advantages and disadvantages of the fuselage arrangement. The horizontal bubble might make a better contribution to the total lift than an upright bubble—such as that shown in Fig. C.2.4. But the fuselage structure would probably be heavier. A horizontal bubble has not the same beam-depth as an upright bubble, and must therefore be heavier to resist bending loads. Pressurization tends to blow out the fuselage into a circular section and, for lightness, hoop-stresses must be met by a line of pillars, or a vertical web, along the cabin centre-line. Such an arrangement inevitably increases the weight over that of an upright bubble, and may limit seat arrangement, passenger services (unless additional galleys and toilets are provided), and the arrangement of doors for passengers and freight.

C.2   Heavy (Long Haul) Transport Aeroplanes

Heavy transport aircraft include both civil freighters and military transports, of which the latter include both strategic and tactical aeroplanes. Most are designed to lift awkward, heavy loads of 30 tons or more. Many civil freighters in present use throughout the world have been developed from military machines, or show clearly that they have been designed with military requirements in mind.

Strategic aeroplanes are those intended to fly intercontinental distances with loads of national importance, such as troops and war material. Tactical aeroplanes have to fly shorter distances within a region, often delivering loads to sites without proper airfield facilities. It can be argued that both strategic and tactical machines should, ideally, be one and the same, so that prepared loads do not have to be broken down— or have time wasted by excessive handling—for carriage by other aircraft. On the other hand there are good arguments, based upon total economics, for designing different aircraft for each role able to handle a common payload. In the tactical role there is a need for V/STOL machines, and an interesting idea is the air-portable package of lifting engines that can be added to each wing of a conventional aircraft to fit it for the V/STOL role. The tactical transport requires a multi-wheel under-carriage with low LCN tyres for operation from soft unprepared surfaces, and the ability to carry all of the equipment needed to operate in the field.

The most significant difficulties with V/STOL aeroplanes are those resulting from noise and cost. Noise is a serious problem when the lifting engines use high induced velocities—a feature of high disc loadings—and the aircraft is large. The high cost is caused by the complexity of such aircraft and reflects in both the first (*i.e.*, production) cost and the rate of depreciation. Fuel consumption is usually high and increases the operating cost appreciably. Depending upon the particular aircraft, VTOL reduces the range to something like a 1/4 to 1/2 of the range in the conventional role.

VTOL does not seem to be entirely suitable for civil work, because of the noise and high cost, except for specialized operations in remote areas—such as landing heavy mining equipment somewhere well beyond the reach of adequate road and rail facilities. The helicopter is much quieter for VTOL, because of the lower disc loading and slipstream velocity, but productivity over long range is poor compared with the aeroplane. It is perhaps significant that the large helicopter has been mainly developed in Russia and America, where long distances can be conveniently flown in short stages without the problems of overflying rights and political barriers.

C.2.1   Freight Carriers

The fuselage of a freighter has large stowage volume, generous sections that are widest at the floor, and easy access for awkward loads. Floors are close to the ground (most aircraft are high winged for this purpose) allowing loads to be run straight off the tailboards of trucks. Ideally there are facilities for nose and tail loading. Most must satisfy the requirement for parachuting loads. This poses a problem in ramp design, for ramps must not be excessively heavy, yet they must be strong enough to support the cantilever load of a heavy pallet, or vehicle, being dragged out of the hold by parachute. Airframe buffeting with tail doors open sometimes causes aerodynamic and structural problems.

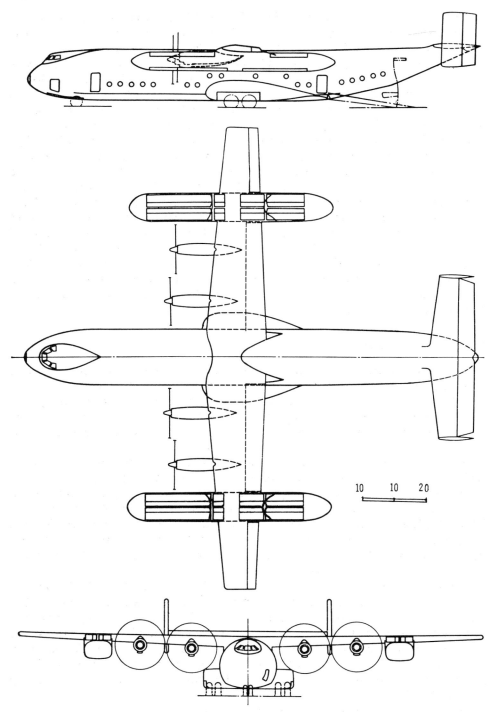

Fig. C.2.1   Strategic freighter, College of Aeronautics, 1961

Two typical designs are shown in Figs. C.2.1 and C.2.2. The first, the F–61 VTOL freighter was the 1961 design study of the College of Aeronautics, Cranfield. The second, the Blackburn B.107A of 1956 was to have been a development of the Beverley. Both are roughly comparable, except that the maximum payloads were 77,000 lb for the F–61 and 53,000 lb for the B.107A for gross weights of 250,000 lb and 175,000 lb respectively. The F–61 carried about 60,000 lb for 1,600 nml, the distance the B.107A carried 53,000 lb. Both had similar Rolls Royce Tyne turboprop engines, but the F–61 also had two pods, totalling 44 lift engines of 8,000 lb nominal thrust. The control system of such a large number of engines posed severe problems in design.

Both aeroplanes are large by Western European standards, but they are small compared with current developments in the U.S.A. and U.S.S.R. Some idea of the size of future developments can be got from Fig. C.2.3, in which a comparison is made between three American projects and four existing aircraft. The top three aircraft are entries for the C–5A design competition, which is reported to call for the carriage of payloads of 100,000 lb for 5,500 nml, and 200, 000 lb beyond 2,500 nml. The initial Douglas C–5A proposal is said to have had a weight of 725,000 lb, a span of 240 ft, a length of 216 ft, a range of 7,000 miles and the ability to carry 300,000 lb over short distances. It is now understood (late 1965) that the Lockheed design has been chosen. The Russian Antonov An 22 is the largest aircraft flying at this time. It made a first appearance at the Paris Salon in 1965.

C.2.2   Passenger Carriers

The future development of the large passenger aeroplane is far from clear. It is impossible to guess whether or not all long range machines will be supersonic, but it would seem irrational to neglect the subsonic aeroplane if fares are lower than by SST. There are two possible lines of development that merit attention: the design of special aeroplanes employing new techniques that bring about radical reductions in cost; or the stretching of well tried aircraft already in service.

For the first, the most promising technique is to laminarize a large part of the surface of an aeroplane—70 per cent or more—to bring about greatly improved lift/drag ratios. In the U.K. Handley Page have made an extensive study of laminarization, and one project, the HP 117, was said to be capable of carrying 300 passengers and 20,000 lb of freight across the North Atlantic for an all-up weight of 330,000 lb. The aeroplane was said to span 148 ft, and was expected to carry 82,000 lb over a 5,000 statute mile stage at $M = 0.8$ with full BOAC reserves. With a smaller payload a range of 6,000 nml was claimed.

By comparison, the second is represented by the 'stretched' BAC (Vickers) Super VC 10, first mentioned in July 1965. The aircraft has a new fuselage 33 ft longer than the standard machine, with a seating capacity for 265 passengers on two decks. The fuselage is a double-bubble in section, carrying 80 per cent of the passengers in the upper saloon and the remainder, with freight, in the lower. The aircraft, known by the company at this time as the DB265, is said to be able to carry a payload of 72,000 lb for 2,800 nml for an all-up weight of 370,000 lb. Both aircraft are provisionally compared in Fig. C.2.4.

Basing deductions on the published and unconfirmed figures, it would appear that, working to the same range, the swept-wing HP117 has a percentage payload of 32 as against the $19\frac{1}{2}$ per cent of the conventional wing-plus-body DB265. The conclusion is that laminarization leads to huge savings in fuel weight, in spite of the increased

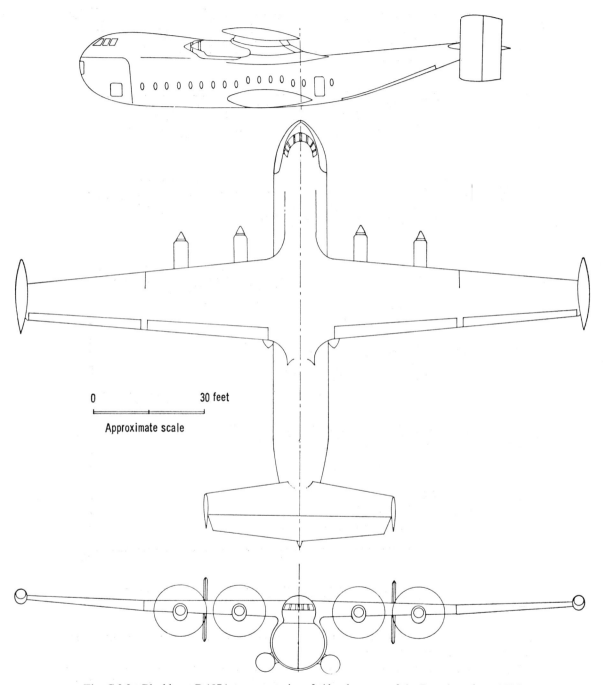

0   30 feet

Approximate scale

Fig. C.2.2   Blackburn B.107A transport aircraft (development of the Beverley, about 1956)

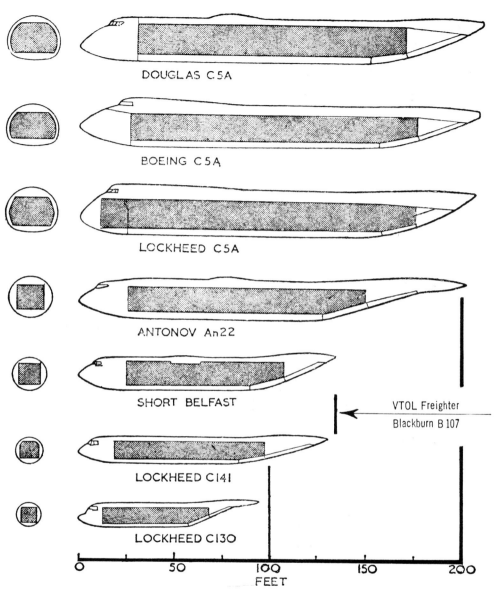

DOUGLAS C5A

BOEING C5A

LOCKHEED C5A

ANTONOV An22

SHORT BELFAST

VTOL Freighter
Blackburn B 107

LOCKHEED C141

LOCKHEED C130

0   50   100   150   200
FEET

Fig. C.2.3   Comparison of approximate cargo space in three projected and four current aircraft, 1965

weight of the BLC system, thus permitting heavier payloads to be carried. Both aircraft weigh well over 160 tons.

Practical laminarization still appears to be a long way off however. Research and development costs tend to work out around $\frac{1}{2}$ of the first cost of a batch of 100 aircraft, and low direct operating costs (around 0·6d per passenger mile) may not be realizeable in practice if a large bill for long term R and D has to be met by the civil operator.

Both projects are representative of current thinking, but there may be a break-

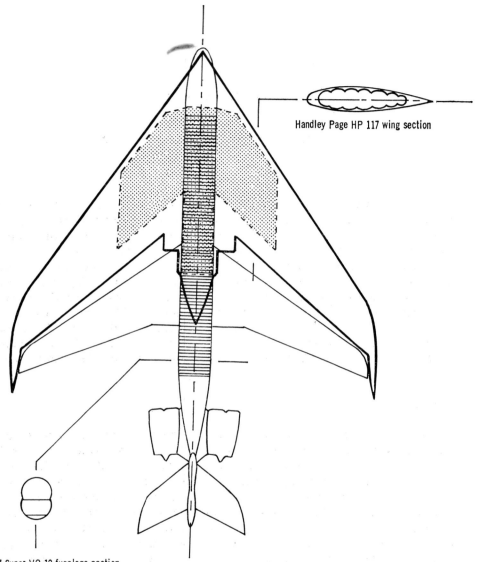

Handley Page HP 117 wing section

'Stretched' Super VC 10 fuselage section

Fig. C.2.4 Provisional comparison between tailless (300 passenger) Handley Page HP117 and 'stretched' version (265 passenger) BAC (Vickers) Super VC10. The laminarized version of the HP117 could have had about double the L/D of an unlaminarized version

through elsewhere that will eventually change the whole picture. An example with some promise is the development of a very large hot-airship, possessing a large volume delta envelope, and powered by a nuclear reactor. The heat would be used to generate static lift, by lowering the weight of air in the envelope, while at speed the aerodynamic shape would generate aerodynamic lift. Propulsion would be by a number of turbo-props, nuclear heat-exchangers being used in place of burning fuel in combustion chambers. Cruising speed would be low, but range global, and only limited by crew and passenger requirements.

Supersonic Transports

The supersonic transport aeroplane, or SST, has attracted much attention for a number of years. In the U.K. the Supersonic Transport Aircraft Committee, formed in 1956, examined the possible lines of development of supersonic transport aircraft. In France, Avions Marcel Dassault and Sud-Aviation planned to cooperate in the production of a Super-Caravelle SST. America showed interest round about the same time, and the U.S.S.R., while not saying very much in public, recently demonstrated a model SST showing that she had also carried out concurrent design studies. The present publicised situation is that the two companies of BAC and Sud, in the U.K. and France respectively, are now building the Concorde—the result of each nation arriving at a similar solution to the problem much earlier on. The Americans are working on several $M=3$ SST designs, whereas the Concorde is designed for $M=2.2$.

D.1 The General Problem

The shape of a supersonic aeroplane depends far more upon its design speed than does a subsonic aeroplane, and the design speed of a transport aircraft depends in turn upon where and how far it will fly. A simple, though revealing, graph is sketched in Fig. D.1.1 in which the flying times are plotted as block times (and include an allowance for take-off, climb, descent and landing) against three stage ranges of 800, 1,400 (European) and 3,000 nml (say London to New York). Starting from a current $M=0.7$, there is a considerable saving in flying time on the longest route if the speed is increased by almost any increment, up to $M=3$. Over the 1,400 nml route time is saved up to $M=1.2$, but above that any further increase is hardly worth the effort. Over the short 800 nml route there is little, beyond prestige, to be gained from supersonic speeds.

Referring back to Eq. (4–12) we see that the range flying efficiency of an aeroplane depends upon how much speed can be bought per unit of fuel flow, how much lift can be got from the air for how little effort, and how much fuel can be loaded into the structure without loss of payload. We have seen that turbojet engines can be used for such speeds—that aerodynamic shapes can be designed to provide the required aerodynamic efficiency—but that kinetic heating raises severe structural problems beyond $M=2.2$. Supersonic aeroplanes are bigger than their subsonic counterparts, payload for payload, because of the additional fuel that must be carried. To carry 100 passengers to New York at $M=2$ we can expect to see aeroplanes around 300,000 lb all-up weight, with 55 per cent of it being taken up with fuel.

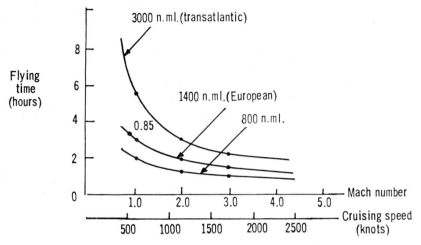

Fig. D.1.1   Variation in block time with stage length and cruising speed

The economy of a design depends upon such factors as block speed, fuel cost, payload, airframe and powerplant weights and costs, stage lengths, and the number of journeys that can be made by one aircraft in a year. Fig. D.1.2 shows the sort of variation that occurs in operating costs with design Mach number. The hump is partly due to inability to design shapes which have enough lift/drag between $M = 1 \cdot 2$ and $1 \cdot 8$. Looking again at Fig. 6.21 we see that L/D falls rapidly in this region, and the rate at which it falls is too fast to be compensated for by the rising M/c', or V/c' of the propulsive efficiency.

Cruising altitudes are above 50,000 ft and this introduces some novel design problems. A $M = 2 \cdot 2$ aircraft cruises about 60,000 ft, while a $M = 3 \cdot 0$ machine cruises nearer 80,000 ft. At the lower altitude neither cosmic radiation nor ozone present excessive hazards, and in emergency a descent can be made more rapidly from

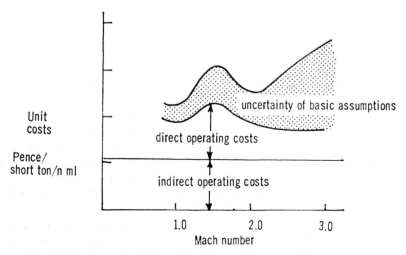

Fig. D.1.2   General variation in total operating cost with cruising speed

60,000 ft than 80,000 ft. Beyond 60,000 ft a sealed cabin is required and a more complicated, heavier, air-conditioning system. Cosmic radiation is likely to be hazardous, and aircrew will be limited in their flying time spent at altitude. An American Federal Aviation Agency doctor is reported as saying that such radiation 'may shorten the life-span by 5 to 10 per cent'.

It was recommended initially that design studies should be made in the U.K. of a $M=1\cdot2$ aircraft with swept wings, and a slender delta aircraft for flight at $M=1\cdot8$. The swept-wing machine had an M-planform, as shown in Fig. D.1.3, while the delta

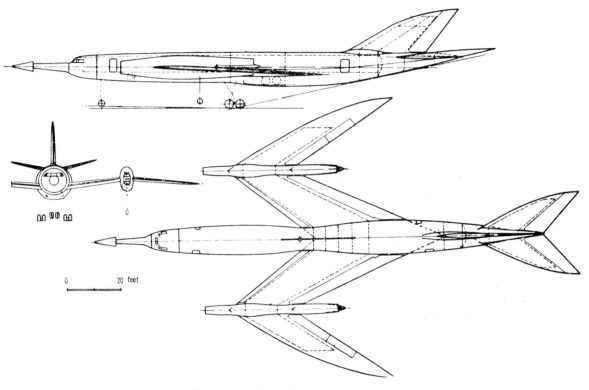

Fig. D.1.3   ($M=1\cdot2$) Medium range SST

was chosen for higher speeds, because of the good lift/drag characteristics, the large internal volume and the good aero-elastic shape.

The fuselage of a supersonic aircraft makes a considerable contribution to the drag of the whole, and of the fuselage drag that of the canopy contributes perhaps 1/3— something like 7 or 8 per cent of the total drag. The optical properties of highly swept, low drag, windscreens leave much to be desired. Refraction, large angle of attack on the approach and poor visibility make the design of satisfactory windscreens a problem with supersonic aircraft, for the surfaces must be highly swept for low drag, but they should be steep (ideally normal to the line of sight) for good vision. The conical spike of the M-wing aeroplane is an attempt to produce a satisfactory airflow with a reasonable windscreen profile. Higher speed aircraft feature retractable visors, drooping noses—and even retractable cockpits have been proposed.

Before discussing certain SST shapes, Fig. D.1.4 is of striking interest, a result of some of the work of Dr. Barnes Wallis, designer of the variable sweep Swallow, shown in Fig. 2.4. The curve relates, in effect, specific fuel consumption and air miles per gallon for different speeds and heights. The same quantity of fuel has been used

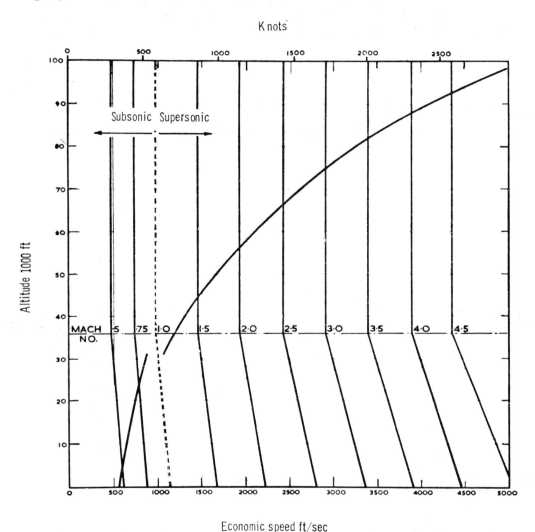

Fig. D.1.4   Economic speed and height

for the calculations throughout, and the curve corresponds very closely with that for a constant EAS of 350 k. It shows that the optimum range speed for best economy is about M=0·5 (500 ft/sec) at sea level, but that this increases steadily to M=4·5 (4,500 ft/sec) a little over 90,000 ft. At that speed steel can no longer be used and we have reached the forseeable limit for present technology. If the curve is assumed to join the design points for best economy, then the configuration of an efficient long range aeroplane must satisfy the speed and height combination at any point.

D.2   M = 2 Aeroplanes

Britain and France decided to build an SST in the M = 2 class because it can be made within the present state-of-the-art, using current aluminium alloys and structural techniques. The aircraft, which has an 'ogee' delta wing, is shown in the published form for 1965 in Fig. D.2.1. Earlier drawings showed the aircraft with marked

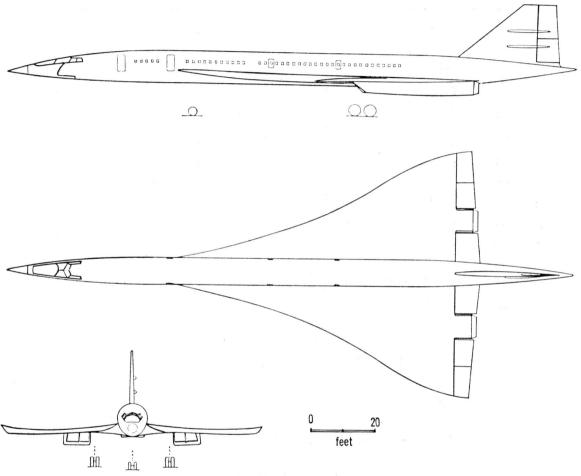

Fig. D.2.1   BAC-Sud Concorde as in 1965. The nose is less cambered than the original, and the fin may be given a lower drag semi-ogee profile similar to the wing. Both alterations would be to reduce cruising drag and improve the rather limited range

camber to the nose, so that the bottom profile appeared as an almost straight line. The nose is now less cambered and there are reports of the fin outline being changed to a semi-ogee profile, similar to a half-wing.

The Concorde is reported to have an all-up weight of 326,000 lb, a maximum payload of 26,000 lb and seating for 118 passengers. The useable fuel capacity (with reduced payload) is 174,000 lb. Using these figures, the maximum payload works out around 8 per cent and the maximum fuel load around 53 per cent of the gross weight.

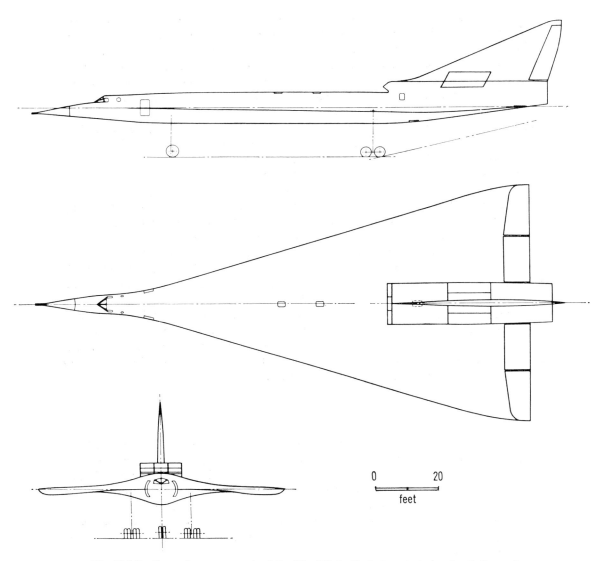

Fig. D.2.2   General arrangement of the M = 2·2 A–60 design study by the College of
Aeronautics, Cranfield, in 1960

The engines are four Bristol Siddeley Olympus 593 of 35,000 lb static thrust each.
The thrust loading on take-off is, therefore, 2·33 lb/lb, which corresponds with a wing
loading of 85 lb/ft².

The windscreen of the Concorde is covered with a retractable visor, and the nose
forward of the windscreen is arranged to droop in order to give the pilots a less
restricted view at low speed.

By comparison the SST shown in Fig. D.2.2 is the A–60 design study of the College
of Aeronautics, Cranfield. The aircraft is broadly similar to the Concorde, except that
there is no separate fuselage, the passengers being housed inside the integrated wing-
body. The cabin is formed by two cylinders, joined in a horizontal double-bubble.

The engine-box houses six 18,000 lb static thrust Olympus 591 engines in two rows, supplied with air from two-dimensional wedge intakes. The arrangement is very different from the twin underwing boxes of the Concorde and rather similar to an early proposal by the STAC. It should be noted that a Russian SST project shown at the Paris Salon in 1965 is very similar to the Concorde, but has the engines mounted in a long box beneath the fuselage, running the length of the centre-section.

The centre of gravity of the A–60 and Concorde will lie slightly forward of the leading pair of main wheels—about 1/12 (8 per cent) of the wheel base forward of the main leg. There is, therefore, a considerable side area ahead of the CG, in fact the centre of lateral area appears to lie forward of the estimated CG. This is a characteristic of high-speed aeroplanes which, for reasons of economy and CG position, cannot afford to carry heavy tail structures around with them. The natural weathercock stability must be augmented artificially with 'black-box' stability, using 'active controls'. Yaw is sensed by a gyro-unit and compensatory signals are fed to the rudder, which is caused to deflect in the correct sense, augmenting the natural fin sideforce. Active controls can be used to achieve all forms of stability.

Both designs have markedly cambered leading edges to the wings and, although no wing sections have been drawn, the amount may be judged from the head-on views. The camber is introduced to improve off-design lift/drag.

It should be noted that, whereas the passengers in the Concorde will have windows, the A–60 has none. The provision of cutouts for windows increases the structure weight, and there is considerable argument in many quarters about the real advantages of letting passengers see what is being done to them. Where no windows are fitted cabin television would have to be carried instead.

D.3   M = 3 Aeroplanes

Compared with the M = 2 SST there are many more problems to be met with the design of a M = 3 aircraft. Aluminium alloy can no longer be used in the high temperature environment, and steel must be used extensively. The Barnes Wallis graph in Fig. D.1.4 shows that the design point must lie around 75,000 to 80,000 ft, and something has already been said of the hazards of flight at such altitudes. Nevertheless, M = 3 designs are being considered in the U.S.A., simply because passengers associate higher speed with superiority of travel, even if they only gain forty minutes in a transatlantic journey.

Although the slender delta wing is attractive aerodynamically and structurally, and has a large volume, for supersonic flight beyond about M = 2·4 it becomes extremely difficult to combine the amount of sweep needed to keep the wing leading edge subsonic with good low speed properties. One particular difficulty is to provide enough elevator power to lift the nose on take-off—the useful lift coefficient is very low in any case and is further reduced by up-elevator.

A typical M = 3 SST is shown in Fig. D.3.1, the A–62 design study of the College of Aeronautics. The aircraft is directly comparable with the A–60 design, except for the higher cruising speed. Power is by four bypass engines of 30,000 lb static thrust, an increase of 66 per cent over that required for flight at M = 2·2 with the same payload and range performance. It was estimated that on a productivity basis an airline would be prepared to pay about £4 million for a M = 2·2 aircraft and £5·3 million for one of M = 3. The extra complication of the faster aircraft was estimated to make the M = 3 design at least 50 per cent more expensive to produce and, if the M = 2·2 machine had cost £4 million, the faster one would have cost at least £6 million, making it an unprofitable proposition for an unsubsidized airline.

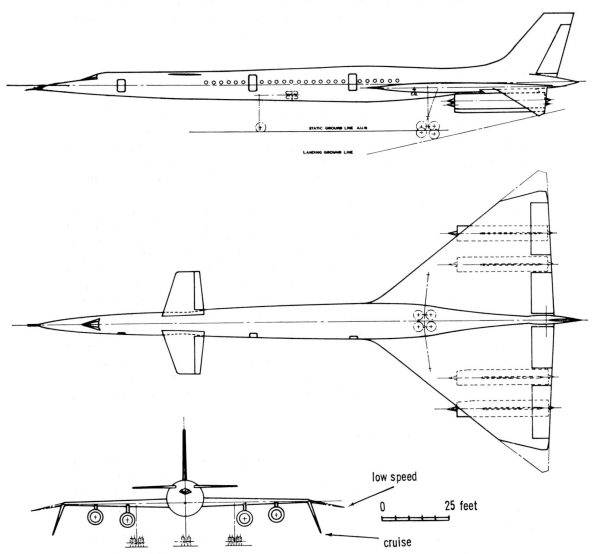

low speed

0   25 feet

cruise

Fig. D.3.1   General arrangement of the M = 3 A–62 design study of the College of Aeronautics, Cranfield, 1962

The aircraft were both designed to carry 108 passengers over 3,250 nml, the payload being 22,700 lb. The all-up weight of the M = 2·2 aircraft was 325,000 lb compared with 390,350 lb at M = 3. The structure weight of the faster (steel) aircraft worked out at 22·5 per cent, compared with the 19·9 per cent of the slower aluminium alloy SST. The payload of the M = 3 design was 5·7 per cent, but that of the M = 2·2 aircraft 7 per cent. One can see, therefore, how slender are the margins that must be worked to in weight control. The faster an aircraft is to fly, the more slender the margin for error.

Examination of Fig. D.3.1 shows how much further aft the CG might be estimated to lie. Apart from artificial directional stability the wing tips can be depressed in flight to improve the effective fin area. Depressing the tips also compensates for the rearward movement of the aerodynamic centre at supersonic speed.

D.4   Other Possible Solutions

The future is full of possibilities. Three alternative solutions to the problem of designing satisfactory supersonic transports are shown here, to emphasize several different approachs. The three solutions are: the Barnes Wallis Swallow with a variable-sweep wing; a 'slewed-wing' design that is completely asymmetric; and a slender 'wingless' airliner employing a large number of lifting engines. All appeared in the period 1958 to 1961 and may well have been shelved completely in the forms in which they were first published.

It will be remembered that the supersonic drag consists of the lift-dependent vortex drag, the wave drag due to both lift and volume, and the drag due to skin friction. The vortex drag is decreased as the span of the wing is increased, while the wave drag terms are decreased as the length of the aircraft is increased fore and aft. As the skin friction drag is roughly proportional to the wetted area of the aircraft it follows that the minimum drag should be obtained by keeping the surface area to a minimum, and then rearranging it so that it occupies a 'box' of the greatest possible area, as defined by the length and span. The proportions of the box would depend, however, upon the actual constants in the drag equations. Three alternative supersonic layouts are shown in this way in Fig. D.4.1. The first represents the slender delta already discussed. The second is the supersonic planform of Swallow-type aircraft. The third represents the slewed-wing. All have the same wetted area, roughly the same sweep, but the slewed-wing should, in theory, have the lowest cruising drag.

D.4.1   The Barnes Wallis Swallow

The Swallow project in Stage II of its development is shown in Fig. D.4.2. The aircraft does not represent the 100-seat SST version, which has a bigger discrete fuselage formed by a slender solid of revolution. In the drawing the pure aerodynamic shape is most clearly seen. The aircraft is by no means definitive but is representative of a wide range of Swallow aircraft.

The argument for the Swallow wing shape is the same as for the slender delta— that the lifting surface lies within the Mach cone—except that the part of the wing is cut away that makes no contribution to the lift and a lot to the drag caused by separated flow. The aircraft cannot land with the supersonic shape, because the undercarriage would have to be impracticably long to achieve a useful angle of attack. Therefore variable sweep is used, and the resulting shape is such that the aircraft would probably chase its M_{crit} as the value rose with increasing sweepback.

The engines are placed outboard, where they make a contribution to the static balance. As they are hinged, they can be used for stability and control in place of aerodynamic surfaces. The version shown has a retractable cockpit.

It is claimed that a supersonic aeroplane of this type would have a wing loading

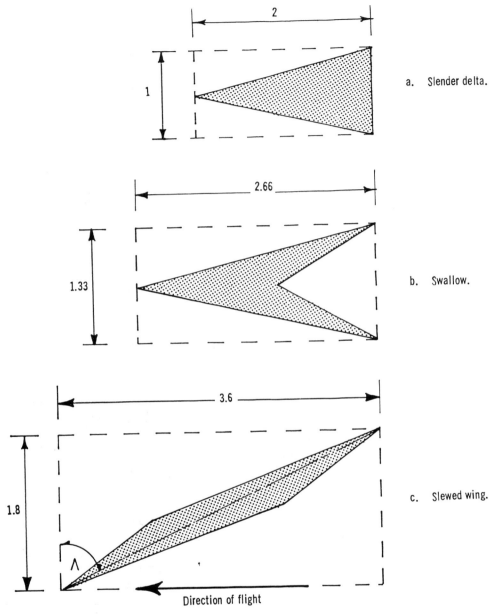

Fig. D.4.1   Three alternative supersonic planforms having the same wing area and, similar
sweep, but occupying different overall space

around 40 lb/ft^2, reversing the present trend towards values of 100 lb/ft^2, and it
would take-off in a few hundred yards at 85 to 90 k. A 60-passenger airliner, expected
to weigh 100,000 lb, would have a spread span of 130 ft, and a similar length with the
wings swept. The most controversial claim reported for the design is that it would be
possible to operate 'a daily return service to Australia with one Swallow—flying
time for the return flight would be about 10 hours'.

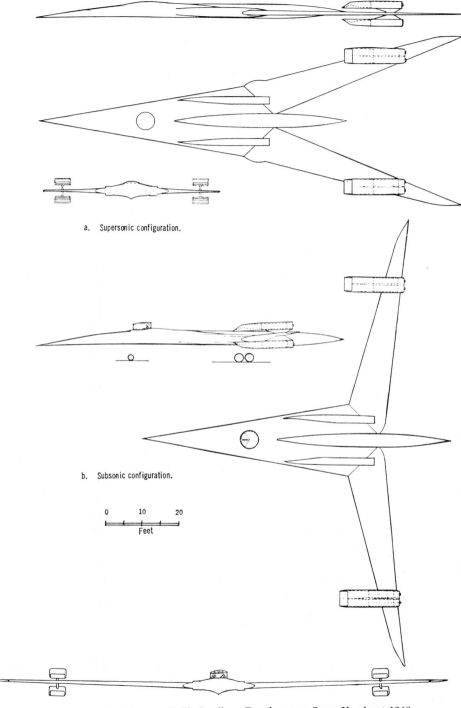

a. Supersonic configuration.

b. Subsonic configuration.

0   10   20
Feet

Fig. D.4.2   The Barnes Wallis Swallow, Development Stage II, about 1960

D.4.2 The Handley Page Slewed-Wing

The proposal for a slewed-wing aircraft was published in 1961, but as far as is known the design has not progressed beyond that shown in Fig. D.4.3. The slew-angle at which such a wing would fly is determined by the setting of the fin and rudder relative to the wing. The variable sweep mechanism would be considerable, involving simultaneous rotation of four engines, a crew nacelle and the fin and rudder. It is claimed that as the wing is supported on an ideal 'air-bearing' the structure is of minimum weight.

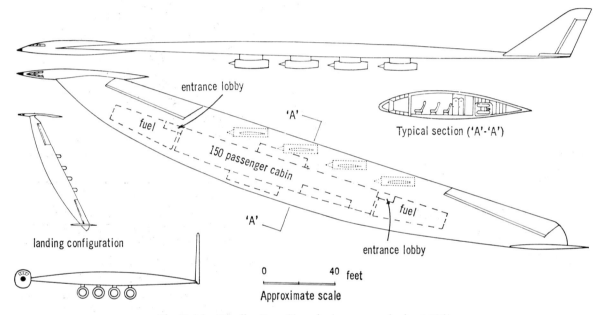

Fig. D.4.3   Handley Page Slewed-wing proposal, about 1961

The slewed-wing is reported to have a theoretical lift/drag 10 to 20 per cent better than a slender delta, requiring 10 to 20 per cent less fuel for the same payload and range. Calculations are said to show that for two $M=2$ aircraft having an all-up-weight of about 350,000 lb, the slewed-wing would require about 24,000 lb less fuel (using $\frac{1}{2}$ when cruising and $\frac{1}{2}$ subsonically), which is approximately equal to the weight of the 120 passengers carried in the slender delta wing. Like the all-wing subsonic transport, there is a certain minimum size below which it is impossible to provide adequate headroom.

The project suggests that slewed-wing aircraft are possible, if not yet probable. A difficulty lies in the cross-coupling of the three stabilities, particularly the longitudinal and lateral modes. Such an aircraft will not be able to make a straight stall, for loss of lift will be accompanied by roll, and corrective action could well aggravate matters.

D.4.3 The Griffith Airliner

The VTO proposal by Dr. A. A. Griffith is a slender delta for flight at $M = 2.6$, and is shown in Fig. D.4.4. Flight at low speed is by a large number of lifting engines, which give the aircraft VTOL capability. It is reported that jet-lift thrust is estimated by Rolls-Royce at 10–15 per cent above all-up weight, but some authorities favour something more like 25 per cent to meet the critical crosswind take-off case, when

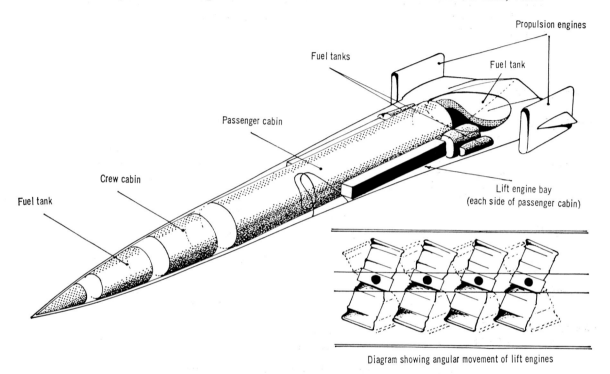

Fig. D.4.4 The Griffith conception of a possible long-range SST, about 1958

acceleration away from the ground must be as high as possible. Yet others favour considerably less than 12·5 per cent. The situation is far from clear, but calculations show that probably more than 50 lifting engines would be required for a transatlantic SST.

Momentum drag of the lifting engines would be high. Flight planning and timing would have to be impeccable. The lift engines would have to be started unfailingly and almost simultaneously, for it is said that they burn up to something like 1/30th of the all-up weight every minute. In spite of the operational problems, such an aircraft may well represent a practical line of development for SSTs of the late 1970s.

APPENDIX E

Strike and Reconnaissance Aeroplanes

If this appendix had been written even ten years ago it would have been split into perhaps two or three smaller appendices. Then there were still distinctive aircraft for high altitude interception (day fighting, night fighting) ground attack, fighter/reconnaissance, medium and heavy bombing, and high altitude reconnaissance. Today the distinguishing features are heavily blurred by the need for economy. An aircraft is designed to carry out a number of roles: night/all-weather fighting, fighter/strike, fighter/recce; tactical strike/reconnaissance; strategic bombing and reconnaissance. Even then it is hard to draw firm distinctions every time. Aircraft little larger than twin-engined, two-seat all-weather fighters now carry strategic nuclear weapons and are designed to make their final attack a little above the tree tops. The large, long-range, strategic bomber is gradually becoming the tanker conversion for in-flight refuelling fighter/strike aircraft, flying intercontinental distances, to reinforce operations in distant parts of the globe. In the U.K., for example, Fighter Command of the Royal Air Force must now provide 'instant air-defence' for overseas allies, in addition to the time-honoured task of defending the British Isles. When there the aircraft, that were basically all-weather interceptors, are used for ground attack in support of ground forces, and reconnaissance—in addition to their interceptor role.

The maritime reconnaissance aeroplane may well embrace several new roles eventually. There is a great similarity in shape between the long-range, relatively slow, maritime aeroplane carrying a lot of fuel and an anti-submarine warload, and the long-range subsonic transport machine. Already there is mention of a maritime version of the Comet airliner. The time may come when there is a subsonic transport version of a maritime aeroplane, for military use if not for civil.

Where the relatively new concept of the very long-range, high-flying, reconnaissance aeroplane is concerned (marked in the first instance by the Lockheed U–2) there is already a sign of such aircraft being fashioned for more than one role. The Lockheed YF–12A, shown in Fig. 8.15, is said to be a two-seat interceptor fighter development of the original A–11, designed for the strategic reconnaissance role. The reconnaissance version of the basic A–11, the SR–71, differs from the fighter primarily in having a large ventral mission-pod carrying reconnaissance equipment. All three machines are basically the same aerodynamically, structurally and propulsively.

E.1   The Basic Military Problem

It will be realized that nothing specific can be said about the problems of military design. One may only generalize, and even then the generalities are idealized, sometimes beyond recognition by those concerned with their reality.

The first difference between the military and civil aircraft is that, historically, military machines must be able to stand up to more punishment than civil, without falling apart. Great care must be lavished upon the basic design of every piece of engine, airframe and equipment. But one constantly comes up against the contrary effect of 'Murphy's Law'—that if a piece of equipment can be assembled or installed wrongly, then eventually someone will do so. Design for ruggedness, simplicity and reliability, all essential in military machines, is often hampered by the resulting ability to assemble wrongly. Whereas thousands of pounds may be saved in the production cost of one interchangeable item, several million pounds may be lost with an aircraft and crew, simply because the item was made interchangeable—and something was installed the wrong way round. A typical example is the use of a common plug for each end of a piece of electrical equipment.

The second difference is that military aeroplanes tend to have lower thrust and power loadings than aerodynamically comparable civil aircraft because high performance (especially manoeuvrability) is a necessity. This is shown in Fig. E.1.1. The curves are based upon information published in the aeronautical press and represent state-of-the-art boundaries within which most aircraft appear to lie. The supersonic transport and the supersonic bomber mark the most noticeable break with the traditionally higher thrust loading of the civil aircraft.

Military development has led civil development for a great number of years, largely because of the need to make the bomber outstrip the fighter, and the fighter catch any bomber. There was a period, just before the Second World War when civil transports became monoplanes while many bombers and fighters remained biplanes, when the civil machine led the military in performance, but it was short-lived. Many recent developments in the civil field are the result of 'spin-off' from military programmes, and something has been said of this already.

E.2   Fighter Strike/Reconnaissance

The original concept of the fighter aeroplane was that of an aircraft that could be used for intercepting enemy raiders and for dog-fighting with enemy fighters. The first specialization of role was the development of 'interceptor' fighters, designed for the sole purpose of destroying enemy bombers. Then came the use of fighters for ground-attack work, using guns and rockets—and it was only a short step to the fighter/strike aeroplane carrying bombs, and the fighter/reconnaissance machine carrying cameras and specially trained sharp-eyed pilots. The distinction between interceptor and fighter is academic—interceptors are specialized fighters. The essential difference lies only in the role. The interceptor is a fighter with a particularly fast climb, insufficient fuel to go anywhere, and no low-level performance. The ordinary fighter climbs more slowly, because it must carry additional fuel in overload tanks ('jugs') to be able to loiter, or fly for longer distances to its quarry. The additional fuel capacity gives it a low-level performance.

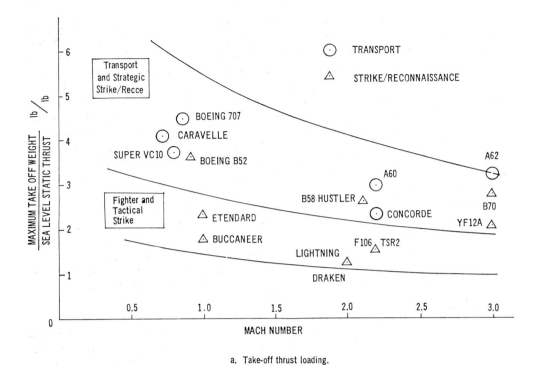

a. Take-off thrust loading.

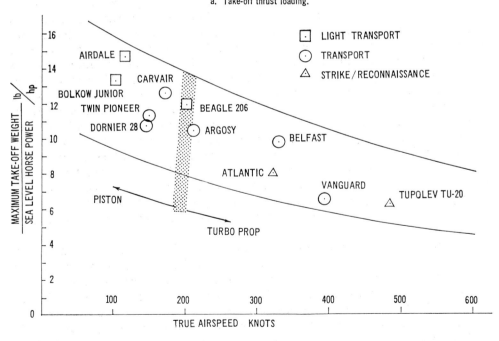

b. Take-off power loading.

Fig. E.1.1   Estimated state-of-the-art thrust and power loadings for current aircraft (1965)

The minimum rate of climb specified for a fighter is based upon the speed and height of the target and the amount of warning time that is available. A diagram of the airspace swept out by a radar scanner shows in section as a lobe. The greatest range of the radar is at high altitude, but the range decreases towards the ground until, at heights of a few hundred feet, the radar sees only a fraction of the distance that it can see at altitude. This characteristic of radar has led to the development of the very low flying strike aeroplane that is claimed to approach 'under the radar screen'. In fact such aircraft can be seen, all that has happened is that they are so close when seen, and flying so fast, that the warning time is shortened to the point where it is very hard to do much about them with anything but missiles. The ideal target for the interceptor is the high flying bomber, seen at great range and giving maximum warning time.

To obtain a high rate of climb we saw in Eq. (4–4) that $(F-D)V/W$ should be large. One may use a powerful engine to climb fast, but big engines are thirsty engines, and there will be little room left in the aircraft for fuel. Drag and weight must be cut to the minimum. The resulting aircraft usually has one large or two slightly smaller engines stowed inside a fuselage that also houses the crew and weapon system. The aim—more than with any other aircraft—is to dispose as much of the aircraft as possible within the minimum frontal area.

Wing loadings are high, but not as high as those of bomber and transport aircraft which cannot afford the degree of manoeuvrability that the fighter must achieve. Wing spans are small and span loading high, and this militates against low lift-dependent vortex drag. One is faced with the need to keep fighters long and slender, in order to reduce wave drag to a minimum, while keeping vortex drag as low as possible, to enable fighter aircraft to cruise efficiently off-design at high altitude and low indicated airspeed. If a fighter can reach 70,000 ft, and yet must descend to 35,000 ft for loitering, then fuel will be wasted in climbing back again through 30,000 ft or more when a target is sighted. Balancing the requirements for flight at the design point and off-design raises many unique problems for the designer of a fighter aircraft.

Eq. (6–16) showed how the planform efficiency and span loading are related. Swept, thin, wings have lower planform efficiencies than straight relatively thick wings with the same aspect ratio. A straight wing with a 7 per cent thick section and an aspect ratio of 2 has a planform 'inefficiency factor', K, of 1·12, compared with a value of 1·48 for a wing of the same thickness and aspect ratio but with 45° sweep to the quarter chord line. It will be remembered that the higher is K the larger is the lift-dependent (vortex) drag, so that the swept wing generates 1/3 more lift-dependent drag than the unswept wing at the same lift coefficient. But, of course, the wave drag is much lower.

It is possible to reduce K considerably by the use of camber and twist if an aircraft is to cruise for long periods at the design point. Bombers can be so treated, but fighters cannot, because they must spend long periods off-design. To offset the inevitably large planform inefficiency fighter span loadings must be kept as low as possible. Furthermore, the lower the span loading of a given wing the larger the residual C_L that can be used for manoeuvring. An aircraft with a $C_{L\max}$ around 0·8, a wing loading of 50 lb/ft² and a span loading around 500 lb/ft will stall in 1g flight at M=0·58 at sea level and M=1·08 at 70,000 ft. In order to handle such an undesirable state of affairs fighters must have span loadings no greater than, say, 600 to 650 lb/ft if they are to fight at high altitude. Fuel is used during the climb to height, so that the span loading on take-off is correspondingly higher.

Most fighter aircraft are fitted with overload fuel tanks which enable them to carry a further 2,000 to 3,000 lb externally. The original idea of the overload fuel tank was that of a cheap container that could be dropped when empty, leaving the clean fighter free to operate in a low drag condition with full internal fuel. Overload tanks are rarely jettisoned except in time of war, and have become standard equipment everywhere. Within the present state-of-the-art 2,000 to 3,000 lb of additional fuel enables the range to be increased by perhaps 200 to 300 nml at altitude, but to only half that at sea level. Overload tanks reduce manoeuvrability and reduce structural reserve factors to a certain extent.

Stowage volume is at a premium inside fighter aeroplanes, and there is an increasing tendency to carry guns (as well as missiles) externally. Missiles of the guided and homing variety are merely suspended on pylons, but guns and unguided rockets are carried in pods. Some very high performance interceptors carry their missiles internally, in weapon bays. In the strike role small nuclear weapons can be carried on pylons in place of missiles.

Modification of a basic fighter for the reconnaissance role usually involves an alteration of shape to the nose, to allow for camera stowage. Cameras and other equipment may also be carried in pods.

Control deflections and forces are large, and such aircraft have fully powered flying controls. Fins and tailplanes (used differentially) may be employed for lateral control in place of ailerons. Wings and tail surfaces are so thin that it is difficult to stow control surface operating jacks within a profile, and large streamlined fairings are usually seen with conventional trailing edge surfaces. In a number of cases tail surfaces are moved as complete slabs, without recourse to flap-like appendages. Control forces, feel, and stability characteristics are built into the systems artificially.

E.2.1 Variable Sweep Fighter

The fighter shown in Fig. E.2.1 was originally designed by the author in 1957, in the form of fixed-sweep interceptor, powered by a turbojet engine and a rocket motor. In that form the aeroplane was intended to be fast climbing, with a good burst of speed at altitude, to enable it to outfly any of the bomber and reconnaissance aeroplanes then in operation. Fighters do not always have to fight, much of the peace time work consists of interception for the express purpose of 'being seen to be there', and investigation of unknown traces that appear on the radar screens.

The aircraft carried two missiles, weighing together something like 1,200 lb, mounted externally on separate pylons. The top speed was $M = 2 \cdot 2$ at the tropopause, and the ceiling a little over 60,000 ft. The rocket engine could be used at the ceiling to give a rate of climb in excess of 30,000 ft/min, and enough oxidant could be carried to enable the machine to reach over 90,000 ft.

The principal disadvantage of the design was that insufficient fuel could be carried to make the tactical radius of action worth while. Bombers were beginning to carry stand-off weapons that could be launched hundreds of miles from their targets, and the aircraft was essentially a target-defence interceptor. Furthermore, the fuel consumption was so high at low altitude that an excessive number of machines would have been needed to achieve a reasonable probability of catching a fast low-level bomber. Long range reinforcement was out of the question without large overload tanks and critically reduced take-off performance.

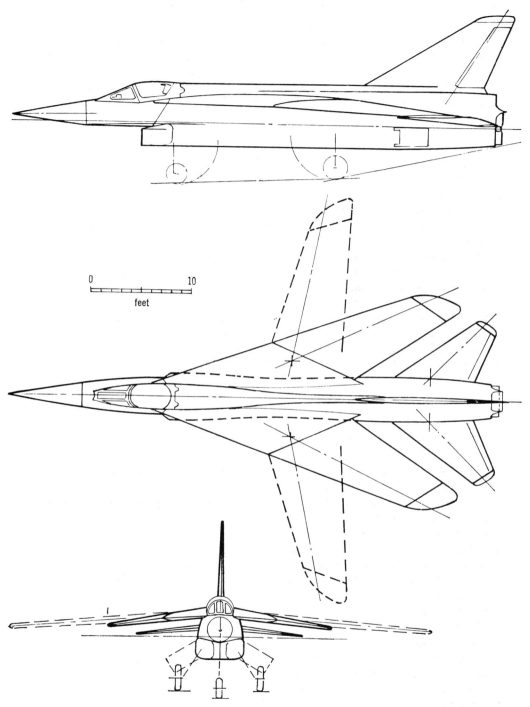

Fig. E.2.1 Variable sweep fighter (bypass engine plus rocket)

In its present form the aircraft has been reshaped around a larger bypass engine and fitted with a variable geometry wing. The rocket motor can still be fitted in the upper part of the rear fuselage. The wing had to be moved from a mid position to the top of the fuselage, to clear the engine and ducting when fully swept. The dihedral effect was then excessive and both wing and tailplane were given anhedral to prevent 'dutch-roll' at high altitude, and during the approach to landing. The undercarriage could not be retracted into the wing, but required the design of a complicated geometry to allow stowage in the fuselage without excessive interference with fuel tanks and ducting.

The engine has reheat, but a thrust sfc about 20 per cent better than the previous turbojet. The most marked improvement in efficiency has come with the variable-sweep wing. Simple trailing edge flaps are fitted, but no ailerons, and the wing (including flaps) is a complete fuel tank. Hinge design is somewhat complicated by the need for fuel and hydraulic lines to run almost through the same point. The tailplane consists of two tailerons, which together form ailerons and elevators.

The aircraft is, aerodynamically, a high winged delta. The rear portion of the centre-section, which contributes little to the lift and much to the drag, has been cut away and lowered to a position well clear of the wing-wake, where it can work as a stabilizer. The stabilizers (tailerons) could have been lowered further, but they have been placed in a mid position where jettisoned missiles will clear them, and where there is ample room between jetpipe and skin for mountings and mechanisms.

It was originally intended to provide the pilot with a complete cockpit capsule and parachute that could be rocket boosted away from the aeroplane in an emergency. An ejection seat was finally selected as being simpler, lighter and more reliable. To save space, electrical flying controls were used, stick and rudder-pedal deflection varying the electrical signal sent to the power control system.

The air intake has a central, variable angle, wedge for establishing the optimum pressure recovery. The nosewheel unit retracts into the structure behind the wedge. A ventral fuel tank can be fitted.

In its present form the range of the aeroplane has been increased by 64 per cent, and the overload ferry range is about 1,300 n ml. The machine is small, however, and lacks much development potential. As an interceptor the dry thrust loading with turbojet alone is about 1·5 lb/lb, and 1·1 lb/lb wet. With rocket and reheat together the thrust loading on take-off is about 0·86 lb/lb—in other words, if the aeroplane could be stood on its tail, it would go straight up. The wing loading is 50 lb/ft^2 with the wings spread, and the span loading 405 lb/ft. With the wings fully swept the equivalent figures are 56 lb/ft^2 and 770 lb/ft.

It is doubtful if such a small aeroplane will ever again be of much use in the present world. The trend is towards bigger, multi-crew aircraft carrying heavy electronic equipment, capable of flying long ranges and carrying out more than one role. A fighter such as that shown lacks utility and is too complicated and costly for what it can do. The advanced systems required for it to carry out its task deny the very elements of ruggedness and flexibility that are so necessary in a true fighter aeroplane.

E.3   Tactical Strike/Reconnaissance

The combination of tactical strike/reconnaissance is, in many respects, a completely new concept, and one that has caused a great deal of agonizing conflict between the military, the government and the aircraft industry in the U.K. over the past few years. Useful published information is comparatively scarce, but enough has been made known to reveal a number of interesting teaching-points.

E.3.1 The TSR.2

The BAC (Vickers) TSR.2, shown in Fig. E.3.1, was designed to meet the General Operational Requirement, GOR.339, circulated direct to the industry as well as the Ministry establishments in the second half of 1957. The aircraft companies were asked to submit feasibility studies. The configuration of the aircraft was determined by three factors: the ability to penetrate to a target at low altitude and high speed; STOL in crosswinds from rudimentary (bulldozed) airstrips; and the ability to fly reasonably long ferry-ranges. The thin delta wing was held to afford the best compromise of low lift slope (low gust response) essential for low-level supersonic flight, while providing a wing large enough for STOL.

The engines were two Bristol Siddeley Olympus 320s, rated at 30,000 to 33,000 lb static thrust with reheat. Estimates indicate that the machine would have been capable of $M = 2.2$ or more, and would have had a take-off weight around 100,000 lb. The take-off span loading would have been about 2,700 lb/ft and the equivalent wing loading about 145 lb/ft^2. One may deduce that the lift-dependent drag would have been very high at altitude and low EAS (the best range with a turbojet is at or above the tropopause). To aid short take-off the nosewheel leg could be extended, setting the aeroplane at a larger angle of attack and providing a thrust component in the vertical plane. The low aspect ratio wing would have no clearly defined stall and would be providing a good working lift at low take-off speeds, despite the high drag, so that time would be saved by avoiding running forward to the speed where enough 'bite' from the tailplane could be used to rotate the aircraft.

With flap down there would have been a strong nose-down pitching moment to be countered by the tailplane, acting on a short moment arm. One may guess that the centre of gravity would lie about 60 per cent of the length from the nose, and larger tail surfaces (more tail-volume) would have imposed heavier weight penalties. The tailplane (or tailerons) had small trailing edge flaps—in effect camber-increasing flaps—to increase the overall slope of the tailplane lift curve. In this way deficient tail volume would be compensated for by the increased effectiveness of the tailplane when deflected.

One may also conjecture that the aircraft would have been deficient in 'natural' directional stability with such a small fin-volume. It is probable that the fin would have required deflection to counter yaw, thus augmenting the natural stability. No doubt the artificial stability would be supplied by picking signal information from a central inertial system, the pick-up then being fed into the flying control system. The conjecture about a deficiency in fin-volume is supported by the wing tip anhedral. It is probable that the aircraft would have suffered from dutch-roll, a lateral and directional oscillatory instability, caused by too much dihedral effect and too little fin. The anhedral tip is the simplest and cheapest structural modification to reduce the lateral stability relative to the apparently deficient natural directional stability.

The wing appeared to have a sweep of 50° at the quarter chord and an aspect ratio of 2. The gross wing area was about 700 ft^2 and the ratio of the wetted area to wing area appears to have been about 5. The span of 37 ft suggests that span^2/wetted area

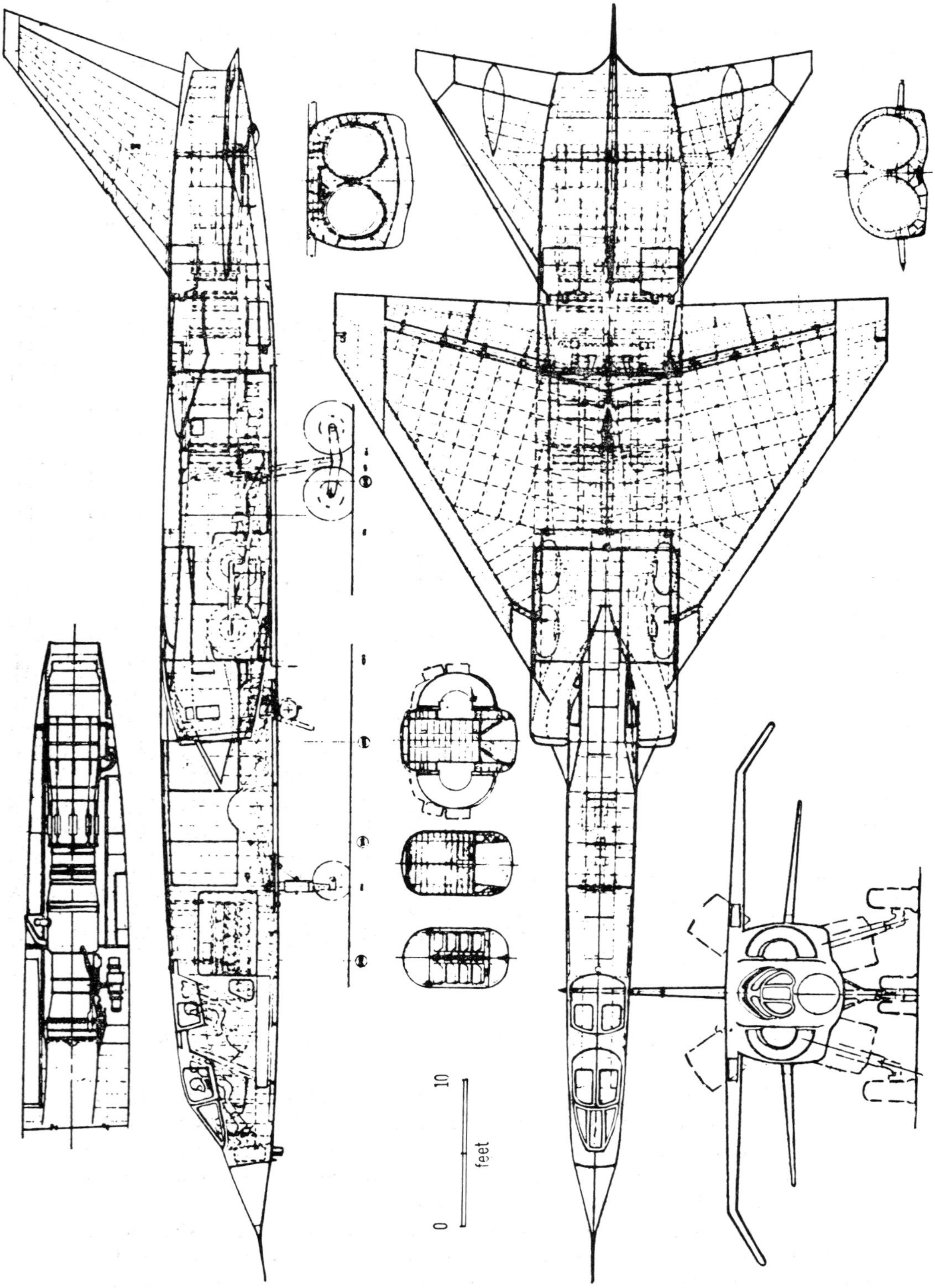

Fig. E.3.1 BAC TSR.2, U.K., first flown 1964

10

feet

0

would have been something like 0·38. Using Fig. 6.23, the maximum subsonic lift/ drag would have been around 8 to 10, say 9 as a reasonable average. At supersonic speed the $(L/D)_{max}$ might have been around $\frac{2}{3}$ of that value—say 6. Some idea of the magnitude of the forces involved begins to emerge. The engines would have developed about $2\frac{1}{2}$ tons of thrust each to move the aircraft through the air at the design point, while burning perhaps one ton of fuel every ten minutes in doing so.

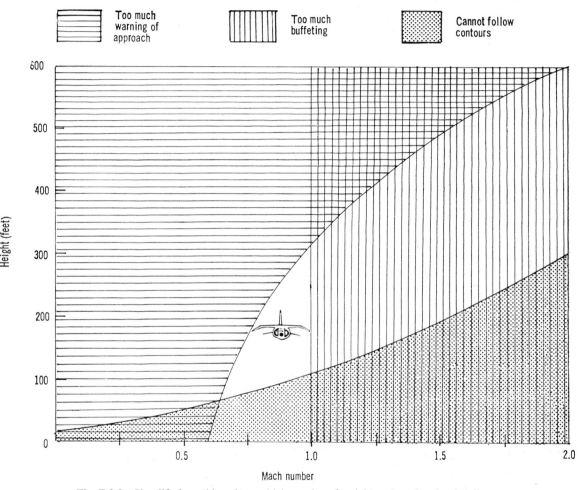

Fig. E.3.2 Simplified corridor along which an aircraft might make a low level strike

The TSR.2 had a crew of 2 and could carry bombs internally. The navigational and other electronic equipment—generally collected within the term avionics—was extremely complicated, and probably very heavy. The whole aeroplane was an airborne weapon system designed to operate at a height of one or two hundred feet. A simplified corridor of operation is shown in Fig. E.3.2.

The low aspect ratio wing, as mentioned earlier, would have had a shallow lift/ angle of attack curve. It may be shown that the normal acceleration imposed by a gust, which changes the angle of attack by an amount w/V, is directly proportional to the lift slope, the wing loading and the velocity of the aircraft. The shallower the slope, and the higher the wing loading, the faster the aeroplane may fly without requiring excessive structure weight and, hence, a reduction in fuel load. At too high a speed it is impossible to follow the ground contours without imposing excessive normal accelerations. It follows that there is a relationship between the type of terrain over which an attack is to be made, the speed at which one must fly, and the minimum height above the ground. If one flies too slowly, or too high, then there is a danger of being seen by the radar and caught by fighters and missiles. Flying too fast causes compressibility buffet. One may deduce from the TSR.2 wing that compressibility would have become critical round about $M = 1 \cdot 0$.

Reports in the press suggest that the TSR.2 became too highly specialized and was overtaken by events, for during the development period defence requirements began to change radically. The aircraft was designed for low level strike and reconnaissance and, one may guess, lacked the aerodynamic efficiency for long-range flight at altitude. A reappraisal of future operations in other parts of the world, where action must be carried out cheaply, would make the aircraft appear as a very expensive and mighty sledgehammer for cracking nuts. It is significant that the project was shelved in 1965, after more money had been spent upon it than upon any other single weapon system in the British armoury. It is also perhaps significant that the manufacturers, the British Aircraft Corporation, were showing a model of a broadly similar aeroplane, but with a variable sweep wing, at the Paris Salon in 1963.

E.3.2   1958 Project Low-Level Bomber

By comparison a particularly interesting project of the College of Aeronautics, Cranfield, is shown in Fig. E.3.3. The aeroplane was designed in the year following the circulation of GOR.339, that led to the TSR.2.

The low-level bomber is smaller than TSR.2 and weighed about $\frac{1}{3}$ of the estimated all-up weight of the former aeroplane. Note the very low aspect ratio wing, and what has been said of wing loading and lift slope. The design speed was $M = 1 \cdot 5$ at sea level. Rockets were to boost the take-off thrust of the six $\times$ 2,200 lb sea level static thrust turbojet engines. The six engines were housed within the wings, the exhaust gases being led across the rear 17 per cent of the upper wing surface. We may assume that the exhaust would increase the lift of the wing by inducing super-circulation.

The operational range was 1,200 nml carrying a 2,000 lb guided stand-off bomb. This was housed in an area-ruled recess in the bottom of the fuselage. The ventral fin would have been more efficient at large angles of attack than a dorsal fin, but the approach and landing speed would have needed close control to maintain the landing attitude within the inevitably narrow limits   One shudders to think of the effects of engine failure.

E.4   Strategic Strike/Reconnaissance

The traditional long range, high altitude bomber/reconnaissance aeroplane is covered by the term strategic strike/reconnaissance   Such aircraft used to carry anti-fighter armament in the form of rearward-firing guns, but this is no longer practicable

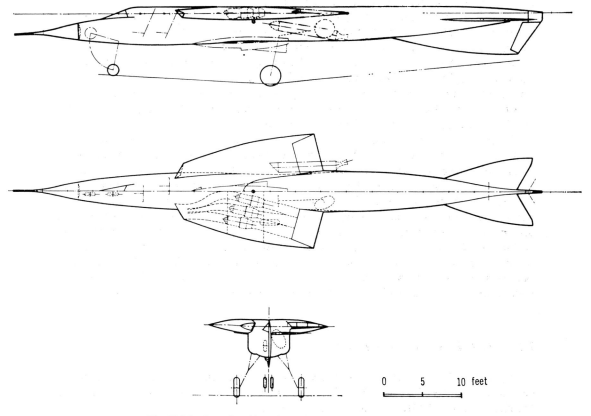

Fig. E.3.3 Low-level bomber. College of Aeronautics, 1958

because of the severe weight penalties involved, and because fighters can attack with guided weapons while staying well out of range

The modern strike/reconnaissance aeroplane must rely on the evasive power of:

(a) High speed, *i.e.*, M = 2 to 3.

(b) Flight at very high altitude, above, say, 65,000 ft (the steady ceiling is usually higher than that of a fighter).

(c) Improved manoeuvrability.

(d) Small size—to reduce the radar reflectivity of the surfaces.

(e) Radio counter-measure (RCM) equipment for jamming enemy radio and radars.

In many ways the design problems are similar to those of the supersonic transport aeroplane, except that one might expect the strike/reconnaissance machine to be smaller. One must achieve maximum economy in fuel consumption, and for this the engine and aerodynamic efficiencies must be of much the same order as for the SST. Radar reflectivity, however, is a function (among other things) of frontal area. If one is to achieve intercontinental ranges with an aircraft of smaller volume than the SST, then we might expect to see a slight difference in structural (and aerodynamic) layout.

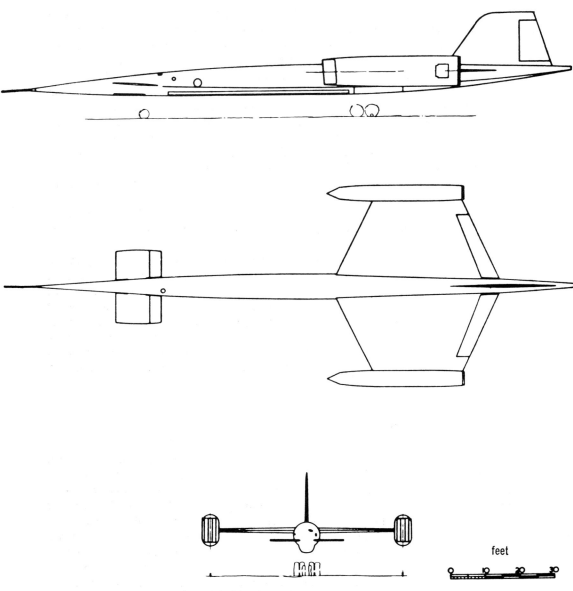

Fig. E.4.1   The Avro 730 (U.K., about 1956)

The most important difference in structural layout would be the use of bending-relief. Instead of mounting engines inboard, within the fuselage, or in centre-section and centre-line boxes, the engines would be hung outboard, along the wings. The wing tips are a most attractive position for the engines, for in that position they not only provide maximum bending relief, but serve as endplates that increase the effective aspect ratio by reducing the effects of the tip vortices.

Arguments have already been stated for the slender delta and canard layouts in Chapter 8, where the aerodynamic sum was balanced. There, Fig. 8.15 showed the general arrangement of the Lockheed YF–12A, and this should be compared with Fig. E.4.1, which shows the cancelled Avro 730 reconnaissance aeroplane of 1955 to 1957. Both aircraft have their engines placed outboard and have similar orders of slenderness, although the Avro 730 would have been much longer overall.

The Avro 730 had centrally mounted mainwheel units—almost a bicycle arrangement (including nacelle outriggers), except that the mainwheels carried most of the weight of the aeroplane. A strike version would have required a rearrangement of the mainwheels, to provide room for weapon stowage in the fuselage. The alteration might have entailed fitting nacelles beneath the wings, to house wheels and fuel, for there would have been no room in the engine nacelles, and some fuel volume would have been surrendered in the fuselage. To meet the runway LCN requirements at maximum weight four extra main wheels were fitted, these could be dropped after take-off.

Instead of a conventional cockpit the pilot had a periscope. This was retracted in flight and raised on take-off and landing. The aircraft would have had a crew of at least three: pilot, navigator and air electronics operator.

Nothing can be said of performance, but from Fig. D.1.4 one might expect the cruising speed to have been $M = 2 \cdot 2$ to $2 \cdot 5$ at 65,000 ft, and the range anything from 4,000 to 5,000 n ml. The structure would be of steel. Payload would be of a similar order to that of the SST (same state-of-the-art) and such supersonic aeroplanes would be able to carry no more than a small number of individual weapons. To obtain the maximum effectiveness weapons would inevitably be nuclear. If one wishes to carry a large number of conventional bombs one is automatically limited to the traditional bomber, similar in size, shape and performance to the long-range subsonic transport aeroplane.

E.5   Maritime Strike/Reconnaissance

Some years ago there was talk of the design of true water-based strike aircraft, and a fighter was built in Britain (the Saunders Roe SR/A1), but little further has been done up to the time of writing. Apart from the report that public interest is being shown in the U.S.A. in a submersible military aircraft (Chapter 10), maritime work is mainly concerned with anti-submarine and shipping strike and reconnaissance from land bases. The Russians have a long-range maritime reconnaissance flying boat, the Beriev BE–10 (NATO code-name Mallow), and the Americans are reported to have operated seaplanes so successfully off Vietnam (1965) that the Department of Defence is believed to be considering afresh the use of amphibians. But on the whole maritime aircraft are now land-based. In this appendix we will not consider water-based bombers and fighters as such. Instead we will accept the continuing need for long-range maritime aeroplanes for anti-submarine and shipping work, and consider the relative merits of a landplane and flyingboat for the same job.

Maritime landplanes are similar in size and configuration to most low-subsonic transport and bomber aircraft and in many cases they are direct developments of airliners and bombers. Aeroplanes designed for maritime work must be able to carry bombs, depth-charges, homing-torpedoes, flares, mines, and a vast assortment of search equipment. Their work involves flying for long hours at low altitudes over the sea, and they therefore require engines that are economical low down. Search and patrol are primary tasks and crew positions are needed with ample room for camera operation. Searchlights may be carried, and a certain amount of electronic counter-measure equipment.

Power is by piston, turboprop, or (in future) by regenerative turboprops, which are being developed to produce fuel consumptions as low as the most economical piston engines. It is doubtful if turbojet propulsion will ever produce wholly satisfactory results with such aeroplanes, simply because they have to spend so much time at speeds and heights where turbojets are grossly uneconomical.

One cannot lay down any hard and fast ruling on the order of percentage payload to be carried by such aircraft. One sortie may involve the carriage of 20,000 lb of mines a few hundred miles, while another may involve a search, without warload, over thousands of square miles of ocean. Clearly, the more fuel that can be carried the better, and one can only say that the disposable load should be as large as possible.

Just as multi-role thinking is affecting other military aircraft, so too is it likely to affect requirements for maritime aircraft. There have been reports published in Britain, for example, of a foreseeable need for aircraft that can be used both for maritime work and in the transport role, carrying troops and equipment over inter-continental distances. This is taken into account in the layout and size of the two aeroplanes to be discussed.

The landplane has been used as the yardstick for measuring the performance of the flyingboat. The two aircraft were specified by the author to have the same all-up-weight and engines, and basically the same aerofoil surfaces. Both were to fly as far as possible, the only real requirement being that it should be possible to carry 15,000 lb of warload, freight, or soldiers and equipment for a minimum distance of 2,000 nml.

E.5.1 Maritime Landplane

Landplane operations are affected by the size of airfield available. Working to state-of-the-art figures as shown in Fig. E.5.1 the basic aircraft had a wing loading of 90 lb/ft², a power loading of a little over 6 lb/hp, an all-up weight of 142,000 lb and a wing area of 1,580 ft². The wing had a basic section of 15 per cent thickness, no sweep, a span of 120 ft and an aspect ratio of 9·1. Power was by four 5,500 to 5,700 ehp turboprops, a low power loading being chosen to give scope for inevitable 'stretching' of requirements, and enough power for the seaplane to still take-off on three engines.

A preliminary drawing of the aeroplane is shown in Fig. E.5.2. The fuselage had a double-bubble section with a large weapon-bay below the wing centre-section. The bottom of the fuselage cleared the ground by about 3 ft, so that the undercarriage might be kept short and light. The bomb doors were double-hinged, to fold horizontally beneath the wings when on the ground, thus facilitating loading of weapons. Overload tanks could be carried within the weapon bay. Wing tip fuel tanks could be fitted.

Search radar was carried, and magnetic anomoly detector (MAD) gear in the tail-sting. A searchlight was carried under the starboard wing and ECM devices in the fin-blister. Four transparent blisters were arranged (two per side) for observation purposes.

With 15,000 lb payload the range was about 2,400 nml, and with maximum fuel load and no payload, a little over 3,200 nml. Carrying 14,000 lb overload fuel the range would have been about 4,000 nml. The cruising speed, depending upon weight, was 300 to 350 k at 15,000 to 20,000 ft. By using twin-engined cruising procedure,

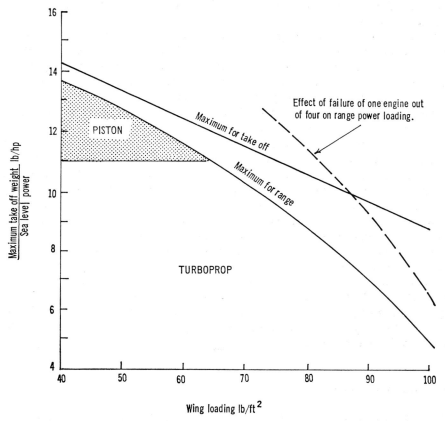

Fig. E.5.1   State-of-the-art wing and power loading limitations for multi-engined propeller driven aircraft

but at a much lower altitude, it would have been possible to extend the endurance to well over 12 hours. In the transport role 40 troops might be carried.

The aircraft was fitted with Fowler flaps. Reverse-pitch propellers were used, for deceleration at maximum weight.

E.5.2   Maritime Flyingboat

The flyingboat is shown in Fig. E.5.2. The aircraft had the same operational features as the landplane, and the hull was to be basically the same as the fuselage above the main deck. A double-bubble hull section was used—the depth of the hull needed for engine spray-clearance allowing the weapon deck to be very deep.

The arrangement of bomb doors, and a retractable radome for search radar in the bottom of the fuselage is a reasonably simple and straight forward matter with a landplane. In the case of a flyingboat there are certain difficulties. If bomb doors are fitted in the planing-bottom, then they must lie in the vicinity of the CG—*i.e.*, forward of the step—in the region that takes the load-on-water when planing, and a correspondingly heavy pounding. Doors have to be strong (heavy), water-tight and

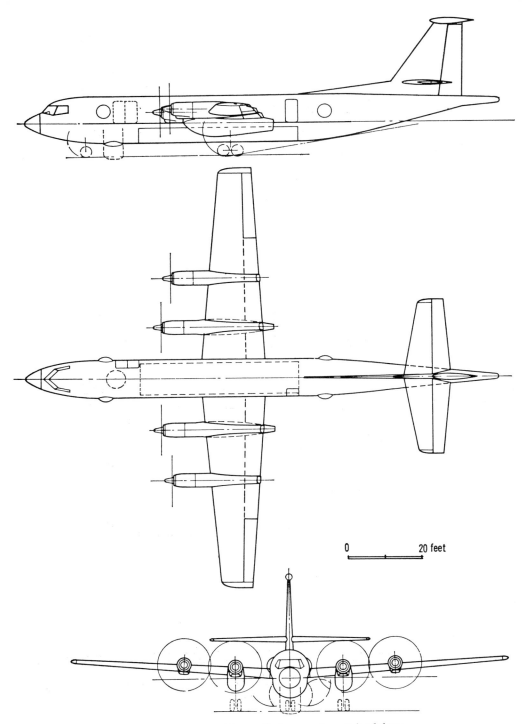

Fig. E.5.2   Maritime strike/reconnaissance landplane

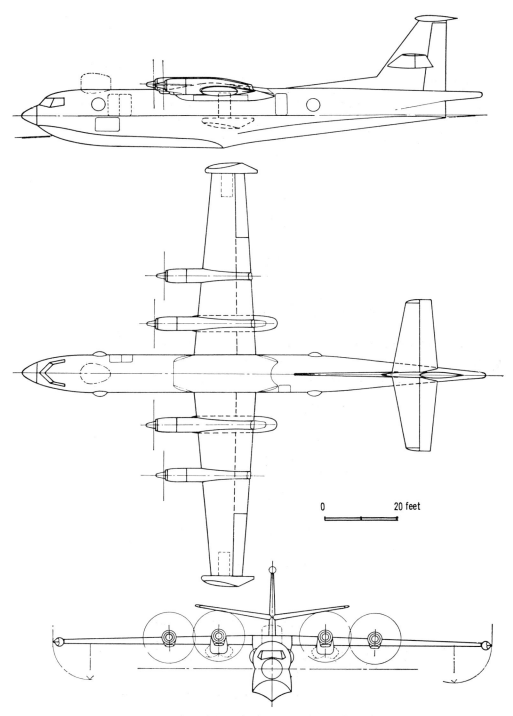

Fig. E.5.3   Maritime strike/reconnaissance flyingboat

0   20 feet

corrosion-proof. Fortunately there is a way out in that stores can be ejected rearwards instead, from chutes in the after planing-bottom. The technique is used for certain supersonic strike aeroplanes. An operational advantage of rearward ejection is that stores can be dispensed with no forward speed, directly over a target, and aiming errors are thus reduced. Weapon bays can be provided under the inboard engine nacelles, and this simplifies matters still further.

The radome is more of a problem. Retraction into the planing-bottom is beset with the same difficulties as for bomb doors—and failure of the retraction mechanism could raise critical difficulties on landing. A retractable radome above the fuselage would reduce the internal space for passengers, and the scanner would be shielded to a certain extent by the hull and wings. A non-retracting radome causes high drag, but could be the simplest solution, depending upon the relative importance of the other requirements. Some radar could be carried in the nose, however, and the problems would be not altogether insuperable.

The structure weight of the aircraft was higher than that of the landplane: about 33 per cent as against 28 per cent. If an undercarriage had been fitted for amphibious work, then the structure weight would have risen to something like 38 per cent. Weight could have been saved by having fixed wing-tip floats, but there were aero-dynamic advantages in making them retractable. The higher structure weight of the flyingboat reduced the fuel load by about $\frac{1}{6}$ with the 15,000 lb payload.

The hull increased the drag of the flyingboat by 8 to 10 per cent. The overall effect of increased drag, reduced cruising speed and fuel load, reduced the range of the flyingboat by 17 to 18 per cent compared with the landplane. Overloading the flying-boat is far less serious than a landplane, however, for by increasing the take-off weight to 171,000 lb the cruising range could have been increased almost to the 4,000 n ml of the overloaded landplane without making excessive spray during the take-off run.

The aircraft would have carried the same payload, but the high wing left the main deck clear beneath the centre-section allowing another 30 or so troops to be carried. With the 15,000 lb payload the range was 2,000 n ml and the cruising speed 280 to 330 k between 15 and 20,000 ft.

TABLE E.5.1

Item	Maritime Landplane	Maritime Flyingboat
Design weight lb	142,000	142,000
Payload, lb	15,000	15,000
	(including 40 troops)	(including 70 troops)
Take-off power loading, lb/ehp	6·2	6·2
Take-off wing loading lb/ft^2	90	90
Percentage structure weight	28	33
		(amphibian 38)
Drag	—	increased by 8 to 10%
Cruising speed, knots	300 to 350	280 to 330
Range with payload, n ml	2,400	2,000
Full fuel range (no payload), n ml	3,200	2,600
Overload fuel, lb	14,000	29,500
Full overload range (no payload), n ml	4,000	4,000

Table E.5.1 compares the landplane and flyingboat. Although the flyingboat has the disadvantages of reduced range, or reduced payload, it would still be a formidable and very flexible aircraft. Such machines can fly well beyond the range of fighters, are not restricted to land bases, and can operate wherever there is a supply ship. They can be more heavily overloaded than a landplane, as was found on a large number of occasions during the Second World War, simply because longer take-off runs are usually available.

Finally, it should be noted that the figures given for both are based upon transport state-of-the-art and not those of military aircraft, which are unobtainable. There is certain published evidence that maritime aeroplanes, smaller than those shown here, fly much further, over ranges of 5,000 or more miles. It is certain that given the right order of payload and equipment weights the figures for the two aircraft could be increased.

E.6 Naval Aeroplanes

From the operational point of view naval aeroplanes are broadly similar in role and in appearance to those that carry out strike and reconnaissance roles from land bases. Design requirements limit naval aeroplanes in different ways, however, and the design limitations are imposed by the physical characteristics of aircraft carriers.

Decks are short and limited in the loads that they can take. A ship rolls and pitches at sea, while runways are stationary (a ship must be under way to create enough wind for launching and landing aircraft back on deck). Lifts for carrying aircraft below decks are necessarily small. Hangar space between decks is cramped, in height and in extent. Operations may take place anywhere between the harsh extremes of Arctic, tropics and Antarctic. Aircraft picketed on deck spend their lives in a perpetually high wind, are frequently drenched by sea water, and permanently coated with corrosive salts.

Because of these limitations naval aeroplanes are small in size (VTOL may one day change the picture) and correspond with most single turbo-prop anti-submarine aircraft with no land-based counterparts. Naval aircraft are also built differently and have different protective finishes.

Undercarriages are stronger than those needed on land. Shock-absorbers have a longer stroke for absorbing the impact of meeting a deck that is rising towards the landing aircraft. Catapult points are incorporated in structures, which must be correspondingly strong enough to take the shock of acceleration to flying speed from a standing start in some 200 feet. Arrester hooks are fitted to decelerate the aircraft from flying speed to rest in similar distances. It should be noted that the use of arrester hooks is being investigated for supersonic land-based aircraft, to ease the problem of designing brakes for emergency stops on take-off and landing (in the U.S.A. hooks are fitted to all Century-series fighters).

Wings and fins are designed to fold so that aircraft can be stowed between decks. Turboprop machines need propeller-brakes to prevent windmilling when picketed on deck.

Because of these design considerations naval aeroplanes are heavier than land-based machines. But their special design requirements put them in a class that, in many ways, indicates a line of future development for many comparable land-based aircraft.

Vertical and Short Take-off and Landing (*VSTOL*) Aeroplanes

Over recent years there has been a widespread movement towards the design of aircraft for more than one role. Counter-insurgent (COIN) aircraft, for which many design studies were investigated in the 1960s, represented an attempt in the U.S.A. to evolve an aircraft capable of close air support, visual and photographic reconnaissance, helicopter escort, artillery fire control, airborne delivery of para-troops, and cargo delivery. From the practical point of view COIN aircraft made no real impact upon the direction of design. Other avenues were opening up, especially one marked by the British Aerospace Harrier (Fig. F.1.1) which has now proved itself to the hilt in battle in ways which are disbelieved by incredulous sceptics whose attitude is: 'Don't confuse me with facts, my mind's made up.' This highly successful aeroplane has operated with both the Royal Air Force and the Royal Navy in support of the Army.

F.1 Design for VSTOL

Design for VSTOL breaks into two: design for vertical take-off; and design for short take-off: both of which imply maximum weight. The landing is usually made at a lighter weight. Although there are design concepts on drawing boards for large VSTOL machines, those which are already in use are necessarily small in size. The Sea Harrier shows that, while small, the folding nose still emphasises the need to watch the dimensions of an aircraft carrier lift. Such machines have given a new lease of life to the concept of the aircraft carrier. The thrust of an engine for vertical take-off (which is, by definition, independent of the size of wing) must be around twenty per cent more than the operational take-off weight, to provide a margin for manoeuvre and acceleration. An excess of thrust bestows the benefit of overload when there is room for a take-off run. It follows that if an aeroplane is designed for VTOL, the wing can be much smaller than for an aircraft wing matched to the take-off requirements. However, when there is a surface which can be used for a take-off ground run, the wing can be relied upon to provide some of the lift, so enabling an operational overload to be carried.

Take-off performance can be shown theoretically as a function of wing loading, thrust (or power) loading, take-off lift coefficient, relative density and thrust/drag. It may be shown that the ground-run depends upon the aerodynamic and propulsive

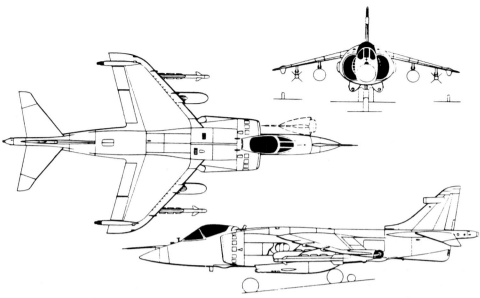

Fig. F.1.1   BAe Sea Harrier Mk1 VSTOL fighter, reconnaissance and strike aircraft (Pilot Press *and* Jane's All the World's Aircraft)

factors in the following equation:

$$K_s = \left(\frac{W}{S}\right)\left(\frac{W}{F}\right)\left(\frac{1}{C_{Lto}}\right)\left(\frac{1}{\sigma}\right)$$

where the terms have their previous meanings, except that C_{Lto} is the take-off lift coefficient (which may be assumed to have a value around 0.75 C_{Lmax}). The take-off distance is shown in Fig. F.1.2 as a function of K_s, which neglects the thrust loading term W/F. The term has been used in the determination of the curve, however, by using typical state-of-the-art values. It should be noted that σ, the relative density, varies with altitude and temperature – and so does thrust.

The aeroplane must be designed so that 0.75 C_{Lmax} can be obtained during the ground run. From Fig. F.1.2, knowing the field length and the aerodynamic properties of a design, the thrust loading can be determined for a number of climatic conditions. In the case of a propeller-driven aeroplane the thrust loading may be converted to power loading, W/P, from Eq. (7–6), where:

$$\frac{FV}{550} = nP \text{ hp}$$

Where there is no component of thrust in the lifting plane the velocity may be taken to be 0.7 of the take-off speed at 0.75 C_{Lmax}. The calculation of thrust and power loading must, of course, take account of engine failure on take-off. But when a component of thrust augments the wing lift of a military aircraft this condition cannot apply.

Take-off distance is usually specified to clear an obstacle of a given height (35 ft or 50 ft) and there is a difference between ground run as such and take-off distance. This is included in Fig. F.1.2 for a 50 ft obstacle. In order to generate take-off lift early the COIN aeroplane had much of the wing span lying within the propeller slipstream.

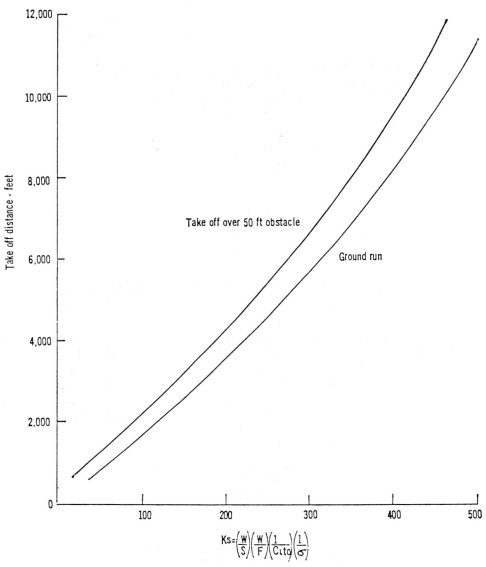

$$Ks = \left(\frac{W}{S}\right)\left(\frac{W}{F}\right)\left(\frac{1}{C_{Lto}}\right)\left(\frac{1}{\sigma}\right)$$

Fig. F.1.2   Take-off distance chart

This necessitated short wing spans quite apart from the carrier lift requirement, and in most cases design for the lowest possible wing loading also led to parallel chord wings with little or no taper. Slotted flaps were used for high efficiency on take-off and landing.

F.2   The North American OV–10A

The winner of the competition for Counter-Insurgent aircraft was the North American OV–10A, shown in Fig. F.2.1. The first aircraft flew in July 1965. Of

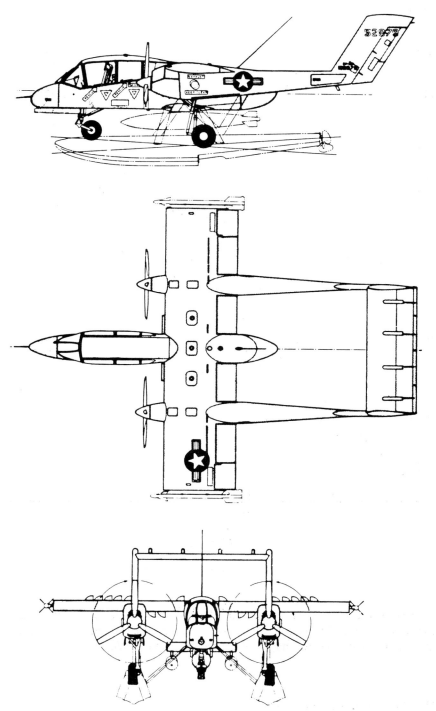

Fig. F.2.1 The North American OV-10A

particular interest were the steps that led to the prototype. It is reported that between 30 and 40 different concepts were studied initially, covering some 250 different design points. A biplane version offered the smallest and most compact arrangement with the least complexity, but fell short in other ways. When operating from a sod runway the OV–10A was claimed to take-off after a run of under 400 ft and clear a 50 ft obstacle in 800 ft at an all-up weight of 8,600 lb. The figures corresponded with power and wing loadings of 6·5 lb/hp and 40 lb/ft². The maximum take-off weight was 13,300 lb, and the wing loading about 61 lb/ft² – with no STOL capability.

F.3   The Wide Airspeed Aeroplane

The author investigated a number of other designs of VSTOL aircraft in the late 1960s, one in particular intended for use in the battlefield, with the flexibility of the helicopter. The target specification was for an aeroplane to be able to take-off and land vertically, carrying 4,000 lb of bombs; with a radius of action of 250 nm at sea level and maximum speed not less than M 0·8. The fuselage was shaped to carry an alternative load of ten troops. Because of fighter opposition it was thought necessary to be able to pull 7 g when flying fast. In the low speed mode it was specified to match a rigid rotor helicopter, which could pull about 2·5 g.

A 'barber's pole' type of rotor incorporating boundary layer control was selected. This, designed by the National Gas Turbine Establishment, was hollow-bladed, each blade having an elliptical cross section. Air tapped from the engine compressors was blown downwards out of a spanwise slot at the trailing edge of each blade and generated a lifting circulation when the blades rotated. A four-bladed rotor was mounted on a Rolls-Royce Adour engine at each tip of a forward-swept wing. Each rotor had two blades which could be turned coaxially to lie along the wind as shown in Fig. F.3.1.

Mechanical problems were marked. Each tip unit weighed more than one ton, with a gearbox needing a reduction ratio around 32 to 1. Also, interference drag would have been significant, particularly in the transition phase from winged to rotor-borne flight.

There followed a requirement to investigate a smaller variant, which led to the two-seater shown in Fig. F.3.2 with four engines: two generating rotor lift, two for propulsion. This aircraft would have been comparable in size with the projected supersonic version of the *Folland Gnat*, but would otherwise have been subsonic.

Both wide airspeed aircraft show forward-swept wings: to achieve better drag characteristics at high speed (Fig. 6.4), while also arranging the fuselage frames and wing root joints more favourably for the carriage of payload.

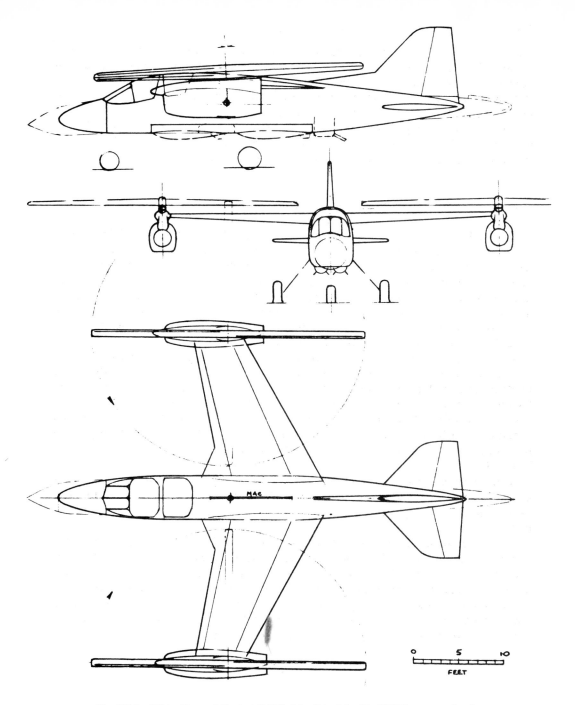

Fig. F.3.1   Wide Airspeed Project (1967), M = 0 to 0·8 with 4,000 lb weapon load

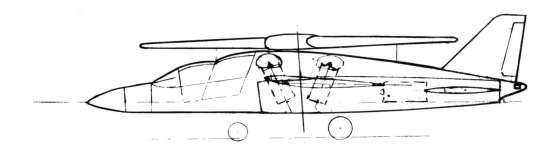

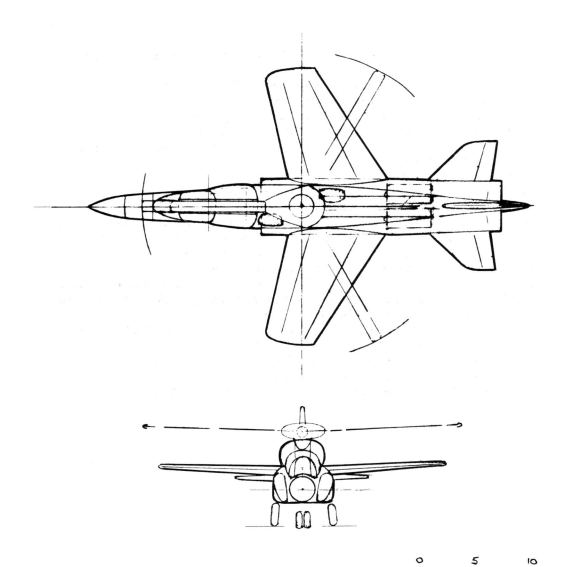

0   5   10
FEET

Suggested Further Reading

1. *Aerodynamics*, A Series of Papers Revised and Reprinted from 'Research', Vol. 10, 1957.
2. BADISTER, A. W., *Aircraft Stability and Control*, Pergamon Press.
3. BEVAN, T., *Theory of Machines*, Longmans.
4. BRADSHAW, P., *Experimental Fluid Mechanics*, Pergamon Press.
5. BROOKS, P. W., *The World's Airliners*, Putnam & Company Ltd.
6. CORNING, G., *Supersonic and Subsonic Airplane Design*, Edward Brothers Inc., Ann Arbor, Michigan, U.S.A.
7. COULTAS, H. W., *Theory of Structures*, Pitman.
8. FEATHER, N., *Mass, Length and Time*, Penguin Books.
9. *Handbook of Aeronautics*, Nos 1 and 2, The Royal Aeronautical Society.
10. GREEN, W., *The Observer's Book of Aircraft*, Frederick Warne & Company Ltd.
11. *Jane's All The World's Aircraft*, Samson Low, Marston & Company Ltd.
12. MARTYNOV, A. K., *Practical Aerodynamics*, Pergamon Press.
13. SCORER, R. S., *Natural Aerodynamics*, Pergamon Press.
14. SECKEL, E., *Stability and Control of Airplanes and Helicopters*, Academic Press.
15. *Supersonic Engineering*, A Symposium held at The Royal College of Advanced Technology, Salford, May 1961, Heinemann.
16. WOOD, K. D., *Aerospace Vehicle Design Volume 1, Aircraft Design*, Johnson Publishing Company, Boulder, Colorado, U.S.A.
17. *The Journal of the American Institute of Aeronautics and Astronautics.*
18. *The Journal of the Royal Aeronautical Society.*
19. STINTON, D., *The Design of the Aeroplane*, BSP Professional Books.

Index

312   INDEX

Bomb, doors 296
  stand-off 292
Bomber
  Command 28
  low-level 292
Boom 244
Bouncing 175
Boundary layer 94
  control 94, 96, 111, 192
  drift 99
  fence 99
  laminar 76
  separation 63, 83, 99, 112
  stagnation 100
  turbulent 76
Brakes
  air 43, 97
Braking
  differential 171
  parachute 43
  wheel 43, 48
Break-even point 24
Breguet
  Atlantic 284
  range equation 45
Bristol Siddeley
  Olympus 591 275, 289, 320
  Olympus 593 274
Britain 273, 296
  Battle of 201
  U.K. of Great 265, 269
Buffeting 263
Bulkhead 206
Buoyancy 179
  centre of CB 179
Burning
  surface 89
Busemann, A. 80
Bypass
  engine 133
  ratio 133
B-52 (see Boeing)
B-70 North American 89, 284

Cabin
  pressure 198, 209
  sealed 271
Camber 57, 80, 285
  changing 94
  conic 99
  nose 271
  reflex 154
Camera 286
Campbell, of NASA 135
Canard 13, 152, 294
Canopy
  blown 245
  drag 271
  optical properties 271
Cantilever 209
Carvair, Aviation Traders 284
Cascade 128, 135
Catapult 301
Cavitation 187

Ceiling 40, 48, 286
Centre
  aerodynamic, ac 61, 79, 91, 146
  of buoyancy 179
  of gravity, CG 61, 79, 140, 227
  calculation 227
Centre, position 230
  of lateral area 275
  of pressure 198
  section 296
Centroid 209
Certificate of Airworthiness 235
Cessna 310, 119
Chord
  aerodynamic mean 64
  centreline 64
  equivalent streamwise 81
  geometric mean 64
  -line 54
  tip 64
Chine 180
Circulation 50, 55, 75
  control 96
  super 96, 97
Classical family 13
Climate 18
Climb 31
  zoom 40
Clouds
  base 44
  cumulo-nimbus 6
  nacreous 6
  noctilucent 3
Cockpit
  (escape) capsule 91, 288
Coefficient
  dimensionless
    (force and moment) 61
    of drag 61
    of lift 61, 85
    of pitching moment 61
College of Aeronautics, Cranfield
  low-level bomber 292
  A-60 SST 213, 274
  A-62 SST 275
  F-61 Freighter 264
Comet, De Havilland 282
  Hawker Siddeley HS 801 132
Composition of atmosphere 1
Compressibility 72, 82, 103, 168
Compressor (engine) 96, 121, 123, 135
Communications 18
Concise Oxford Dictionary viii
Cone, mach 277
Concorde, BAC-Sud 269, 273
Configuration 15
Contract 28
Control 139, 163, 213
    active 163, 275
    cross-coupling 163
    electrical 168, 288
    manual 168
    power 168
    reversal 217
    surface trail 152, 217

DATE DUE